A Short Cut to Happiness...

The Greeks had a word for it—ataraxia: a state in which mental serenity is combined with physical well-being. How to achieve it has been the quest of religion and philosophy for thousands of years. But because these paths call for long and arduous self-discipline, men have also sought a short cut to happiness through herbs and chemists' concoctions.

In this immensely readable and informative book, Robert S. de Ropp, a biochemist who specializes in work on drugs and whose **Man Against Aging** has also received wide acclaim from critics and specialists alike, offers us the first overall view of a world still largely unknown to the general public: ancient herbs and modern drugs, and the unspeakable joys and tortures they produce. From the hashish salons of Beirut to the common forms such as coffee, tea, tobacco, and alcohol, this book is a journey of discovery into the chemistry of the brain and the emotions.

Drugs and the Mind
by Robert S. de Ropp

Foreword by Dr. Nathan S. Kline

An Evergreen Black Cat 🐱 *Book*

Grove Press, Inc.   **New York**

Contents

The author is indebted to Dr. William J. Turner for many valued comments and suggestions regarding the material presented in this book. Permission was kindly granted by Harper and Brothers for the use of quotations from Aldous Huxley's *The Doors of Perception;* by the Cambridge University Press for the use of an excerpt from Sir Charles S. Sherrington's *Man on His Nature;* and by Alfred A. Knopf, Inc., for use of the quotation from John Roy Carlson's *Cairo to Damascus.*

Foreword

"The desire to take medicine," wrote the great Osler, "is perhaps the greatest feature which distinguishes man from animals." Although from time to time animals may accidentally ingest such things as loco weed (astragulus) or similar products they are not apt to repeat the process deliberately. To some extent this may be due to a lack of ability to isolate such substances since, given the opportunity, Masserman's neurotic cats took to alcohol like the proverbial fish to water. We have all seen or heard of dogs or even horses that preferred a good stein of beer above all else. Desire to "transcend" oneself, as Huxley has pointed out, seems to have existed with man from the earliest times.

The great uniqueness of man is not so much his consciousness as his selfconsciousness; and once he had achieved the ability to be aware of how he was feeling and thinking, it inevitably followed that he would attempt to see to what extent his emotions and thoughts could be altered. Part of this undoubtedly arose out of natural curiosity, but more likely fear, guilt, shame, anxiety, depression and like states of discomfort were the prime movers. One type of escape is of purely psychological origin resulting in such diverse manifestations as hermits and libertines, Simeon Stylites and King Priapus; others are psychosocial such as the Bacchanalian orgies, and lynch mobs. The most convenient escape (often in combination with the first two) has been the use of natural or synthetic chemical agents capable of altering states of emotions and consciousness. It is to these latter that Dr. de Ropp has so brilliantly devoted himself in the pages which follow.

Pascal has said, "Most of men's troubles come from their not being able to sit quietly in their chambers" and the present volume is really a profound history of man's attempt to wiggle, worm, and squirm his way out of himself—often at the cost of what are regarded as "basic drives." Such essential functions as nutrition, elimination, and reproduction are carried out not only because they are necessary for survival, but also because they relieve discomfort or alter our emotional or mental state. We know that when chemical agents (or psychosocial activities) can be found that provide more satisfactory relief, eating, sexual activities and sometimes elimination are neglected even at the cost of life itself. As demonstrated by page after page of Dr. de Ropp's book there is no more profound way of understanding the course of history than in terms of this effort to escape from one's own "sweating self" and to experience even temporary states of euphoria or relief of discomfort regardless of the cost.

As I have had occasion to point out in a number of publications, it is these very "dis-eases" that have produced civilization (for good or bad), for without the rumblings of the empty bowel, the pressure of the full bladder, the unsated sexual urges and the parched throat there would be little motivation to do much of anything. Add to these the equivalents that arise with selfawareness—guilt, anxiety, shame, and so on, and motivation is provided for activities beyond mere animal satisfaction. Although alcohol and the opiates have been used from times immemorial, the after effects have led to such discomfort that frequently these "escapes" have either been avoided or used only in moderation.

But what of the future? At the present time I am in the throes of completing a book for the use of my medical colleagues on a group of pharmaceuticals introduced within the past three years which have had a staggering impact on the treatment of human psychiatric ailments. For the first time in the history of public mental hospitals in the United States there was, last year, a decrease of over seven thousand in the patient population instead of the projected ten to twelve thousand increase—a difference of almost twenty thousand. The use of electric shock therapy has been cut by some 80 per cent (according to figures from the Veterans Administration) and the use of restraints and seclusion has been dramatically reduced. At no time in the past has the prospect for the understanding and treatment of mental and emotional aberrations been as promising as it is today.

The tranquilizing drugs, as I have repeatedly and strongly urged, should be used only for the treatment of those whose mental and emotional state *disables* them. They should not be resorted to for the treatment of anything less than an incapacitating illness. The picture of the snarling vicious dangerous monkey transformed by a few milligrams of a chemical into a friendly "tranquil" and "happy" animal fascinates me in an horrendous way. Such a creature is a pleasure to have around the laboratory, but he would not last ten minutes in his native jungle. Similarly, mankind is perfectly capable of tranquilizing itself into oblivion. The one salvation to date has been the disagreeable side effects that these chemicals produce.

At the opposite end of the scale from the tranquilizing drugs is a whole new series of chemical agents which might be described as "psychic energizers." The psychological effects of one of these we recently described for the first time. This drug, iproniazid, was originally used in the treatment of tuberculosis, but it may also represent a "break through" into a new area of treatment in respect to mental disease. Instead of being a psychomotor stimulant, it appears actually to increase the total amount of psychic energy. As with any potent drug it may be dangerous if not properly administered. Used under proper medical supervision, however, it appears of great value in the treatment of those patients whose excessive tranquility verges on total apathy.

Perhaps it is in this direction that we may be able to transcend ourselves upward instead of downward. It is not beyond the realm of possibility that, after concentrating on correcting the aberrations of thinking, feeling, and acting, man is capable of focussing his attention firmly on the achievement of something more than mere surcease of sorrow. The exaltation of heightened awareness, strong positive affective relationships and the pride of useful accomplishment may, at this moment, lie within our grasp.

NATHAN S. KLINE,
*Research Facility,
Rockland State Hospital
Orangeburg, N.Y
May, 1957*

DRUGS AND THE MIND

Mind and Matter

The Greeks, who had a word for almost everything, often spoke of a condition they called *ataraxia*. It was a happy state in which mental serenity was combined with physical well-being, a balanced condition, free from those violent ups and downs that disharmonize the emotional life of the average man. *Ataraxia* was best cultivated by the exercise of philosophy, by inner discipline, by the practice of virtue. The Epicurean philosophers regarded it as the highest possible good.

The Greeks were not alone in holding this condition in such high esteem. Steadiness, inward calm, and harmony have been extolled by all the great religious systems—Christian, Buddhist, Taoist, Vedantist; nor need one be a saint or a philosopher to hunger after this inner tranquillity. It is natural to desire such a state, for without it no real happiness is possible. The hustled inhabitants of the modern world, driven at an increasingly furious tempo in an atmosphere of clamor and violent distraction, must particularly long for this inward peace. It is a pearl of great price; perhaps *the* pearl of great price. The question is how to obtain this pearl.

There have, in the past, been two main methods by which it could be obtained: the practice of religion and the practice of philosophy. But because both these methods call for long and arduous self-discipline men have searched from the earliest times for a *short cut to happiness*, seeking in the realms of pharmacy a means of attaining the desired condition by a procedure no more laborious than the swallowing of a pill.

Teachers of religion and philosophy may declare that such a quest is essentially immoral. It is wrong, they may state, to expect from a drug those gifts which saints and sages have striven to attain by means of the most intensive spiritual efforts. What can you gain from a drug? these critics may ask. What can it possibly give you except slavery? You will become dependent on the contents of a bottle. You will no longer be your own master, but merely the plaything of a chemical substance. The peace you may buy in such a way will be purchased at the expense of your self-respect. You may become a happier being but you will also become a weaker one. Is happiness, on such conditions, worth having? Are you not paying too much for your chemically engendered peace of mind?

Such objections are quite valid. There are a number of very interesting moral problems connected with the use of drugs for the attainment of mental tranquillity or happiness about which a great deal might be said. In this book, however, these problems will not be discussed. It is the author's aim to place before the reader facts regarding several classes of drugs which influence, in one way or another, the mind or the emotions of man. On the basis of these facts the reader himself can decide whether these various agents really do offer happiness or merely an imitation of happiness, whether the peace they give is genuine peace or merely a general numbing of the intelligence and senses. One can, after all, give a man peace of a sort simply by hitting him over the head with a club. If this is the only sort of peace that drugs can offer we might prefer to do without it.

Louis Lewin, the famous German toxicologist, wrote in 1924 a book called *Phantastica: Narcotic and Stimulating Drugs,* which dealt with this problem of the action of drugs on the mind. His book was intended not only for doctors but also for laymen. The writer of the present book has built on the foundations laid by Lewin and endeavored to bring the subject up to date, for many advances have recently been made.

Lewin distinguished five classes of drugs that influence mind and emotions. He called them *euphorica, phantastica, inebriantia, hypnotica,* and *excitantia.* Today we use somewhat different terms. Instead of *phantastica* we speak of *hallucinogens,* drugs capable of producing hallucinations, of which LSD-25 and mescaline are examples. His *hypnotica,* sleep-producing drugs such as the barbiturates, are more commonly referred to now as *sedatives.* In addition we have a new group of drugs, the *ataraxics* (a term recently introduced by Dr. Howard Fabing), that tranquilize without producing drowsiness. Finally Lewin's *excitantia,* a class which includes such stimulants of the nervous system as cocaine or "Benzedrine," are more generally known today as *analeptics.* They have an action opposite to that of the sedatives, arousing and stimulating instead of soothing and calming.

Drugs that exert these effects have long been endowed with a halo of divinity by the people who used them. The *peyotl* was sacred to the Aztecs, the *coca* to the Incas. The gods in the Vedas drank *soma,* those of the Greeks *ambrosia.* *Nepenthe* was praised by Homer as the "potent destroyer of grief" and the hemp plant with its potent resin *charas* was described by the sages of India as the "delight giver."

The properties of these plants were discovered accidentally, in many cases so long ago that we have no idea when their virtues first became known. Our hairy ancestors gained their knowledge of drugs the hard way. Impelled by hunger, they ate what they could find, root or berry, leaf, flower, or fungus. Often they sat in their caves ruefully clutching their stomachs, wondering what they had eaten that had caused them to feel so desperately ill. They purged, they vomited, they convulsed, they collapsed, and the sum of their writhings and spewings, accumulated through the ages, provided the basis for the science of pharmacology. Knowledge of the poisonous properties of plants was cherished by individuals, more discerning than their fellows, who guarded their secrets jealously and employed their understanding of poisons to further their own interests. Gradually, as religions evolved, these discerning characters became priests or witch doctors and their familiarity with poisons became a part of their sacred lore. Most precious of all to these early priests and witch doctors was their knowledge of the plants which affect the workings of the mind, which soothe griefs and relieve sufferings and flood the imagination with delightful visions.

Today the modern chemist is the heir to all this painfully accumulated knowledge. He is the lineal descendant of a long line of witch doctors, shamans, sorcerers, and alchemists. Their carefully guarded secrets have become his stock in trade but he has improved and enormously enlarged his heritage. The crude and often nauseous decoctions which our forefathers swallowed to soothe their griefs or delight their imaginations have now been fractionated by the skill of the analysts. The crystalline essences on which their effects depend have been isolated and characterized. The very places of the component atoms within their molecules have been determined. Nor has the modern chemist been satisfied with these triumphs of analysis but, liberating himself from his dependence on roots and berries, he has embarked on a voyage into the realm of synthesis, creating compounds not found in nature, the properties of which frequently represent a vast improvement on any known natural substance.

All these drugs act by affecting the chemistry of the brain, for it is out of this chemistry that what we call "mind" emerges. The mind of man does not exist in a vacuum. It is associated with the chemistry of the brain and this chemistry underlies all our manifestations. Neither thought nor emotion can occur without some chemical change. The cruelty of the tyrant, the compassion of the saint, the ardor of lovers, the hatred of foes all are based on chemical processes. However hard we may try, however earnestly we may wish to do so, we cannot separate mind from matter or isolate what we call man's soul from his body. Were this not so the action of drugs on the mind could never be understood. It is precisely because all mental and emotional processes have a chemical basis that these drugs exert an action. If mind existed in a vacuum apart from matter we would not be able to influence it by drugs.

What then is the "stuff of the mind"? On what chemical processes do our thoughts and emotions depend? This is a question abstruse enough to make any honest chemist shudder. The scientist who attempts to study the chemistry of thought and feeling resembles a burglar attempting to open the vault of one of the world's major banks with a toothpick He cannot enter the mind; he does not even know where mind is located. Merely to bring the brain within reach of his test tubes he must break open the skull, expose the brain, tear out a portion of its substance. But just how much can he learn from a slice of brain in a test tube? How is he to equate the processes he observes with the thoughts and feelings of an intact man?

The difficulties are immense. The brain, that modest bowl of pinkish jelly which each man carries under the dome of his skull, is a chemical laboratory of incredible complexity. Its soft warm mass, of the consistency of porridge, is the scene of a seething profusion of transformations which never cease even when a man sleeps. This loom of ten billion spindles endlessly weaves the fabric of man's life, the thoughts, emotions, actions, hopes, and fears which form the very basis of his being. Some patterns are common, some are rare, and all are changing. No sooner is one design formed than it is swept away and replaced by another.

Our study of the action of drugs on the mind will hardly be intelligible unless the brain, "the organ of the mind," is visualized at least in its main divisions. Such a visualization can best begin with the nerve cell. This cell, the ultimate building block of thought and sensation, is a really amazing structure. No other cell in the body can compare with it in complexity. A man enters the world with a certain number of these cells and, barring accidents, they live as long as he does. If killed, they cannot be replaced. If seriously damaged, they cannot be repaired. Nothing, therefore, that a human being possesses is more precious than this mass of nerve cells, for every aspect of his physical, mental, and emotional life depends on their well-being.

A glance at the structure of the extraordinary cells reveals the reason for their vulnerability. Most cells in the body are compact and fairly symmetrical. They may be flat or round or somewhat elongated but are rarely much longer than they are broad. They are little boxes of protoplasm containing a round nucleus surrounded by more or less watery cytoplasm.

The nerve cell also contains nucleus and cytoplasm but the cytoplasm is spread out in an extraordinary manner. From one end of the nerve cell there extends a thin fiber of cytoplasm which connects the body of the nerve to the organ, muscle, or gland to which it supplies nervous impulses. This long process is the axone or the "nerve fiber." In man it is generally about a thousandth of an inch thick and may be several feet in length, a prodigious outgrowth for a cell of microscopic size. It is a living, working mechanism which uses energy even when it is not transmitting an impulse. Its life is dependent upon the cell body from which it grew and if cut off from the cell body it dies within a few days. The white threads which traverse our arms and legs and which are loosely called nerves are in fact masses of nerve fibers bound together in bundles. The nerve cells from which these fibers arise lie hidden in the spinal cord. In man and in all higher animals the nerve cells have retreated into the safest and most central parts of the body, relying on their long slender fibers to transmit their orders. Thus a man with both legs and both arms amputated does not, in that process, lose a single nerve cell. The cells remain safely in the spinal cord. The parts that are severed are the bundles of fibers.

From the side of the nerve cell opposite the axone emerge a number of shorter processes called the dendrites. These dendrites make contact with the axone fibers from other nerve cells, forming, in this way, a set of connections. As we ascend through the spinal cord toward the brain these axone-dendrite connections become more and more numerous until, in the brain itself, we find untold billions of such connections. This infinitely complex nerve net and the chemical processes which keep it in ceaseless activity constitute the physical basis of mind, emotion, and sensation. The nerve cell, a tiny speck of protoplasm with a slender, enormously elongated extension, is an electrochemical unit of a very complex type. Nerve fibers are often compared to telephone wires and they do, in fact, transmit an electrical message and can be stimulated by an electric current. Here the resemblance ends. In the telephone wire the electric impulse passes along the wire at a velocity up to 20,000 miles per second. In the nerve fiber the electric impulse moves much more slowly. The fastest messages carried by the largest fibers travel at a mere 300 feet per second, about as fast as a DC-3 transport plane cruises. The slowest messages, traveling in the smallest fibers, move at a rate of about one meter per second—about as fast as a man walks. Nerve fibers can conduct impulses like a telephone wire but the conduction is so poor that, after traversing about one fifth of an inch in this manner, the message is lost.

There are many nerve cells in the body. The brain alone contains about ten billion. They penetrate everywhere, a network of immense complexity, supplying muscle or gland cells with the impulse to act, transporting messages from our various sense organs. At all times a two-way traffic pours along the thoroughfares of the nervous system—not, however, along the same path, for nerve cells conduct impulses in one direction only. Impulses from the sense organs stream in toward the brain, impulses from the brain pass outward to glands and muscles. Never from the day of his birth to the day of his death does man's nervous system rest. Even in sleep it continues to operate. In sleep, however, large parts of the system are disconnected and only those areas necessary for the essential operations of the body continue to function actively.

There is in man a hierarchy of brains. They rise above one another in a sort of pyramid, each one more complex than the one below, reaching their ultimate complexity in the massive cerebral cortex with 15,000 cellular elements crowded into every square millimeter of its surface. Each level in the nervous system of man roughly corresponds to a different level of his being. Man's conscious mind, the part to which he refers as his "I," is not even aware of the operations which take place day and night within the lower levels of the brain. It is on these humble lower functions, however, that the continuation of his physical existence depends. The rate of beating of the heart, the diameter of the blood vessels, the rhythmic movement of the bowels, the activity of various glands, all these and countless other processes must be regulated by the "instinctive brain," ruling by its own wisdom the chemistry of the body. This instinctive wisdom is not possessed by the conscious mind, which frequently frustrates the instinctive brain by imposing all sorts of harmful conditions at the dictates of fashion or under the stress of unnatural conditions of life.

This instinctive brain is located in the spinal cord, the medulla oblongata, and the pons. Above it lies the hypothalamus and the thalamus, regulating and co-ordinating part of man's instinctive life and profoundly affecting his emotional being. Many secrets relating to the chemistry of mind and emotion are hidden in this region of the brain. Lodged at the base of the cranium in the very center of the head, completely surrounded by massive bony structures, the hypothalamus with the attached pituitary gland rules like a conductor over the glandular orchestra, influencing every aspect of man's material and spiritual existence. At least six master hormones flow from the pituitary into the blood stream, chemical messengers which bear their varied tidings to lesser glands in different parts of the body. Thyrotropin arouses the thyroid gland, stimulating it to pour out thyroxin, which increases the rate of metabolism of the body. ACTH (adrenocorticotropic hormone) rouses the adrenal cortex, causing it to produce cortisone and related substances. The gonado-tropins, male and female, carry a message from the pituitary to the ovaries or testes. Ovaries are stimulated to produce progesterone or estrone; the testes are stimulated to produce testosterone, the chemical essence of masculinity without which the strutting muscular male is transformed to a flabby eunuch. From the pituitary also is produced somatotropin, the vital growth hormone which regulates the length of the bones and which, produced in excess, gives rise to giants.

Probing deeply and skillfully into these almost inacessible regions of the brain, the modern neurophysiologist has revealed still more astonishing functions. What, we may ask, is pleasure? What is that nebulous condition we call happiness, the free pursuit of which is defined as one of the ends of existence in no less a document than the Declaration of Independence? There are those philosophers who take the view that happiness and pleasure are mere negative qualities, dependent on the absence of any positive pain. Not so, says the neurophysiologist. Pleasure and pain are alike brain functions. Deep in the hypothalamus, among the vital centers controlling digestive, sexual, excretory, and similar processes, there are "pleasure areas," the electrical stimulation of which produces some exquisite form of titillation the nature of which we can at present only guess.

Rats with electrodes embedded in this region of the brain can be placed in a cage with a movable bar. Each time the animal presses the bar a tiny electric current flows for an instant from the electrode into its brain. By means of such a device students of behavior can differentiate between stimuli felt as pleasure and stimuli felt as pain, for the rat, being at liberty to press the bar or leave it alone, and being, like any normal creature, dedicated to the pursuit of happiness and avoidance of pain, will press the bar often when the stimulus is pleasurable and avoid pressing it when the stimulus has proved painful.

A clever arrangement this. It is called a Skinner box (after Harvard's B. F. Skinner) and is proving of enormous value in several kinds of psychological study. Dr. James Olds has described this research into the origins of pleasure in a recent article in the *Scientific American:*

> Electrical stimulation in some of the regions of the hypothalamus actually appeared to be far more rewarding to the animals than an ordinary satisfier such as food. For example, hungry rats ran faster to reach an electric stimulator than they did to reach food. Indeed, a hungry animal often ignored available food in favor of the pleasure of stimulating itself electrically. Some rats with electrodes in these places stimulated their brains more than 2,000 times per hour for 24 consecutive hours!

Amazing discovery! What curious vistas of depravity open up before our eyes. What an "abyss of divine enjoyment," to borrow De Quincey's phrase, gapes here before us. Here we see a passion similar to that of the alcoholic for his bottle, the heroin addict for his drug. This pleasure-crazed rat, were he human, would present just such a picture of moral degradation as does the soused alcoholic staggering from tavern to tavern while wife and children starve in some wretched hovel. The rat, it is clear, will sacrifice all life's duties and even its more mundane pleasures for the exquisite delights to be obtained from pressing a bar. Is it possible that these neurophysiologists have accomplished what even the devil has been unable to do in all his centuries of experience? Can it be that they have actually devised a *new form of sin?* And

what, one may ask, is the nature of this pleasure so potent
that even the pangs of hunger are powerless against it? In
some cases it may approximate to sexual pleasure. Life for
the rat becomes one long orgasm; he enjoys the delights of
love without its labors, its perils, or any wear and tear on the
organs involved. But some of these pleasure centers are
seemingly unconnected with sex. What form of pleasure,
then, is experienced by the rat? What new ecstasies, what
esoteric joys does the creature obtain each time it presses
the bar?

Clearly we cannot answer any of these questions until
human subjects are employed in place of rats. It is not impossible, however, that the ecstasies of mystics, the raptures
of poets, the lofty joys obtained by artists from the work of
creation may all be produced artificially by a minute electric
current localized in one tiny area of the inner brain. These
researches are of quite extraordinary significance, for they
bear directly on the ultimate motivation which underlies
every form of human behavior. They bear directly also on the
subject of this book, for drugs affecting the mind appear to
exert their action by raising or lowering the sensitivity of
these pleasure centers to stimulation.

On the same level as the hypothalamus but at the back of
the head is the much-convoluted cerebellum, the "little
brain," concerned with the elaboration of skilled movements. The grace of the dancer, the skill of the craftsman,
the finely co-ordinated efforts of the athlete all depend on
the functioning of this region of the brain.

Over all these lower brains the massive cerebral cortex
extends like a roof, the "neopallium" or new mantle, a
recent product of evolution attaining in man its most magnificent development. There are regions of the cerebral
cortex that control movements. There are other regions that

receive sensations. Others again—for instance, the temporal lobe—are associated with memories. Large parts of the cerebral cortex are, to use the phrase of the neurophysiologist, "silent areas"; that is to say, they give neither sensation nor movement when stimulated by an electric current. The massive "frontal lobes" that fill the dome-shaped brow of man, distinguishing him from the apes and his low-browed ancestors, are silent areas. They can be chopped out and a man still lives. He does not become demented though his personality may change. Indeed, provided the motor and sensory areas are left intact, it is amazing what large amounts of the cerebral cortex can be sacrificed without any very marked change taking place in the behavior of the patient. One cannot help wondering at times whether man's massive cerebrum has not become too big, a sort of overgrown fungus which is merely filling up space in the cranium. Or has man, perhaps, more brain than he knows what to do with? Is his huge "neopallium" merely a wasted asset, like a powerful engine installed in a decrepit automobile which can never utilize more than a fraction of the available horsepower? There is a good deal of evidence to suggest that man's brain power is in fact very poorly utilized, that the full potentials of the cerebral cortex are very rarely developed. Man reaches the end of his life span with a brain only partly utilized. The other organs fail while the cerebrum is still youthful. Perhaps this, in part, is the explanation of the human tragedy.

To visualize this great network of nerve cells in operation is an almost impossible task but a general picture of its operation has been given by Sherrington (*Man on His Nature*) in a passage of extraordinary beauty and power:

A scheme of lines and nodal points, gathered at one end

into a great ravelled knot, the brain, and at the other trailing
off to a sort of stalk, the spinal cord. Imagine activity in this
shown by little points of light. Of these some stationary flash
rhythmically, faster or slower. Others are travelling points,
streaming in serial trains at various speeds. The rhythmic
stationary lights lie at the nodes. The nodes are both goals
whither converge, and junctions whence diverge, the lines of
travelling lights. The lines and nodes where the lights are, do
not remain, taken together, the same even a single moment.
There are at any time nodes and lines where lights are not.

Suppose we choose the hour of deep sleep. Then only in
some sparse and out of the way places are nodes flashing and
trains of light-points running. Such places indicate local activity still in progress. At one such place we can watch the
behavior of a group of lights perhaps a myriad strong. They
are pursuing a mystic and recurrent manoeuvre as if of some
incantational dance. They are superintending the beating of
the heart and the state of the arteries so that while we sleep
the circulation of the blood is what it should be. The great
knotted headpiece of the whole sleeping system lies for the
most part dark, and quite especially so the roof brain. Occasionally at places in it lighted points flash or move but soon
subside. Such lighted points and moving trains of lights are
mainly far in the outskirts, and wink slowly and travel slowly.
At intervals even a gush of sparks wells up and sends a train
down the spinal cord, only to fail to arouse it. Where however the stalk joins the headpiece, there goes forward in a
limited field a remarkable display. A dense constellation of
some thousands of nodal points bursts out every few seconds
into a short phase of rhythmical flashing. At first a few lights,
then more, increasing in rate and number with a deliberate
crescendo to a climax, then to decline and die away. After
due pause the efflorescence is repeated. With each such rhyth-

mic outburst goes a discharge of trains of travelling lights along the stalk and out of it altogether into a number of nerve-branches. What is this doing? It manages the taking of our breath the while we sleep.

Should we continue to watch the scheme we should observe after a time an impressive change which suddenly accrues. In the great head-end which has been mostly darkness springs up myriads of twinkling stationary lights and myriads of trains of moving lights of many different directions. It is as though activity from one of those local places which continued restless in the darkened main-mass suddenly spread far and wide and invaded all. The great topmost sheet of the mass, that where hardly a light had twinkled or moved, becomes now a sparkling field of rhythmic flashing points with trains of travelling sparks hurrying hither and thither. The brain is waking and with it the mind is returning. It is as if the Milky Way entered upon some cosmic dance. Swiftly the head mass becomes an enchanted loom where millions of flashing shuttles weave a dissolving pattern, always a meaningful pattern though never an abiding one; a shifting harmony of subpatterns. Now as the waking body rouses, subpatterns of this great harmony of activity stretch down into the unlit tracks of the stalk-piece of the scheme. This means that the body is up and rises to meet its waking day.

This loom with its millions of flashing shuttles requires, like any other very active machine, a constant supply of fuel. The fuel of the brain is glucose, a simple sugar which is brought to the brain by the blood. Glucose is vital to the working of the brain; a fall in the level of sugar in the blood at once affects the working of man's brain cells. If it falls far enough he loses consciousness, a condition seen at times in diabetics who have injected themselves with too much insulin, a hormone which causes a drop in the level of sugar in the blood. "Insulin coma" may also be induced artificially and for some unknown reason proves helpful in the treatment of certain forms of mental illness.

To burn its fuel the brain needs oxygen and, as the activity of the brain never ceases, a steady stream of this element is needed to maintain its inward fires. No other organ in the body uses oxygen at a faster rate than does the brain; no other organ is so swiftly or irreparably damaged by oxygen lack. A baby who fails to breathe for some time after birth may suffer permanent brain injury and go through life crippled with cerebral palsy. Carbon monoxide poisoning, an overdose of anesthetic, the failure of a pilot's oxygen supply at high altitudes may all inflict serious damage on the brain.

An abundant supply of blood flows constantly to the brain to keep it supplied with the substances vital for its working. No blood, however, comes into contact with the brain itself. Between brain and blood is a subtle chemical barrier which denies entry to many substances which might harm the brain. This "blood-brain barrier" has an important influence on the effect of drugs on the brain, for only those chemicals which can pass the barrier can have any direct action on the brain's substance.

The messages that reach the brain, from which the entire inner life of man is constructed, are simple impulses of electrical charge which travel at varying speeds along the fibers of the nerves. There is only one kind of message, a simple unit signal which does not vary in quality from one nerve to another. Its passage along the nerve fiber can be compared to the burning of a fuse and, just as a fuse has to have applied a certain amount of heat to start it burning, so a nerve fiber must receive a stimulus of definite size to set the impulse moving. Once it has been started it goes on moving. A second stimulus will start a second impulse but only a limited number of impulses can pass along a nerve fiber per second.

During every moment of man's conscious or unconscious life uncountable billions of these impulses are surging through the nerve fibers, both inward toward the brain and outward to glands and muscles. The differences both in sensation and in reaction which a human being manifests from moment to moment result from great patterns composed of millions of impulses, assembled and co-ordinated at every level from the spinal cord to the cerebral cortex. From the eye alone about one million private lines of communication enter the brain and each one, while the eyes are open, transmits nerve impulses at the rate of several hundred per second. To this are added messages from touch receptors, from the organs of hearing, of balance, the organs of taste and smell, of muscular tone, pain, temperature, visceral sensation. These surging floods of information moment by moment pour into the brain. This organ would surely be overwhelmed by the very plethora of its own information and a man would be drowned by the profusion of his sensations were there not filters in the brain which cut off from consciousness the irrelevant impulses, enabling a man to "attend" to only one thing at a time.

The nerve impulses resemble separate stones in a mosaic. They pour into the brain, are sorted and assembled, and the resulting design is the stuff of our conscious life. All our experiences are made up of these mosaics of simple impulses. Whether we perceive an odor, a sound, or a sight, whether we feel pain, heat, cold, stomach-ache, or fatigue, our experience is made up of the same ultimate units. The way in which we interpret these messages depends on the part of the brain in which they are received and on the connections we have built up. Our very perception of the outside world exists not in that world itself but solely in our brain. A rose is a rose is a rose, says Gertrude Stein. Nonsense, says the neurophysiologist. A "rose" is a pattern of nervous impulses, patterns in the visual area interpreted as color, patterns in the olfactory area interpreted as scent, patterns of memory, of language, of past experience which inform us that this indeed is a rose and not a geranium or a slice of raw beef. What a rose really is we cannot tell. We can never know the true nature of anything. All the properties which we bestow on objects in the world about us are merely mosaics of nerve impulses projected outward by a magician who dwells in the brain and who deludes us into thinking that we have contact with the outside world whereas we are actually aware only of impulse mosaics occurring within the darkness of our skulls.

All sensations, all perceptions, all impressions are brain-born. Normally they arise from impulses brought to the brain by the sensory nerves, but sensations and perceptions do not have to be produced in this way. They can be produced by electrical stimulation of the brain. They can also be produced by drugs. When Havelock Ellis, sitting by the fire in his quiet room in London, saw "thick, glorious fields of jewels, solitary or clustered, sometimes brilliant and sparkling, sometimes with a dull rich glow," he certainly was not interpreting any sensory messages. There were no fields of jewels in his simple room, only the firelight flickering on the bare walls. His "jewels" were mental processes, brain reactions, chemical events in some brain area associated with vision which resulted from his having swallowed, some time earlier, a decoction of the sacred cactus of the Aztecs. Similarly that "most delightful experience" when the air seemed "flushed with vague perfume" corresponded to chemical events initiated in the olfactory regions of the brain, again the result of the action of *peyotl*, for no such delightful perfume pervaded his room but only the raw aroma of the London fog blended with the exhalations of his fire, which probably smoked as is the habit of English coal fires. And what of those fabulous monsters which Théophile Gautier "saw" when he and his fellow members of Le Club des Hachischins assembled in the Hotel Pimodan to enjoy their favorite drug? "I saw passing by me the creatures of phantasy, owls, sea storks, satyrs, unicorns, griffons, vultures, a whole menagerie of monsters trotting, vaulting, gliding, yelping, about the room." There certainly were no unicorns in the Hotel Pimodan, and few if any owls, vultures, or satyrs. Again the fantastic menagerie, "seen" as if it actually existed, corresponded only to chemical events in Gautier's brain, this time the result of the action of certain active principles which reside in the drug *hashish*.

Electrical stimulation of the brain can also produce hallucinations; indeed, as every sensation is accompanied by an electrical pattern of neurone activity, it ought theoretically to be possible, by feeding suitable patterns into the brain, to produce any desired sensation, visual, tactile, gustatory, or olfactory. What vistas open up! What future prospects for the entertainment industry! No longer need we dispense amusement by the clumsy procedure of projecting an image on a screen and feeding it through the retina to the brain. We will say farewell to all that and ask our patrons merely to sit facing a blank wall while we apply the necessary stimulation directly through the skull into the visual cortex. Lo and behold, every detail of the scene appears on the wall, in full color and also in three dimensions.

But why stop at mere visual stimulation? Stimulate the olfactory lobes, the very aroma of the scene is added. Stimulate the tactile area, the situations are actually felt, that lingering kiss, that melting embrace, that desperate struggle, that daring ride to the rescue! Why, we can even stimulate the hypothalamus and set the adrenals pouring out their juices so that, without ever leaving his armchair, our patron actually feels the terror of the heroine as the villain rushes upon her with intentions anything but honorable. The possibilities are endless and have all been foreshadowed by that versatile prophet of the modern age, Aldous Huxley. No doubt this form of amusement will be perfected and will be called, as he suggested, the "feelies," and men and women of our "Brave New World" will become less than ever capable of thinking their own thoughts or even of experiencing their own sensations.

While messages are pouring into the brain from the sense organs others stream out in the opposite direction to activate muscles and glands that we may run, shout, laugh, blush, weep, and generally play our role in life's drama. When the nervous impulse reaches the end of a nerve fiber it does not pass into the gland or muscle cell. It acts in a more subtle fashion by releasing a chemical called a neurohormone (nerve hormone) and it is this chemical which causes the cell to react. These nerve hormones are generated with flashlike suddenness at the end of the fiber and are destroyed no less swiftly, yet every aspect of our behavior depends on the production of these minute traces of chemical substances.

Best known of the nerve hormones is adrenalin (also called epinephrine), which is produced not only by certain nerves but also by the central portion of the adrenal glands. The nerves which work by producing adrenalin (adrenergic nerves) belong to a part of the nervous system which operates beyond the reach of the will and is for this reason called the autonomic nervous system. It plays an important part in the emotional life of man, especially at moments of crisis. Faced with an emergency that threatens his survival, man, like any other animal, instinctively mobilizes his chemical resources to meet the danger, and does so by means of his autonomic nervous system. In the words of W. B. Cannon, whose experiments first brought to light the chemical reaction underlying rage and fear, this is what happens:

> Respiration deepens; the heart beats more rapidly, the arterial pressure rises, the blood is shifted away from the stomach and intestines to the heart and the central nervous system and the muscles, the processes in the alimentary canal cease, sugar is freed from the reserves in the liver; the spleen contracts and discharges its content of concentrated corpuscles, and adrenalin is secreted from the adrenal medulla. The key to these marvellous transformations in the body is found in relating them to the natural accompaniments of fear and rage—running away in order to escape from danger and attacking in order to be dominant. Whichever the action, a life or death struggle may ensue.

A second substance associated with expression of emotion is nor-adrenalin, closely related to adrenalin in chemical structure (see Appendix) and also liberated through the action of the autonomic nervous system. According to Dr. D. H. Funkenstein, the emotional manifestations which result from a production of nor-adrenalin are those of outwardly directed anger accompanied by aggressive behavior, whereas adrenalin prepares the organism for flight or, in man, may be associated with the manifestation of anxiety or depression. The well-known difference in behavior between the fierce, aggressive meat eaters and the timid, readily frightened herbivores appears to be associated with a difference in production of these two chemicals. In the adrenal medulla of the lion, nor-adrenalin predominates; in the adrenal medulla of the rabbit, adrenalin predominates. As for man, his reactions depend largely on type. The muscular, athletic mesomorph (to use Sheldon's terminology) who delights in hunting big game, assaulting mountains, and generally challenging nature and his fellow men has a system favoring the production of nor-adrenalin. The more rabbitlike ectomorph, timid, retiring, and of slender physique, will rely in his reactions on flight rather than fight and possesses a system favoring the production of adrenalin.

The third nerve hormone is called acetylcholine, and the nerves which operate by the production of this substance are called cholinergic. All movements of our voluntary muscles depend on the flashlike production of acetylcholine and on its no less rapid destruction by the enzyme cholinesterase. Without both the substance and the enzyme we literally could not move a muscle. That tragic affliction, *myasthenia gravis*, in which muscular weakness becomes so great that the sufferer often has not strength enough even to swallow, is due to some failure in the production of acetylcholine. This neurohormone is also responsible for several effects beyond the reach of our will, for one segment of the autonomic nervous system (parasympathetic) operates by means of acetylcholine rather than adrenalin.

Practically all those manifestations which form the outward and visible signs of our inward emotional lives result from the action of these chemical agents: adrenalin, nor-adrenalin, and acetylcholine. Their effects form a part of the stock in trade of every novelist who, though he may never have heard of them, never wearies of describing their more obvious modes of action. So, when we read that "her heart stopped beating for a moment," we can guess that the vagus has secreted acetylcholine; when the same organ starts "pounding like a sledge hammer," we can safely assume that the "accelerans" nerve has been stimulated and has produced adrenalin. If the heroine goes "pale as a sheet" we can be reasonably sure that contraction of her surface blood vessels has resulted from the production of nor-adrenalin by her sympathetic nerve endings. If she blushes we can assume that vasodilation instead of constriction has occurred and that the chemical cause is a whiff of acetylcholine, generated, this time by nerves of the parasympathetic division.

Thus, underlying the sparkling play of the emotions, the ecstasies of lovers, the fury of foes, we see these three fundamental chemicals playing their roles like the three basic characters in the old harlequinade. It must not be imagined, however, that the display of emotion—its outward expression—is the same thing as the emotion itself. Behind the scenes there takes place a more subtle drama concerning the chemistry of which we know much less. For all our blushings and palings, the speeding or slowing of our hearts, our cold sweats, our tremblings and other outward manifestations are but the expressions, not the emotions themselves. The actual *experience* of emotion takes place, as Papez has shown, within the depths of the "old brain," in the thalamus or hypothalamus. So we can *experience* an emotion we do not express and, if we are any good at acting, can *express* an emotion we do not experience. The chemical processes involved are different and the difference is important. Thus, if an actor in a highly emotional drama really experiences those emotions which, night after night, he must portray on the stage, there is every probability that he will develop a nervous breakdown. Ability to express without experienc-

ing is the essence of great acting, and the chemistry of the
two processes is quite different, the James-Lange theory of
emotions notwithstanding.

This short introduction does scant justice to the work of
such scientists as Sir Henry Dale and Dr. Otto Loewi, whose
magnificent researches have shed so much light on the
chemical mechanisms which underlie the workings of the
nervous system. It was not the author's intention, however,
to delve deeply into the mysteries of either neurophysiology
or neurochemistry, but only to offer a framework for the
benefit of the non-scientific reader within which the effects
on the mind produced by drugs could be described more
intelligibly. Without further delay we can proceed to the
main subject.

The Mind and Mescaline

On the mesas of Tamaulipas and Jalisco, in the dry un-
fertile regions of Mexico south of the Rio Grande, a cactus
grows amid the rocks and sand. It is not erect and magnificent like the Saguaro or the bearer of gorgeous flowers like
the night-blooming Cereus. It is, in fact, a thoroughly insignificant little·pincushion projecting a bare three inches
above the barren soil, a round, dark green protuberance
connected to a carrotlike taproot, its surface covered with
tufts of silky hairs. Though utterly uninspiring in appearance, this humble cactus, *Lopophora Williamsii,** produces
in its fleshy top one of the strangest drugs in the pharmacologist's collection. The properties of this drug have already
been briefly mentioned. It is necessary now to describe them
in more detail.

.Antiquity shrouds the origins of the cactus cult. We do
not know, nor are we likely to discover, by what accident
some wanderer in the Mexican deserts first stumbled upon
the secret of the plant's effects. We may assume that the discovery of the drug resulted from the usual causes, a quest

* Formerly *Anhalonium Lewinii.*

for food on the part of some wanderer, reduced to extremity by hunger and thirst, devouring anything containing moisture and nourishment, however evil-tasting that something might be. We can envisage that long-forgotten man, Aztec or pre-Aztec, chewing the nauseous, bitter cactus tops and lying down to rest, then, in a rising tide of astonishment, finding himself ringed on all sides with fantastic visions, with shapes, colors, odors of which he had never even dreamed. Small wonder that, when he found his way back to his tribe, he informed them that a deity dwelt in the cactus and that those who devoured its flesh would behold the world of the gods.

So, by the time the Spaniards arrived in Mexico, they discovered that, along with such gods as Quetzalcoatl and Huitzilopochtli, the Aztecs also worshiped a triad of plants called *teonanaçatl, ololiuqui,* and *peyotl.* Of these three the *peyotl* was the chief, a veritable divine substance, the "flesh of the gods." This presented a challenge to the Spanish priests, who had their own ideas on the subject of God's flesh and had no intention of tolerating any rival claims to that dignity. They promptly dubbed the *peyotl* "raiz diabolica," and persecuted all who used it without bothering to investigate its nature or its properties. Thus the divine *peyotl* languished in the shadow of the Church's displeasure for some three centuries, officially excommunicated, secretly enjoyed. The Indians, having other values and other memories, were little moved by the priestly denunciations nor could these bringers of a foreign creed root out so easily a practice that had been established for centuries. Though Montezuma was dead and the glory of the Aztecs had passed away the worship of the divine plant continued. It was still regarded as the flesh of God, the flesh of Christ rather than that of an Aztec deity. Had not the Lord declared, giving bread to his disciples, "Take, eat, this is my Body, which is given for thee and for many. Do this in remembrance of me"? And who would dare to find fault with the humble Indian if, in his eagerness to obey the command of Christ, he chose to eat not a sacramental wafer but a plant having properties so wonderful that it unrolled before his eyes all the glories of the New Jerusalem?

And so over the dry plateaus in northern Mexico in the states of Tamaulipas, San Luis Potosí, Nuevo León, Coahuila, Querétaro, Zacatecas, and Chihuahua, the seekers of the divine plant would set out to gather the cactus. God, they maintained, had provided maize as food for the body and *peyotl* as nourishment for the soul. Should they then merely live on maize like hogs? Ought they not rather to go and gather the divine food that both body and soul might receive appropriate nourishment?

In San Luis Potosí the sacred cactus is gathered in October just before the dry season. So holy a plant is not to be dragged from the earth without proper respect and those who go forth to gather the *peyotl* do so with awareness of the sacred nature of their mission. For several weeks before the expedition starts those who are to take part prepare themselves with prayers and fasting. Abstinence from sexual intercourse is imposed upon them, as both strength and purity are required for the success of the expedition. Chanting prayers and reciting sacred verses, the leaders of the party proceed over the rocky mesas, followed by pack animals which will bing back the harvest. Before reaching the holy place the members of the expedition perform a public penance Then, displaying every sign of veneration, they approach the plants, uncovering their heads, bowing to the ground, and censing themselves with copal incense. The more devout cross themselves in the name of the Father,

the Son, and the Holy Ghost. Then, having discharged
arrows to right and left of the plant to ward off evil spirits,
they dig the cacti with care so as not to hurt them, brush off
the soil from the roots, and place the plants in jars. As the
expedition returns there is great rejoicing in all the villages
through which it passes. *Peyotl* is offered on the altars and
fragments given to every person met. Sufficient is kept for
the great festivals and the rest is sold to those who took no
part in the expedition.

In order to dry and preserve it the plant is cut into thick,
fleshy slices which are laid in the sun to dry. These slices,
when dried, become wrinkled brown discs more or less covered with tufts of short white hairs. In this form they are
commonly known as "mescal buttons." The word "mescal"
here is confusing, for it is also used to describe an intoxicant
made from the agave. The mescal button, however, is entirely non-alcoholic and, with its dirty color and covering of
spiny fluff, is about as unpromising a passport to an artificial
paradise as can be imagined. Its taste is as unpleasant as its
appearance; indeed anyone who has chewed his way through
one of these "buttons" must marvel at the hardihood of the
Indian Peyotist, for the flesh of the cactus is not only bitter
but possessed of a peculiarly nauseating odor. Yet the Indian
not only swallows as many as twelve of these morsels but is
also able to retain them in his stomach, a feat which the
squeamish might envy.

As means of communication became easier the *peyotl* rite
spread steadily among the Indians. It crossed the border and
invaded the United States, becoming established first in that
region of the Rio Grande in Texas where the cactus grows.
It spread steadily among the Apaches, Omahas, Kiowas,
Comanches, and was employed even by tribes as far north
as Wisconsin. As a result of the outcries of Christian mis-

sionaries efforts were made to prevent the Indians from ob-
taining the plant. Why the missionaries wished to prevent
them is not clear, for there is no evidence whatever that
peyotl is associated with debauchery. Their efforts, however,
resulted in prohibitions and legal actions, one of the most
curious of which was the trial in Wisconsin of the Indian
Nah-qua-tah-tuck, whose crime, it appears, consisted in having imported a shipment of *peyotl* from Texas by parcel
post. Considerable efforts were made to prove that *peyotl*
was harmful and that its employment led the user straight
to the pit of hell; that it was, in fact, the "raiz diabolica"
described by Padre José Ortega. From this standpoint the
Indians in the trial proved most unco-operative. Far from
describing *peyotl* as a short cut to hell, they insisted that by
its means they were brought several steps nearer to heaven.
Before taking the drug they "invoked God, begging Him to
make all of them good and to keep them from evil." They
took *peyotl* that their souls might ascend toward God.
"Peyotl helped them to lead better lives and to forsake
alcoholic drinks." The Reverend Thomas Prescott, who also
testified at the trial, declared that for seven years he had
officiated as a priest in a society known as the Union Church
Society and to its Indian members as the Peyote Society.
Peyotl was either eaten or taken as tea at weekly services
and those that took it derived benefit from its use. "They
gave up drink, established themselves in regular homes, and
lived sober and industrious lives." As for himself, "it stopped
me from drinking, and now since I used this peyotl, I have
been sober, and today I am sober yet." "This," writes Norman Taylor, "was too much for the government experts, and
Uncle Sam decided to go back to Washington, where the
records of this fantastic trial still molder."

Even so, those warped individuals who seem happy only

when forbidding something to their fellow men continued
to seek to suppress the now Christianized form of *peyotl*
worship. As recently as 1951 efforts were made to declare
illegal the use of *peyotl* among various Indian tribes. So
energetic were these attempts that LaBarre and four other
professional anthropologists who had made extensive studies
of Peyotism and participated in the rites felt it their duty
"to protest against a campaign which only reveals the ignorance of the propagandists concerned." After pointing out
that *peyotl* is neither a narcotic nor an intoxicant in the true
sense of the word they went on to describe the aims of that
intertribal organization incorporated under the name of
"The Native American Church of the United States" as
given in its articles of incorporation.

> The purpose for which this corporation is formed is to
> foster and promote religious belief in Almighty God and the
> customs of the several tribes of Indians throughout the
> United States in the worship of a Heavenly Father and to
> promote morality, sobriety, industry, charity and right living
> and cultivate a spirit of self-respect and brotherly love and
> union among the members of the several tribes of Indians
> throughout the United States   with and through the
> sacramental use of peyotl.

> by eating the sacramental peyotl [these writers con-
> tinue] the Indian absorbs God's Spirit, in the same way that
> the white Christian absorbs that spirit by means of the sacra-
> mental bread and wine   The traditional practice of
> many Indian tribes was to go off in isolation to contemplate
> and fast until a supernatural vision was achieved. This is
> now replaced by a collective all night vigil in which, through
> prayer, contemplation and eating peyotl, the Peyotist re-
> ceives a divine revelation. For the Peyotist this occurs be-

cause he has put himself in a receptive spiritual mood and has absorbed enough of God's power from the peyotl to make him able to reach God. . . . The all night rite is highly formalized. One man functions as priest, with the help of three assistants. During the rite they pray for the worshippers at fixed intervals, while the other men and women pray to themselves in low voices. Early in the rite everyone takes four pieces of peyotl; later, anyone may take as many more as he or she thinks proper. Most of the time is occupied in having each man, in rotation, sing four religious songs that correspond to hymns sung in white churches. . . . It will be seen from this brief description that the Native American Church of the United States is a legitimate religious organization deserving of the same right to religious freedom as other churches; also that peyotl is used sacramentally in a manner corresponding to the bread and wine of the white Christians.

Among the Kiowa Indians the rite of peyote eating generally takes place on a Saturday night. The men sit quietly on the carefully swept earth, forming themselves into a circle about a flickering campfire. All bow their heads in prayer, then, taking the mescal buttons from the jar in which they are stored, the leader of the ceremony hands four buttons to each man. One of these, freed from the tufts of hair that cover it, is put into the mouth and thoroughly softened, ejected into the palm of the hand, rolled into a bolus, and swallowed. In this way as many as twelve buttons may be taken at intervals between sundown and 3 A.M. with the accompaniment of occasional prayers and rites. Throughout the ceremony the campfire is kept burning brightly and attendants maintain a continual beating of drums. The Indians remain seated from sundown to noon of the following day. As the effect wears off they get up and go about their work without experiencing unpleasant aftereffects. On the following day, purely for ritual reasons, they abstain from using any salt with their food.

It was not until the end of the nineteenth century that Western scientists became aware of the existence of *peyotl* and began to wonder what properies this insignificant cactus possessed to cause the Indians to encompass it with so splendid a halo of veneration. Earliest of these investigators to describe his own experiences was the American physician, Weir Mitchell, who swallowed "on the morning of a busy day," one and a half drams of an extract of mescal buttons, followed by further doses in the afternoon. By 5:40 P.M. Mitchell found himself "deliciously at languid ease," and observed floating before his eyes luminous star points and fragments of stained glass. Going into a dark room, he settled down to enjoy the performance evoked by the mysterious action of the drug on the cells of his visual cortex.

The display which for an enchanted two hours followed was such as I find it hopeless to describe in language which shall convey to others the beauty and splendor of what I saw. Stars, delicate floating films of color, then an abrupt rush of countless points of white light swept across the field of view, as if the unseen millions of the Milky Way were to flow in a sparkling river before my eyes . . . zigzag lines of very bright colors . . . the wonderful loveliness of swelling clouds of more vivid colors gone before I could name them.

A white spear of grey stone grew up to huge height, and became a tall, richly furnished Gothic Tower of very elaborate and definite design, with many rather worn statues standing in the doorways or on stone brackets. As I gazed every projecting angle, cornice and even the face of the stones at their jointings were by degrees covered or hung with clusters of what seemed to be huge precious stones, but uncut, some being more like masses of transparent fruit. These were green, purple, red, and orange, never clear yellow and never blue. All seemed to possess an interior light, and to give the faintest idea of the perfectly satisfying intensity and purity of these gorgeous color fruits is quite beyond my power. All the colors I have ever beheld are dull in comparison to these. As I looked, and it lasted long, the tower became a fine mouse hue, and everywhere the vast pendant masses of emerald green, ruby reds, and orange began to drip a slow rain of colors.

After an endless display of less beautiful marvels I saw that which deeply impressed me. An edge of a huge cliff seemed to project over a gulf of unseen depth. My viewless enchanter set on the brink a huge bird claw of stone. Above, from the stem or leg, hung a fragment of the same stuff. This began to unroll and float out to a distance which seemed to me to represent Time as well as immensity of Space. Here were miles of rippled purples, half transparent, and of ineffable beauty. Now and then soft golden clouds floated from these folds, or a great shimmer went over the whole of the rolling purples, and things like green birds fell from it, fluttering down into the gulf below. Next, I saw clusters of stones hanging in masses from the claw toes, as it seemed to me miles of them, down far below into the underworld of the black gulf. This was the most distinct of my visions.

In his last vision, Mitchell saw the beach of Newport with its rolling waves as "liquid splendors, huge and threatening, of wonderfully pure green, or red or deep purple, once only deep orange, and with no trace of foam. These water hills of color broke on the beach with myriads of lights of the same tint as the wave."

The author considered it totally impossible to find words to describe the colors. "They still linger visibly in my memory, and left the feeling that I had seen among them colors unknown to my experience."

News of the remarkable properties of *peyotl* spread to Europe, where Havelock Ellis, famed for his pioneer studies in the field of human sexual behavior, decided to experiment with this singular drug. Having obtained in London a small sample of mescal buttons, he settled down in his quiet rooms in the Temple and prepared a decoction from three of the buttons which he drank at intervals between 2:30 and 4:30 P.M

The first symptom observed during the afternoon was a certain consciousness of energy and intellectual power. This passed off. and about an hour after the final dose I felt faint and unsteady; the pulse was low, and I found it pleasanter to lie down. I was still able to read, and I noticed that a pale violet shadow floated over the page around the point at which my eyes were fixed. I had already noticed that objects not in the direct line of vision, such as my hands holding the book, showed a tendency to look obtrusive. heightened in color, almost monstrous. while, on closing my eyes, after-images were vivid and prolonged. The appearance of visions with closed eyes was very gradual. At first there was merely a vague play of light and shade which suggested pictures, but never made them Then the pictures became more definite, but too confused and crowded to be described. beyond saying that they were of the same character as the images of the kaleidoscope, symmetrical groupings of spiked objects. Then, in the course of the evening, they became distinct, but still indescribable—mostly a vast field of golden jewels, studded with red and green stones, ever changing. This moment was, perhaps, the most delightful of the experience, for at the same time the air around me seemed to be flushed with vague perfume—producing with the visions a delicious effect—and all discomfort had vanished, except a slight faintness and tremor of the hands, which, later on, made it almost impossible to guide a pen as I made notes of the experiment; it was, however, with an effort, always possible to write with a pencil. The visions never resembled familiar objects; they were extremely definite, but yet always novel; they were constantly approaching, and yet constantly eluding, the semblance of known things. I would see thick, glorious fields of jewels, solitary or clustered, sometimes brilliant and sparkling, sometimes with a dull rich glow. Then they would spring up into flower-like shapes beneath my gaze, and then seem to turn into gorgeous butterfly forms or endless folds of glistening, iridescent, fibrous wings of wonderful insects; while sometimes I seemed to be gazing into a vast hollow revolving vessel, on whose polished concave mother-of-pearl surface the hues were swiftly changing. I was surprised, not only by the enormous profusion of the imagery presented to my gaze, but still more by its variety. Perpetually some totally new kind of effect would appear in the field of vision; sometimes there was swift movement, sometimes dull, somber richness of color, sometimes glitter and sparkle, once a startling rain of gold, which seemed to approach me. Most usually there was a combination of rich, sombre color, with jewel-like points of brilliant hue. Every color and tone conceivable to me appeared at some time or another. Sometimes all the different varieties of one color, as of red, with scarlets, crimsons, pinks, would spring up together, or in quick succession. But in spite of this immense profusion, there was always a certain parsimony and aesthetic value in the colors presented. They were usually associated with form, and never appeared in large masses, or if so, the tone was very delicate. I was further impressed, not only by the brilliance, delicacy, and variety of the colors, but even more by their lovely and various textures—fibrous, woven, polished, glowing, dull-veined, semi-transparent—the glowing effects, as of jewels, and the fibrous, as of insect's wings, being perhaps the most prevalent. Although the effects were novel, it frequently happened, as I have already mentioned, that they vaguely recalled known objects. Thus, once the objects presented to me seemed to be made of exquisite porcelain, again they were like elaborate sweetmeats, again of a somewhat Maori style of architecture; and the background of the pictures frequently recalled, both in form and tone, the delicate architectural effects as of lace carved in wood, which we associate with the mouchrabieh work of Cairo. But always the visions grew and changed without any reference to the characteristics of those real objects of which they vaguely reminded me, and when I tried to influence their course it was with very little success. On the whole, I should say that the images were most usually what might be called living arabesques. There was often a certain incomplete tendency to symmetry, as though the underlying mechanism was associated with a large number of polished facets. The same image was in this way frequently repeated over a large part of the field; but this refers more to form than to color, in respect to which there would still be all sorts of delightful varieties, so that if, with a certain uniformity, jewel-like flowers were springing up and expanding all over the field of vision, they would still show every variety of delicate tone and tint.

Weir Mitchell found that he could only see the visions with closed eyes and in a perfectly dark room. I could see them in the dark and with almost equal facility, though they were not of equal brilliancy, when my eyes were wide open. I saw them best, however, when my eyes were closed, in a room lighted only by flickering firelight. This evidently accords with the experience of the Indians, who keep a fire burning brightly throughout their mescal rites.

The visions continued with undiminished brilliance for many hours, and as I felt somewhat faint and muscularly weak, I went to bed, as I undressed being impressed by the red, scaly, bronzed, and pigmented appearance of my limbs whenever I was not directly gazing at them. I had not the faintest desire for sleep; there was a general hyperaesthesia of all the senses as well as muscular irritability, and every slightest sound seemed magnified to startling dimensions. I may also have been kept awake by a vague alarm at the novelty of my condition, and the possibility of further developments.

After watching the visions in the dark for some hours I became a little tired of them and turned on the gas. Then I found that I was able to study a new series of visual phenomena to which previous observers had made no reference. The gas jet (an ordinary flickering burner) seemed to burn with great brilliance, sending out waves of light, which expanded and contracted in an enormously exaggerated manner. I was even more impressed by the shadows, which were in all directions heightened by flushes of red, green, and especially violet. The whole room, with its whitewashed but not very white ceiling, thus became vivid and beautiful. The difference between the room as I saw it then and the appearance it usually presents to me was the difference one may often observe between the picture of a room and the actual

. room. The shadows I saw were the shadows which the artist puts in, but which are not visible in the actual scene under normal conditions of casual inspection. I was reminded of the paintings of Claude Monet, and as I gazed at the scene it occurred to me that mescal perhaps produces exactly the same conditions of visual hyperaesthesia, or rather exhaustion, as may be produced on the artist by the influence of prolonged visual attention. I wished to ascertain how the subdued and steady electric light would influence vision, and passed into the next room; but here the shadows were little marked, although the walls and floor seemed tremulous and insubstantial, and the texture of everything was heightened and enriched.

About 3:30 A.M. I felt that the phenomena were distinctly diminishing—though the visions, now chiefly of human figures, fantastic and Chinese in character, still continued—and I was able to settle myself to sleep, which proved peaceful and dreamless. I awoke at the usual hour and experienced no sense of fatigue nor other unpleasant reminiscence of the experience I had undergone. Only my eyes seemed unusually sensitive to color, especially to blue and violet; I can, indeed, say that ever since this experience I have been more aesthetically sensitive than I was before to the more delicate phenomena of light and shade and color.

So impressed was Havelock Ellis by his experiences that he persuaded an artist friend to try the drug. After consuming four of the buttons this artist became violently ill. Paroxysmal attacks of pain in the region of the heart were combined with a sense of imminent death while so great was the dread of light and the dilation of the pupils that the eyelids had to be kept more or less closed. The colored visions did indeed begin at this time but so preoccupied was the artist with his other less pleasant sensations that he had little opportunity to enjoy the strange hues he now perceived.

I saw an intensely vivid blue light begin to play around every object. A square cigarette box, violet in color, shone like an amethyst. I turned my eyes away and beheld this time, on the back of a polished chair, a bar of color glowing like a ruby. Although I was expecting some such manifestation as one of the first symptoms of the intoxication, I was nevertheless somewhat alarmed when this phenomenon took place. Such a silent and sudden illumination of all things around, where a moment before I had seen nothing uncommon, seemed like a kind of madness beginning from outside me, and its strangeness affected me more than its beauty. A desire to escape from it led me to the door, and the act of moving had, I noticed, the effect of dispelling the colors. But a sudden difficulty in breathing and a sensation of numbness at the heart brought me back to the armchair from which I had risen. From this moment I had a series of paroxysms, which I can only describe by saying that I felt as though I were dying. It was impossible to move, and it seemed almost impossible to breathe. My speedy dissolution, I half imagined, was about to take place, and the power of making any resistance to the violent sensations that were arising within was going, I felt, with every second.

The first paroxysms were the most violent. They would come on with tinglings in the lower limbs, and with the sensation of a nauseous and suffocating gas mounting up into my head. Two or three times this was accompanied by a color vision of the gas bursting into flame as it passed up my throat. But I seldom had visions during the paroxysms; these would appear in the intervals. They began with a spurting up of colors; once, of a flood of brightly illuminated green

water covering the field of vision, and effervescing in parts,
just as when fresh water with all the air bubbles is pumped
into a swimming bath. At another time my eye seemed to be
turning into a vast drop of dirty water in which millions of
minute creatures resembling tadpoles were in motion. But
the early visions consisted mostly of a furious succession of
colored arabesques, arising and descending or sliding at
every possible angle into the field of view. It would be as
difficult to give a description of the whirl of water at the
bottom of a waterfall as to describe the chaos of color and
design which marked this period.

Now also began another series of extraordinary sensations. They set in with bewildering suddenness and followed
one another in rapid succession. These I now record as they
occur to my mind at haphazard: (1) My right leg became suddenly heavy and solid; it seemed, indeed, as if the entire
weight of my body had shifted into one part, about the thigh
and knee, and that the rest of my body had lost all substan-
tiality. (2) With the suddenness of a neuralgic pang, the back
of my head seemed to open and emit streams of bright color;
this was immediately followed by the feeling as of a draft
blowing like a gale through the hair in the same region.
(3) At one moment the color, green, acquired a taste in my
mouth; it was sweetish and somewhat metallic; blue again
would have taste that seemed to recall phosphorus; these
are the only colors that seemed to be connected with taste.
(4) A feeling of delightful relief and preternatural lightness
about my forehead, succeeded by a growing sensation of contraction. (5) Singing in one of my ears. (6) A sensation of
burning heat in the palm of my left hand. (7) Heat about
both eyes. The last continued throughout the whole period,
except for a moment when I had a sensation of cold upon
the eyelids, accompanied with a color vision of the wrinkled

lid, of the skin disappearing from the brow, of dead flesh, and finally of a skull.

Throughout these sensations and visions my mind remained not only perfectly clear, but enjoyed, I believe, an unusual lucidity. Certainly I was conscious of an odd contrast in hearing myself talk rationally with H.E., who had entered the room a short time before, and experiencing at the same moment the wild and extraordinary pranks that were taking place in my body. My reason appeared to be the sole survivor of my being. At times I felt that this, too, would go, but the sound of my own voice would establish again the communication with the outer world of reality.

Tremors were more or less constant in my lower limbs. Persistent, also, was the feeling of nausea. This, when attended by a feeling of suffocation and a pain at the heart, was relieved by taking brandy, coffee or biscuit. For muscular exertion I felt neither the wish nor the power. My hands, however, retained their full strength.

It was painful for me to keep my eyes open above a few seconds; the light of day seemed to fill the room with a blinding glare. Yet every object, in the brief glimpse I caught, appeared normal in color and shape. With my eyes closed, most of the visions, after the first chaotic display, represented parts of the whole of my body undergoing a variety of marvellous changes, of metamorphoses or illumination. They were more often than not comic and grotesque in character, though often beautiful in color. At one time I saw my right leg filling up with a delicate heliotrope; at another, the sleeve of my coat changed into a dark green material, in which was worked a pattern in red braid, and the whole bordered at the cuff with sable. Scarcely had my new sleeve taken shape than I found myself attired in a complete costume of the same fashion, mediaeval in character, but I

could not say to what precise period it belonged. I noted that
a chance movement—of my hand, for instance—would immediately call up a color vision of the part exerted, and that
this again would pass, by a seemingly natural transition, into
another wholly dissimilar. Thus, pressing my fingers accidentally against my temples, the fingertips became elongated,
and then grew into the ribs of a vaulting or of a dome shaped
roof. But most of the visions were of a more personal nature. I happened once to lift a spoon of coffee to my lips,
and as I was in the act of raising my arm for that purpose a
vision flashed before my closed (or nearly closed) eyes, in all
the hues of the rainbow, of my arm separated from my body,
and serving me with coffee from out of dark and indefinite
space. On another occasion, as I was seeking to relieve slight
nausea by taking a piece of biscuit passed to me by H.E., it
suddenly streamed out into blue flame. It was a sight of
wonderful beauty. But this was not all. As I placed the biscuit in my mouth it burst out again into the same colored
fire and illuminated the interior of my mouth, casting a blue
reflection on the roof. The light in the Blue Grotto at Capri,
I am able to affirm, is not nearly as blue as seemed for a
short space of time the interior of my mouth. There were
many visions of which I could not trace the origin. There
were spirals and arabesques and flowers, and sometimes objects more trivial and prosaic in character. In one vision I
saw a row of small white flowers, one against the other like
pearls of a necklace, begin to revolve in the form of a spiral.
Every flower, I observed, had the texture of porcelain. It was
at a moment when I had the sensation of my cheeks growing
hot and feverish that I experienced the strangest of all the
color visions. It began with feeling that the skin of my face
was becoming quite thin and of no stouter consistency than
tissue paper, and the feeling was suddenly enhanced by a

vision of my face, paper-like and semitransparent and somewhat reddish in color. To my amazement I saw myself as
though I were inside a Chinese lantern, looking out through
my cheek into the room.

This artist particularly noted the curious dualism, the
split of personality, so often observed by those who enter the
strange world to which *peyotl* is the key. On returning to
the normal state he experienced that sense of unreality
which sometimes assails the spectator of a particularly fascinating play who emerges suddenly into the gray light of the
everyday world.

As one pours out with the crowd into the street, the ordinary world, by force of contrast with the sensational scenes
just witnessed, breaks in upon one with almost a sense of unreality. The house, the aspect of the street, even the light of
day appear a little foreign for a few moments. During these
moments everything strikes the mind as odd and unfamiliar,
or at least with a greater degree of objectivity. Such was my
feeling with regard to my old and habitual self. . . . It was
as if I had unexpectedly attained an objective knowledge of
my own personality. I saw, as it were, my normal state of
being with the eyes of a person who sees the street on coming out of the theatre in broad day.

This sensation also brought out the independence of the
mind during the period of intoxication. It alone appeared to
have escaped the ravages of the drug; it alone remained sane
during a general delirium, vindicating, so it seemed, the
majesty of its own impersonal nature. It had reigned for a
while, I now felt, as an autocrat, without ministers and their
officiousness. Henceforth I should be more or less conscious
of the interdependence of body and brain; a slight head-

ache, a touch of indigestion, or what not, would be able to effect what a general intoxication of my senses and nerves could not touch.

As the year continued Havelock Ellis was tempted to use more of his friends as human guinea pigs to unravel the mysteries of the world of *peyotl*. One, a poet, with an interest in mystical matters and a knowledge of various vision-producing drugs, found the effect of *peyotl* mainly unpleasant and decided he much preferred *hashish*. Another poet was particularly impressed by the "sound-colors" which flowed about him as he played the piano. Havelock Ellis himself found that music had a potent effect on his visions. This was particularly true of Schumann's music, especially of his *Waldscenen* and *Kinderscenen*.

"The Prophet Bird" called up vividly a sense of atmosphere and of brilliant feathery birdlike forms passing to and fro, "A Flower Piece" provoked constant and persistent images of vegetation, while "Scheherazade" produced an effect of floating white raiment, covered by glittering spangles and jewels. In every case my description was, of course, given before I knew the name of the piece. I do not pretend that this single series of experiments proves much, but it would certainly be worth while to follow up this indication and to ascertain if any light is hereby thrown on the power of a composer to suggest definite imagery, or the power of a listener to perceive it.

After Havelock Ellis, the next student of *peyotl* was the French pharmacologist Alexandre Rouhier, who described the reactions of one of his subjects to a dose of 2 grams of *peyotl* extract. The subject, who took the drug at 8 P.M., experienced visions which began an hour and forty minutes later and which "continued to unfold without interruption for the next twenty-three hours, nor did the pleasure with which L. contemplated the unfolding of these colorful scenes decrease during this time." The visions were complex and varied. Only a few examples will be given here.

An ornate ring of diamonds. The large central stone emits great quantities of green, violet, or rose-colored fire which inundates the whole scene with a strange glow, complex in color, the product of the fusion of the multiple fires. One of the diamonds opens revealing within it a little angel which leaps from the ring, picks it up and carries it with an effort. A woman appears, "beautiful as a goddess." Her features are noble, her nose aquiline, her color yellowish bronze, her curly auburn hair floats unrestrained. She plays with the little angel. A group of women appears, of which some are clad in pink and some in blue robes. In the midst of them is a dancer who makes rhythmic movements. Soon all of them are dancing, sometimes in couples, sometimes in vari-colored groups. The little angel dances on her hands, her legs in the air. She goes and fetches a placard on which is written "I am love." She flies up onto a cloud.

The dancers are going. The goddess remains alone; her features bear the marks of infinite sorrow; she weeps, then throws herself onto the ground, sobbing "as if she would die." She grows dim and disappears.

Visions of a virgin forest; luxuriant tropical vegetation; trees with trunks draped with giant creepers, the soil covered with tall dense grass. Hanging from a branch there appears a monkey holding a coconut. Below there appears a large beast, strange and ferocious of aspect, its mouth agape, displaying terrible white teeth. Above appears another monkey and plays with the first.

A glade illuminated by the light of the sun which sifts through the thick foliage. Beautiful tone contrasts are seen in the shadows. In the middle is a pond covered with water lilies whose leaves are filled with toads. Frightened, they all jump briskly into the water. A vermillion colored man approaches carrying a bow and a quiver. His hair is ornamented with feathers. A fine graceful antelope emerges from the undergrowth and comes to drink at the pond "with infinite delicacy." The Indian kills and dismembers it and departs, carrying its head. L., overwhelmed by the intensity of the visions, cries with indignation. "What a brute! He cannot understand the beauty of nature! How graceful the animal is even in death."

Several of Rouhier's subjects commented on the tiny figures they saw under the influence of *peyotl*. These "lilliputian hallucinations" are contrasted by Rouhier with the gigantic figures, the "Brobdingnagian illusions," seen under the influence of *yage*, another hallucinogen which will be described later.

After these studies little further work was carried out on the effects of crude *peyotl*. The chemists, ever on the lookout for new worlds to conquer, had taken the divine plant into their laboratories, bent on determining the nature of those substances that endow it with its vision-provoking properties. The brown malodorous decoction of the mescal buttons was progressively purified and one crystalline compound after another was separated from the crude material. No less than nine alkaloids were finally crystallized, several of which influenced the behavior of experimental animals. Most poisonous of these alkaloids was lophophorine, which, in doses of about 12 milligrams. per kilogram body weight, would produce in rabbits violent convulsions of the type seen in sufferers from tetanus or strychnine poisoning. The substance pellotine produced in man a drowsiness suggesting that it might be of use as a sedative. Anhalonidine, on the other hand, had a stimulating effect on the central nervous system.

But of all the substances isolated from this curious cactus the most important and interesting was called mescaline. To this substance and to this substance alone the extraordinary visions of the *peyotl* eater could be attributed. Mescaline is not a complex substance. It belongs to the large and important group of chemicals known as amines, many of which (for instance, adrenalin and nor-adrenalin) have a powerful action on the chemistry of the body. To be more specific, mescaline is a derivative of ammonia (NH_3) in which one of the hydrogens has been replaced by a chain of carbon atoms grouped as shown in the Appendix. Chemically it is 3, 4, 5-trimethoxy phenyl ethylamine, a substance which can be synthesized without too much difficulty so that those who wish to enjoy the *peyotl*-induced visions need not depend on the cactus for their supply of the drug.

With pure mescaline available, investigators of the properties of the drug no longer had to chew the nauseating cactus or swallow revolting decoctions brewed from its buttons. They left such questionable pleasures to the Indians and continued their studies with the purified essence of the sacred plant, either swallowing or injecting the solution into their persons. Research continued vigorously. From the laboratory of Dr. Beringer in Heidelberg emerged a tome, three hundred and fifteen pages in length, a worthy example of German *Wissenschaftlichkeit,* which remains the most massive contribution on the subject to date. Dr. Beringer's subjects generally took their mescaline in the form of an injection, the dose employed being usually 400 milligrams. Their experiences had much in common with those described by Weir Mitchell and Havelock Ellis, but the metaphysical bent of the Teutonic mind, its tendency to seek the ultimate, the infinite, the inexpressible, added to the already rich spectrum of the mescal experience certain deeper hues not noted by the earlier investigators.

I ceased my reading of Weil's book on *Internal Secretions* because the day was filled with the phenomena evoked by mescaline. Soon there began on the carpet before me a wonderful display. From the edge of the field of vision there crept across the green carpet beasts like the monsters from a fairy tale stretching out tongues and claws. I watched their play with pleasure only regretting that the beasts appeared in various shades of gray. Scarcely had this thought passed through my mind before the eyes of the beasts glittered with green or red lights. Soon their tongues and claws became touched with crimson and began to flicker like the play of flames in a fire. . . . Somewhat later I fixed my eyes on a point on the ceiling on which were a few small flies in the web of a spider. Suddenly the flies began to multiply lit up by beautiful colors within the ever-changing form of the spider's web.

Now there appeared before my eyes splendid architectural forms which seemed to hang from the ceiling divided into hexagonal segments like honeycombs. Above the ceiling each honeycomb rose up and developed into a painted Gothic arch. While I delighted in the upward striving of these slender arches they towered to ever greater heights before my eyes. Extraordinary joy overcame me—a strong and beautiful feeling of eternity and infinity. This so overwhelmed me that soon everything appeared infinite. There they were again, the deep beautiful perspectives which I had seen during my first experience with mescaline, but now they never stood still, they grew constantly deeper. As with space so with time. The ordinary human concept of time seemed contemptible. I would not even think of it. The sense of drifting in the infinite, of flowing into the ocean of eternity occupied me entirely and was most closely and intimately associated with my self-awareness. I experienced a unique pleasure from exploring the endlessness of my own ego, the boundlessness of every one of my psychic functions. . . . My psychological equilibrium was constantly changing. At one moment I would experience pleasure because I could go to sleep in my own little world; at another I stood astounded by profound riddles, by the mystery of the magic play within me. I even felt fear at the thought of that wild secret force at work within my being.

Similarly pervaded with what Baudelaire has called "The Taste of the Infinite" were the experiences of another of Beringer's subjects:

My ideas of space were strange beyond description. I could see myself from head to foot as well as the sofa on which I was lying. About me was nothingness, absolutely empty space. I was floating on a solitary island in the ether. No part of my body was subject to the laws of gravitation. On the other side of the vacuum—the room seemed to be unlimited in space—extremely fantastic figures appeared before my eyes. I was very excited, perspired and shivered, and was kept in a state of ceaseless wonder. I saw endless passages with beautiful arches, delightfully colored arabesques, grotesque decorations, divine, sublime and enchanting in their

fantastic splendor. These visions changed in waves and billows, were built, destroyed, and appeared again in endless
variations first on one plane and then in three dimensions,
at last disappearing into infinity The sofa island disappeared. I did not feel my physical self; an ever increasing
sense of dissolution set in. I was seized with passionate
curiosity, great things were about to be unveiled before me.
I would perceive the essence of all things, the problem of
creation would be unravelled I was dematerialized!

The mystical aspects of the mescaline experience have
very recently been investigated again Aldous Huxley, a
representative of that "universal man" commoner in the
Renaissance than in our overspecialized age, has studied the
subject from the standpoint of a creative writer who is at
the same time a mystic and a scientist. His own experiences,
after swallowing 400 milligrams of mescaline, involved a
change not in the identity of things perceived but in the
content of perception He describes no fields of gorgeous
jewels, none of the Gothic arches so popular with the German investigators, none of the strange beasts, the "delightful dragons balancing white balls on their breath," which
visited one of Havelock Ellis's poets. There is nothing in
Aldous Huxley's account which even suggests that mescaline might be, as some have described it, a hallucinogen—
that is to say, an agent capable of generating hallucinations.
The essence of a hallucinogen is that it causes those under
its influence to hear, see, or feel things which are not present.
Havelock Ellis's rotating flower beds, Weir Mitchell's tower
dripping jewels, these were hallucinations in the true sense
of the word. No such phenomena are described in Aldous
Huxley's book

The change which, for him, was brought about by mescaline concerned the manner in which familiar objects were perceived. "How wonderfully supernatural and how miraculous this," wrote the Zen patriarch, "I draw water and I carry fuel!" It was exactly this transformation of simple things which Aldous Huxley described, and this element of the miraculous, enhaloing ordinary objects, was for him far more significant than any color vision or elaborate phantasy. Certainly he experienced that enrichment of color values which is an almost universal feature of descriptions of the mescaline experience. His books, for example, took on a gemlike glow.

Red books, like rubies; emerald books; books bound in white jade; books of agate; of aquamarine, of yellow topaz; lapis lazuli books whose color was so intense, so intrinsically meaningful, that they seemed to be on the point of leaving the shelves to thrust themselves more insistently on my attention.

But this enrichment of the quality of colors was secondary to the extraordinary significance with which simple objects became endowed. An hour and a half after taking mescaline Aldous Huxley found himself looking intently at a small glass vase.

The vase contained only three flowers—a full blown Belle of Portugal rose, shellpink with a tint at every petal's base of a hotter, flamier hue; a large magenta and cream-colored carnation; and, pale purple at the end of its broken stalk, the bold heraldic blossom of an iris. Fortuitous and provisional, the little nosegay broke all the rules of traditional good taste. At breakfast that morning I had been struck by the lively dissonance of its colors. But that was no longer the point. I was not looking now at an unusual flower arrangement. I was seeing what Adam had seen on the morning of his creation—the miracle, moment by moment, of naked existence.

What the rose, the iris, and the carnation so intensely signified when viewed with perception modified by mescaline was

. . . nothing more, and nothing less, than what they actually were—a transience that was yet eternal life, a perpetual perishing that was at the same time pure Being, a bundle of minute particulars in which, by some unspeakable and yet self-evident paradox, was to be seen in the divine source of all existence.

I continued to look at the flowers, and in their living light I seemed to detect the qualitative equivalent of breathing, but of a breathing without returns to a starting point, with no recurrent ebbs but only a repeated flow from beauty to heightened beauty, from deeper to ever deeper meaning. Words like "grace" and "transfiguration" came to my mind, and this, of course, was what, among other things, they stood for. My eyes travelled from the rose to the carnation, and from that feathery incandescence to the smooth scrolls of sentient amethyst which were the iris. The Beatific Vision, *Sat Chit Ananda*, Being-Awareness-Bliss—for the first time I understood, not on the verbal level, not by inchoate hints or at a distance, but precisely and completely what those prodigious syllables referred to.

The foregoing descriptions of the effects of mescaline will probably have left the reader with the impression that this purified product of the sacred cactus offers the key to a very remarkable world. To many people it does indeed offer such a key and its virtues have been summarized very clearly by Havelock Ellis:

Mescal intoxication may be described as chiefly a saturnalia for the specific senses, and, above all, an orgy of vision. It reveals an optical fairyland, where all the senses now and again join the play, but the mind itself remains a self-possessed spectator. Mescal intoxication thus differs from the other artificial paradises which drugs procure. Under the influence of alcohol, for instance, as in normal dreaming, the intellect is impaired, although there may be a consciousness of unusual brilliance; hasheesh, again, produces an uncontrollable tendency to movement and bathes its victim in a sea of emotion. The mescal drinker remains calm and collected amid the sensory turmoil around him; his judgment is as clear as in the normal state; he falls into no oriental condition of vague and voluptuous reverie. The reason why mescal is of all this class of drugs the most purely intellectual in its appeal is evidently because it affects mainly the most intellectual of the senses. On this ground it is not probable that its use will easily develop into a habit. Moreover, unlike most other intoxicants, it seems to have no special affinity for a disordered and unbalanced nervous system; on the contrary, it demands organic soundness and good health for complete manifestation of its virtues. Further, unlike the other chief substances to which it may be compared, mescal does not wholly carry us away from the actual world, or plunge us into oblivion; a large part of its charm lies in the halo of beauty which it casts around the simplest and commonest things. It is the most democratic of the plants which lead men to an artificial paradise. If it should ever chance that the consumption of mescal becomes a habit, the favorite poet of the mescal drinker will certainly be Wordsworth. Not only the general attitude of Wordsworth but many of his most memorable poems and phrases cannot—one is almost tempted to say—be appreciated in their full significance by one who has never been under the influence of mescal. On all these grounds it may be claimed that the artificial paradise of mescal, though less seductive, is safe and dignified beyond its peers.

The author, however, would not be doing his duty as an impartial reporter if he did not add that even the glamorous world of mescaline has its darker side. Not everyone can enter its colorful kingdom.

"Along with the happily transfigured majority of mescaline takers," writes Aldous Huxley, "there is a minority that finds in the drug only hell and purgatory." This is undoubtedly true, nor is it easy to be sure just how correctly we can claim that the "happily transfigured" are in the majority. The following description by Tayleur Stockings of the general appearance of a group of individuals under the influence of mescaline seems hardly that of "happily transformed beings":

The lips and tongue become dry and coated with sordes; the skin is flushed at first, and later becomes dry and harsh with an earthy pallor; the conjunctiva are injected, and the eyes appear unnaturally bright. The urine is scanty and highly colored, and there is absolute insomnia, anorexia (loss of appetite) and in the later stages, restlessness. . . . There is always nausea and occasionally vomiting in the early stages.

This nausea may not interfere with the subject's enjoyment of his strange experiences. As Klüver points out, "In spite of marked nausea many subjects 'have a good time'; being in a state of mental exhilaration they become talka- tive and jocular, they commit social errors and enjoy com- mitting them—harmless remarks, even a potato salad or a catsup bottle, are considered unusually funny." In other sub- jects, however, the unpleasant symptoms produced by the drug are unrelieved by any consoling experience, visual or otherwise.

One might suppose such individuals to be degraded types whose "doors of perception" are so hopelessly muddied that even the potent cleansing action of mescaline makes no im- pression on the encrusting grime. This can hardly be true. That prince of psychologists, William James, was certainly no stranger to the realm of mystical experience. He remains one of the few psychologists of any standing who has ever taken the trouble to investigate religious phenomena. Yet William James, who received *peyotl* from Weir Mitchell, derived from the sacred cactus nothing more than a stom- ach-ache. "I ate one bud three days ago," he wrote in a letter to his brother Henry, "was violently sick for twenty- four hours, and had no other symptoms whatever except that and the Katzenjammer the following day. I will take the visions on trust." Even Weir Mitchell, whose experiences were much more promising, commented, "These shows are expensive. . The experience, however, was worth one such headache and indigestion but was not worth a second."

Quite apart from the nausea, anorexia, and insomnia, the mescaline visions themselves are by no means always divine:

In some individuals the "ivresse divine" of which Rouhier speaks comes nearer to being an "ivresse diabolique." Vague terrors and the sense of impending disaster often mingle with the cosmic experiences. The immensity of the new realms perceived may frighten more than they enlighten the mescaline taker . . . the experiences in the mescal state are not easily forgotten. One looks "beyond the horizon" of the normal world, and this "beyond" is often so impressive or even shocking that its aftereffects linger for years in one's memory. No wonder some subjects are disinclined to repeat the experiment . . . [Klüver].

For this reason it is improbable that mescaline will ever become widely popular as a means of fleeing the drab realities of the ordinary world. The artificial paradise to which it holds the key is too strange a realm to appeal to the average taste and the cost of getting there, in terms of unpleasant physical reactions, would seem excessive. Many, in fact, would agree with William James that the experience is not worth the *Katzenjammer*. * As a euphoriant it is unlikely to replace alcohol, though its effects are infinitely more interesting, and it "does not drive the taker into the kind of uninhibited action which results in brawls, crimes of violence and traffic accidents" (Huxley). It has no addiction-forming properties. Indians who have consumed it for years can still manage perfectly well without the drug. It seems to have no lasting ill effect on any organ in the body, including the liver on which falls the task of detoxifying this particular poison, for mescaline is poisonous, albeit the effects are interesting and the toxic symptoms rarely alarming. It belongs to the class of poisons which the great toxicologist, Lewin, labeled phantastica, a class of materials now more commonly referred to as hallucinogens. It is probably one of the most

* This expressive German word means, literally, caterwauling. In the sense used above it describes the unpleasant symptoms left by an alcoholic debauch, in short a "hangover."

harmless members of this group of drugs, but is nonetheless quite toxic for certain people.

As regards the way in which mescaline exerts its effects, we have to admit that we are almost entirely ignorant. Quastel and Wheatley have shown that mescaline and several related substances interfere with oxidative processes in minced brain tissue. Aldous Huxley has accepted this finding as the explanation of mescaline's mode of action. He envisages the brain as a kind of reducing valve which protects our little human minds from the overwhelming pressure of "Mind at Large." When the efficiency of the reducing valve is impaired by mescaline "Mind at Large," or the mind of the macrocosm, pushes its way into the mind of the microcosm, which explains the overwhelming character of certain mescaline experiences. To assume, however, that mescaline exerts its characteristic action simply by lowering the brain's capacity to utilize oxygen would not seem warranted by the evidence. The barbiturates also cut down oxidation in brain slices but these substances do not produce the color visions or other experiences typical of mescaline. They merely put the one who takes them to sleep. Further, it must be emphasized again that between minced brain in a test tube and living brain in a man's skull there is a very wide gap. We dare not even assume that mescaline taken by mouth or even injected into the blood necessarily enters the brain itself. It may be checked by the blood-brain barrier. It may be transformed in the liver into something chemically different. This, say the German workers Patzig and Block, is actually what does happen. When mescaline is "labeled" by building into it an atom of radioactive carbon, its presence can be detected in the liver but hardly a trace of the substance can be found in the brain. Its effects, these workers believe, are due to its combining with liver protein to form a toxic substance which, like a number of other toxic substances, interferes with brain function and causes hallucinations.

F. M. Sturtevant and V. A. Drill, who injected mescaline directly into the brains of cats, thus forcing the drug past the blood-brain barrier, have shown that it produces dramatic effects on the animal's behavior. The cats began a loud continuous yowling which was unlike any normal cat sound. They retched, they salivated, they defecated, and their breath came in short gasps. Particularly noticeable was the change in their behavior toward mice. Cats which, before treatment with mescaline, had instantly caught and killed a mouse, merely ignored the animal while under the influence of the drug. Indeed, so great did their forbearance become that one submitted placidly to having his ears and nose nibbled. The drug evidently made pacifists out of the cats and filled them with brotherly love which extended even to mice. They appeared to derive enjoyment from rubbing their cheeks against the mice and allowing them to crawl over and under their bodies. The happy state foretold by the prophet was thus realized; the lion lay down with the lamb and did not hurt nor destroy. For the next eighteen to twenty hours the peace continued, after which the fondling became progressively rougher, ending with typical cat-and-mouse play in which the mice were killed and eaten. It is clear from this work that mescaline does have some direct effect on the chemistry of the brain; the nature of this action is at present unknown.

The Mind and Marihuana

Now the three statues advanced towards him, and approached the couch on which he was reposing, their feet hidden in their long white tunics, their throats bare, their hair flowing like waves. Assuming attitudes which the gods could not resist but which saints withstood they turned upon him looks inflexibly ardent such as those with which a serpent charms a bird. Then he gave way before looks which held him in a torturing grasp and delighted his senses as with a voluptuous kiss. Now followed a dream of passion like that promised by the Prophet to his Elect. Lips of stone turned to flame, breasts of ice became like heated lava, so that to Franz, yielding for the first time to the sway of the hashish, love was a sorrow and voluptuousness a torture, as burning mouths were pressed to his thirsty lips, and he was held in cool serpentlike embraces. The more he strove against this unhallowed passion the more his senses yielded to its spell, and at length, weary of the struggle that strained his very soul, he sank back yielding, breathless and exhausted, under the kisses of those marble goddesses, wrapped in the enchantment of his marvellous dream.

What goes on here? It is the fertile pen of Alexandre Dumas busying itself with a theme unfailing in its appeal to the average novel reader—the effect on the mind and emotions of a mysterious oriental drug. Dumas chose well. There is hardly another drug in or out of the pharmacopoeia more shrouded in mystery, more richly encrusted with big and little misconceptions than that substance which in Arabia is called *hashish,* in Persia *beng,* in Morocco *kif,* in South Africa *dagga,* in India *charas, bhang,* or *gangha,* in Mexico and the United States *marihuana,* and in scientific circles "the flowering tops of the female plant of *Cannabis sativa.*"

Scarcely seen in Europe until the middle of the nineteenth century, the drug was known only by reputation from the tales of travelers returning from the Orient. It was always associated with romantic stories colorful and gorgeous as the interminable yarns of Scheherazade. The very word *hashish* carries romantic overtones. This substance, so ran the legend, was fed to his followers by Hasan-i-Sabbah, "The Old Man of the Mountain," who built his stronghold on the craggy peak of Alamut. For the sake of the glimpse of paradise which the drug afforded, his fanatical henchmen would gladly ride across the desert to Basra or Baghdad, there stealthily to murder certain individuals of whom Hasan happened to disapprove. For this reason the furtive secret political murderer is known even today as an assassin, a name supposedly derived from that of the drug. As to the nature of those joys for which Hasan's followers were willing to commit murder, we have a description of them from the pen of no less an orientalist than Marco Polo:

In the centre of the territory of the Assassins there are delicious walled gardens in which one can find everything that can satisfy the needs of the body and the caprices of the most exacting sensuality. Great banks of gorgeous flowers and bushes covered with fruit stand amongst crystal rivers of living water. About them lie verdant fields and from the shaded turf burst bubbling springs. Trellises of roses and fragrant vines cover with their foliage pavilions of jade or porcelain furnished with Persian carpets or Grecian embroideries.

Delicious drinks in vessels of gold or crystal are served by young boys or girls, whose dark unfathomable eyes cause them to resemble the Houris, divinities of that Paradise which the Prophet promised to believers. The sound of harps mingles with the cooing of doves, the murmur of soft voices blends with the sighing of the reeds. All is joy, pleasure, voluptuousness and enchantment.

The Grand Master of the Assassins, whenever he discovers a young man resolute enough to belong to his murderous legions, invites the youth to his table and intoxicates him with the plant *hashish*. Having been secretly transported to the pleasure gardens the young man imagines that he has entered the Paradise of Mahomet. The girls, lovely as Houris, contribute to this illusion. After he has enjoyed to satiety all the joys promised by the Prophet to his elect, he falls again into a state of lethargy and is transported back to the presence of the Grand Master. Here he is informed that he can enjoy perpetually the delights he has just tasted if he will take part in the war of the Infidel as commanded by the Prophet.

Before we plunge further into the myths and marvels which have become associated with this peculiar drug it will be as well if we examine the plant from which it comes. *Marihuana, hashish, bhang, charas,* and the rest are all de-

rived from the hemp plant, *Cannabis sativa.** As a drug
plant cannabis is extremely ancient. Even in the days of
Hasan-i-Sabbah, who staged his deviltries toward the end of
the eleventh century, the plant had a long and varied history. Norman. Taylor, in a vivid account of the plant's
romantic story, describes it as being well known to the
Chinese emperor, Shen Neng, whose work on pharmacy was
written in the year 2737 B.C. An aura of suspicion hung
even then about the plant, for that which gave easy happiness was, then as now, an object of disapproval. The active
preparation from the plant was therefore labeled "Liber-
ator of Sin." Later a more indulgent generation of Chinese
sages called it "the delight giver," while the tolerant Hindus
termed it "the heavenly guide" and "the soother of grief."

A tall gangling weed which may reach a height of ten feet,
the hemp plant has long been grown in Kentucky for its
fiber, but the hardy pioneers who brought it to that state
either knew nothing of its effect on the mind or, despising
its seductions, refused to avail themselves of its artificial
paradise. In India, however, the plant is cultivated especially for the drug. There, in three small villages adjoining
Ahmadnagar in Bombay, special varieties of hemp grow in
the tropical climate, filling the humid air with a fragrance
drowsy and balsamic, faintly reminiscent of the odor which
pervades the hop fields when the ripening cones are about to
shed their golden dust. This dust from the hops is not pollen
but a special resin from which beer derives its bitterness, its
aroma, and its slightly soporific qualities. Hemp and hops
are related and the potent spirit of the hemp also resides in
a resin, sticky and aromatic, which coats the female flowers.
Crushed and rolled into flat cakes, these flowering tops form
the *gangha* of Bengal. Gathered without further treatment,

* The older name, *Cannabis indica*, refers to the same plant.

they constitute the *marihuana* of Mexico. The most potent of all the hemp drugs, *charas,* is produced in Yarkand, in Central Asia. There, in the scented hemp fields, sweltering laborers run to and fro clad only in leather aprons to the surface of which the sticky resin adheres. It is scraped off and pressed into cakes which are green at first but become brown on aging. *Charas* is imported into India via Tibet. In Tibet itself is prepared *momea,* that weird concoction consisting of *charas* incorporated into human fat. It is used by the Dugpas in their unholy rites and is taken from a cup made from a human skull.

In less esoteric circles the hemp drugs are used in a variety of ways. In Bombay the potent *charas* is often incorporated into a sweetmeat called *maajun,* which is popular among members of the female sex. In Egypt and the Middle East *hashish* is smoked in special pipes called *josies,* along with glowing charcoal, the carbon monoxide from which doubtless contributes to the physiological effects. In Mexico and the United States the drug is smoked in the form of *marihuana.* In Algeria a special delicacy is made from cannabis which goes under the name of *dawamesc.* It is prepared by grinding the hemp tops with sugar, orange juice, cinnamon, cloves, cardamom, nutmeg, musk, pistachios, and pine kernels. These are all ground together and served in portions no bigger than a filbert. Meunier mentions that, to increase the aphrodisiac effect of the hemp, the Oriental sometimes adds a "pinch" of nux vomica or cantharides. A toxicologist must shudder to think of these potent poisons handled in so casual a fashion. Without these added ingredients, however, *dawamesc* is a relatively harmless confection.

It was with *dawamesc,* brought from Algeria by Dr. Moreau de Tours, that the members of Le Club des Hachischins carried out those experiments whose descriptions enliven the writings of Théophile Gautier and Baudelaire. These European devotees of the hemp met by invitation in the old Hotel Pimodan in the Latin Quarter of Paris. In the middle of the nineteenth century when they held their meetings the maze of forbidding legislation which now surrounds the drug like a barbed-wire entanglement had not been constructed. The Hachischins therefore were free to indulge as they saw fit without running the risk of spending five years in jail as would any contemporary group rash enough to experiment in the same field and to publish its experiences.

Much can be learned from the writings of members of this group, not only about the effects of cannabis but also about the motives, mental and emotional, that lead men to seek "artificial paradise" and to turn from the world of reality to that of drug-induced unreality. On this subject no one is better qualified to speak than poor, embittered, devil-ridden Baudelaire, rotted with syphilis and addicted to both opium and alcohol, whose face, in the photograph which prefaces his collected works, seems etched with the acid of every form of human grief and frustration. Baudelaire's study, *Les Paradis artificiels*, is in some respects the finest prose he ever wrote. It has more than merely literary value, for Baudelaire, unlike Dumas, Gautier, and the American *hashish* eater, Ludlow, was a careful observer not unduly given to hyperbole. His phrases thus have a flavor of accuracy which is absent from the more colorful accounts by the other writers. Here is his description of the peculiar craving which leads men to seek for the "Taste of the Infinite":

> Those who are able to observe themselves and can remember their impressions often have occasion to note in the observatory of their thoughts strange seasons, luxurious after-

noons, delicious minutes. There are days when a man awakens with a young and vigorous genius. Hardly have his eyelids cast off the sleep which sealed them before the outer world presents itself to him in strong relief, with a clearness of contour and wealth of admirable color. The man gratified with this sense of exquisite loveliness, unfortunately so rare and so transitory, feels himself more than ever the artist, more than ever noble, more than ever just, if one can express so much in so few words. But the most singular thing about this exceptional state of the spirit and of the senses, which without exaggeration can be termed paradisiacal as compared with the hopeless darkness of ordinary daily existence, is that it has not been created by any visible or easily definable cause.

This acuity of thought, this vigor of sense and spirit, has at all times appeared to man as the highest good. For this reason, purely for his immediate enjoyment, without troubling himself about the limitations imposed by his constitution, he has searched in the world of physical and of pharmaceutical science, among the grossest decoctions and the most subtle perfumes, in all climates and at all times, for the means of leaving, if only for a few moments, his habitation of mud and of transporting himself to Paradise in a single swoop.

Alas! Man's vices, horrible as they are supposed to be, contain the positive proof of his taste for the Infinite. *Man will never believe that he has entirely given himself over to evil.* He forgets, in his infatuation, that he is playing with someone stronger and keener than himself, and that the spirit of Evil, even if one gives it no more than a single hair, will eventually carry away the head. Therefore this visible lord of visible nature (I speak of man) desired to create paradise with the help of pharmacy, exactly like a maniac who would replace his solid furniture and real gardens with decorations painted on canvas and mounted on easels. I believe that in this depraved sense of the Infinite lies the reason for all guilty excesses, from the solitary and concentrated intoxication of the man of letters who, obliged to turn to opium for relief of some physical suffering, little by little makes it . . . the sun of his spiritual life, to the drunkard who, his brain afire with glory, hideously wallows in the filth of a Paris street.

Concerning the world of *hashish*, Baudelaire writes as follows in his chapter intriguingly entitled "The Theatre of the Seraphim":

Ignorant people suppose that the intoxication of hashish represents a prodigious land, a vast theatre of jugglery, in which all is miraculous and unexpected. That is a prejudice, a complete mistake. . . . In the intoxication of hashish there is nothing of the kind. Our dreams are natural, our intoxication will always keep the peculiar tonality of the individual. Men who are eager to experience unusual pleasures should know that in hashish they will find nothing miraculous, absolutely nothing but what is extremely natural. The brain and the organism on which hashish operates give only their ordinary individual phenomena, increased it is true as to number and energy but always faithful to their origin. Man cannot escape the fatality of his physical and moral temperament. Hashish will be for man's familiar thoughts and impressions a mirror that exaggerates but always a mirror.

Over the surface of man's ordinary life the power of hashish spreads a magic glaze, coloring it with solemnity, bringing to light the profoundest aspects of existence. Fleeting horizons, perspective of cities, pale in the cadaverous light of storms or blazing beneath the concentrated ardor of a crouching sun—profundities of space—allegories on the profundities of time—the dance—the gestures and the declamations of actors if you happen to be in the theatre—the first phrase your eyes chance to fall on if you are reading a book—in short the universality of being reveals itself to you with a glory never before experienced.

Now Baudelaire approaches the drug itself, explaining, for the benefit of those wishing to experience its effects, the rather special conditions under which it must be taken if unpleasant effects are to be avoided:

Here is the drug before your eyes; a morsel of green jam, no more than a nutful, singularly odorous, to such a point that it sickens the stomach and makes one faintly nauseous. Here, then, is your happiness! It hardly exceeds the capacity of a teaspoon! Happiness with all its intoxication, all its follies, all its absurdities! You can swallow it without fear. No one ever died of it. It will not injure your physical organs. Later perhaps a too frequent appeal to this magic may undermine the strength of your will, perhaps you will be less a man than you are today, but the punishment is so distant and the future disaster to one's nature so hard to define! What do you risk? Tomorrow a little nervous fatigue. Do you not every day risk greater punishments for smaller rewards?

So. You have diluted your hashish in a cup of black coffee to endow the drug with greater strength and effect. You have been careful to have an empty stomach, postponing your dinner until nine or ten o'clock to give the poison adequate time to act, at the most in an hour or so from now you might take some soup. You have now enough ballast for a long and strange voyage. The whistle blows, the sails are set and you have the curious advantage over the ordinary traveller of not knowing where you are going. You wanted it. Hurrah for fatality!

I presume that you have chosen the right moment for this expedition. Every perfect debauch requires perfect leisure. Besides, hashish not only magnifies the individual but also the circumstance and environment. You must have no duties to accomplish that require punctuality or exactitude, no pangs of love, no domestic preoccupations, griefs, anxieties. The memories of duty will sound a death knell through your intoxication and poison your pleasure. Anxiety will change to anguish, grief to torture. But if the conditions are right and the weather is good, if you are in a favorable environment as in the midst of a picturesque landscape or in a room artistically decorated, if, moreover, you can hope to hear some music, then all's for the best.

There are, says Baudelaire, three stages in the *hashish* intoxication:

Most novices, during the first step of their initiation, complain of the slow effects of hashish. Then, like the signs of an approaching storm, comes a certain hilarity, irresistible, ludicrous. The simplest words, the most trivial ideas take on new and strange shapes, incongruous resemblances and associations impossible to foresee, interminable puns, comical absurdities, rush continually through your brain. From time to time you laugh at yourself, at your foolishness and your folly, and your friends, if you have any, laugh just as boisterously at their condition and your own, but, as they are without malice, you bear no rancor.

This hilarity, now languishing and now poignant, this uneasiness in joy, this insecurity, this sick indecision usually lasts only a short time. New events soon manifest themselves as a sensation of chill in the extremities and weakness in the limbs. Your hands tremble. In your head and your whole being you feel an awkward stupor. Your eyes dilate, your face grows pallid, your lips thin. The throat is contracted so to speak, the palate dried by thirst. You heave deep raucous sighs, as if your old body could not endure the desires and activity of your new soul. From time to time you shudder and make involuntary movements, like those nervous jumps which, at the end of a day's work, or during a stormy night, precede one's real sleep.

It is at this period of the intoxication that a new sensitiveness, a superior acuteness, manifests itself in all the senses. Smell, sight, hearing, touch, participate equally in this improvement. The eyes have a vision of Eternity. The ear hears almost inaudible sounds in the midst of a vast tumult. It is then that the hallucinations begin. Exterior objects slowly and successively assume singular appearances; they become deformed and transformed. Then the equivocations commence, the errors and the transposition of ideas. Sounds take on colors and colors contain music. This, one might say, is quite natural, and any poetical mind in a sane and normal state easily imagines such analogies. But I have already warned the reader that there is nothing supernatural in the intoxication by hashish. These analogies merely assume an unusual vivacity; they penetrate, they invade, they overpower the mind because of their despotic nature. Musical notes become numbers and, if you have a gift for mathematics, melody, audible harmony, while it preserves its voluptuous and sensual character, transforms itself into a vast arithmetical operation in which numbers beget numbers and where you may follow the phrase and progressions with inexplicable rapidity and an agility equal to that of the performer.

It often happens that personality disappears and that objectivity develops so abnormally that the contemplation of objects outside yourself makes you forget your own existence and causes you to lose yourself in them. Suppose you look at a tree gracefully waving in the wind; in a few seconds what, in the mind of a poet, might be merely a natural comparison, becomes for you a reality. First you attribute to the tree your passion, your desire or your melancholy, its murmurs and its writhing become yours, and before long you *are* the tree. In the same way, a soaring bird first *represents* the immortal desire to fly above things human, but already you are yourself the bird. Similarly if you are smoking, by some sort of transposition or intellectual *quid pro quo*, you will feel yourself evaporating and will attribute to your pipe, in which you feel yourself crouching and packed together like tobacco, the strange power of *smoking yourself.*

Baudelaire is careful to explain that the "hallucinations" induced by *hashish* are not true hallucinations. The hallucination is progressive, almost voluntary, and ripens only through the action of the imagination. Sounds may seem to say strange things, but there always was a sound in the first place. Strange shapes may be seen, but before becoming strange the shapes were natural. *Hashish,* in short, may distort but it does not create that which is not there.

Concluding his account of the *hashish* experience in a section entitled "The Man-God," Baudelaire describes that triumphant euphoria, that prodigious glorification and uplift which, on certain occasions, floods the soul of the *hashish* eater.

Now my imaginary man, the spirit of my choice, has reached that peculiar state of joy and serenity in which he finds himself *compelled* to admire himself. All contradictions disappear, all philosophical problems become clear or at least seem to. All is food for pleasure. A voice speaks inside him and says to him, "You now have the right to consider yourself superior to all men; no one knows or could understand all that you think and all that you feel; they would even be incapable of appreciating the good will with which they inspired you. You are a king unrecognized by the crowd and who lives alone in his belief: but who cares? Do you not possess a sovereign contempt that strengthens the soul?"

But we can suppose that from time to time some biting memory enters and corrupts his joy. Does not one's past reveal many a vile or stupid action which is truly unworthy of a king? But the man that takes hashish will courageously face these reproachful ghosts of memory—he will analyze curiously the action or sentiment, the memory of which disturbed his glorification "This ridiculous, cowardly or vile action, the memory of which disturbed me for a moment, is a complete contradiction of my true nature The very energy with which I condemn it, the inquisitorial care with which I analyze and judge it, proves my high and divine aptitude for virtue How many men are there in the world clever enough to judge themselves or strict enough to condemn themselves?"

Shall I continue my analysis of this victorious monomania Shall I explain how under the influence of the poison, the man I have imagined supposes himself to be the center of the Universe? All things about him act as suggestions activating a world of thoughts within him more alive, more colored, more subtle scintillating with a magic glaze "These magnificent cities where superb houses are set as intervals like stage scenery, those fine ships balanced in nostalgic indolence by the waves of the bay, these museums which contain such beautiful forms and such intoxicating colors, these libraries in which are gathered the labors of Science and the dreams of the Muses, these instruments of music which, when placed together, seem to speak with one voice, these enchanting women made more charming still by the science of adornment and the rare magic of their glances —all these have been created *for me, for me, for me!* For me has humanity labored, been martyred, been immolated, to serve as pasture for my implacable thirst for emotion, for knowledge, for beauty!"

None now should be astonished by the final, the supreme thought born in the dreamer's mind—"*I have become God!*" That ardent, savage cry bursts from his lips with so intense an energy, with so tremendous a power of projection, that, if the will and belief of an intoxicated man had effective virtue, the cry would topple the very angels scattered about along the roads of heaven: "I am a god!" But soon this hurricane of arrogance becomes transformed. A mood of calm, muted and tranquil, takes its place; the universality of man is announced colorfully, and lighted as it were by a sulfurous dawn. If perchance a vague memory reaches the soul of this poor happy man that possibly there is another God, be certain that he will rise up and question *His* commands and that he will face him without terror. Who is the French philosopher who said, with the intention of mocking modern German doctrines, "*I am a god who has dined poorly*"? This irony would not touch a man intoxicated by hashish. He would quietly reply: "*Perhaps I did dine poorly, yet I am a god.*"

So much for the experiences of Baudelaire. Turning now

to the writings of another member of Le Club des Hachischins, Théophile Gautier, we note at once how correctly
Baudelaire has observed that *hashish* serves only to magnify
that which is already present in the soul of man and that
every man receives the vision which his nature dictates. So
while Baudelaire, always preoccupied with moral and philosophical problems, found in the world of *hashish* huge ab-
stractions centering about the problems of god and devil,
Gautier's brilliant visual imagination discovered a realm of
fantastic shapes and colors. We have no reason to suppose
that Gautier had ever heard of *peyotl* but his description of
his experiences under the influence of *hashish* are so like
those of other investigators under the spell of the sacred
cactus that one is tempted to suppose that the two drugs
must produce within the brain a similar reaction, despite
the chemical dissimilarity of their active principles.

A certain numbness overcame me. My body seemed to dissolve and I became transparent. Within my breast I perceived the hashish I had eaten in the form of an emerald
scintillating with a million points of fire. My eyelashes
elongated indefinitely, unrolling themselves like threads of
gold on ivory spindles which spun of their own accord with
dazzling rapidity. Around me poured streams of gems of
every color, in ever changing patterns like the play within
a kaleidoscope. My comrades appeared to me disfigured, part
men, part plants, wearing the pensive air of Ibises. So strange
did they seem that I writhed with laughter in my corner and,
overcome by the absurdity of the spectacle, flung my cushions
in the air, making them turn and twist with the rapidity of
an Indian juggler.

The first attack passed and I found myself again in my
normal state without any of the unpleasant symptoms that

follow intoxication with wine. Half an hour later I fell once
again under the domination of hashish. This time my visions
were more complex and more extraordinary. In the diffusely
luminous air, perpetually swarming, a myriad butterflies
rustled their wings like fans. Gigantic flowers with calyxes
of crystal, enormous hollyhocks, lilies of gold or silver rose
before my eyes and spread themselves about me. with a
sound resembling that of a fireworks display. My hearing
became prodigiously acute. I actually listened to the sound
of the colors. From their blues, greens and yellows there
reached me sound waves of perfect distinctness. A glass in-
verted, the creak of an armchair, a word pronounced in a
deep voice vibrated and rumbled about me like the reverbera-
tions of thunder My own voice seemed so loud that I dared
not speak for fear of shattering the walls with its bomblike
explosion. More than five hundred clocks seemed to an-
nounce the hour in voices silvery, brassy or flutelike Each
object touched gave off a note like that of a harmonica or an
aeolian harp. Floating in a sonorous ocean. like luminous
islands, were motifs from *Lucia* and the *Barber of Seville*
Never has greater beauty immersed me in its flood I was so
lost in its waves. so separated from myself, so disembar
rassed of my ego. that odious appendage that accompanies
us everywhere, that for the first time I understood the nature
of existence of elementals. of angels and spirits separated
from the body I hung like a sponge in the midst of a warm
sea; at each moment waves of happiness traversed me enter
ing and emerging by my pores Because I had become per
meable my whole being became tinged by the color of the
fantastic medium in which I was plunged Sounds lights.
perfumes reached me through tendrils fine as hairs in which
I heard magnetic currents vibrating By my calculation this
state lasted about three hundred years. for the sensations

which followed one another were so numerous and pressing that any real appreciation of time was impossible. The rapture passed. . . . I saw that it had lasted just a quarter of an hour.

A third rapture, the last and most bizarre, terminated my oriental soirée. In this one my vision doubled itself. Two images of every object were reflected on my retina in perfect sympathy. Soon the magic ferment began once again to act with power in my mind. For a full hour I became completely insane. In Pantagruelian dreams I saw passing by me creatures of fantasy, owls, sea storks, satyrs, unicorns, griffins, vultures, a whole menagerie of monsters trotting, gliding, vaulting, yelping about the room. . . . The visions became so baroque that a desire to draw them took hold of me. In less than five minutes I made a sketch of Dr. X . . . who appeared to me seated at the piano, dressed as a Turk with a sunflower on the back of his waistcoat. My drawing represented him emerging from the keyboard in the form of a corkscrew of capricious spirals. Another sketch bore the legend "an animal of the future," and represented a living locomotive with the neck of a swan terminated by the jaws of a serpent from which emerged billows of smoke and monstrous paws composed of wheels and pulleys. Each pair of paws was accompanied by a pair of wings and above the tail of the animal hovered the antique god Mercury, who advanced upon it victoriously in spite of its talons. By the grace of hashish I had been able to draw a "Farfardet" from nature.

Now, leaving the Club of the Hachischens behind us, we travel some three thousand miles westward to that place on the banks of "the broad and noble Hudson" where the American *hashish* eater, Fitz Hugh Ludlow, takes his walks

by the river somewhere in the neighborhood of Poughkeepsie. A curious character, this Ludlow, intensely imaginative,
with that inwardly directed habit of mind which causes its
possessor to be more concerned about events of his inner
than those of his outer world. He began his experiments
with *hashish* at the surprisingly early age of sixteen and did
not abandon his regular use of the drug until he had gradu-
ated from college and assumed the duties of a teacher in
Watertown, New York. This rather prolonged rendezvous
with My Lady of the Hemp provided him with material for
his book, *The Hasheesh Eater*, an effusion of some 365 pages
published anonymously in 1860. No one seriously interested
in the effects of drugs on the mind should fail to read Ludlow's book. Though, from the modern standpoint, it is
grossly overwritten and though in many places scientific
impartiality has been sacrificed in the interests of literary
effect, it still remains one of the most interesting products
of its kind. It certainly provides, at least in the present
writer's opinion, more lively and more colorful reading than
do the grossly overrated confessions of that "English opium-
eater," Thomas De Quincey.

It should be pointed out here that Ludlow, like Baudelaire, was strongly influenced by the confessions of De
Quincey and that much of his agonizing and handwringing
over his "addiction" to *hashish* is purely imitative. No one
would deny that De Quincey had good reason to wring his
hands over his condition. Opium addiction is a serious matter and De Quincey was an addict in the fullest sense of the
word. But when Ludlow starts sighing and groaning over
his enslavement to *hashish* the reader who is familiar with
the properties of the drug will lift a skeptical eyebrow.
There is no such thing as genuine addiction to *hashish* or
any other preparation of cannabis. Those terrible and ago-

nizing withdrawal symptoms which chain the opium addict to his poison do not affect the *hashish* eater. He can take the drug or leave it alone. It is, by all unbiased accounts, even less habit-forming than tobacco. So Ludlow's literary lamentations over his terrible "slavery" must be taken with a large grain of salt as must a good many of his other remarks. One would not, however, wish to be so unkind as to suggest that Ludlow was a liar. It is sufficient if we realize that he suffered from hypertrophy of the imagination and an excessive dependence on the works of De Quincey. These weaknesses were further exaggerated by the influence of *hashish,* for, as Baudelaire points out, the drug magnifies all characteristics of an individual's psychology.

So we find Ludlow in the apothecary's shop in Poughkeepsie buying his extract of cannabis which in those innocent days, when no one had even heard of *marihuana* or its "menace," was a perfectly legal and normal thing to do. Ludlow, as we have mentioned, was a mere boy of sixteen but a boy of unusual imagination and curiosity. He had been reading *The Arabian Nights,* not, we suspect, in Burton's original translation, which is hardly suitable food for innocent minds, but in some suitably Bowdlerized version, from which material likely to offend had been removed. One thing which had not been removed, however, was the accounts of the effects of *beng* or *hashish.* It was these accounts which roused the curiosity of the youthful Ludlow. How, he asked, did these spinners of oriental yarns contrive to dream up such magnificent compositions? With what magical stimulant did they fertilize their imaginations that they could ornament their tales with such gorgeous embroidery? The answer, Ludlow finally decided, was *hashish.* Being afflicted, even at that early age, with the urge to create literary masterpieces, he determined to try the drug himself, so he made haste to the nearest apothecary, placed his six cents on the counter, and received his extract. Back in his room he examined his purchase, an oily green-black sludge with a balsamic odor. With some excitement he rolled the mess into a bolus, downed a total of 10 grains, and waited eagerly for his gorgeous dreams. He experienced nothing whatever. Disappointed, he tried again on the following day, raising his dose to 15 grains. Still nothing happened. Again he upped the dose, 20 grains, no effect, 25 grains, no effect. He was disgusted. The celebrated effects of the mysterious drug were evidently just one more oriental fabrication. Nonetheless he decided to give the *hashish* one more opportunity to reveal to him its wonders. He rolled an even larger bolus, 30 grains, the size of a small grape, and swallowed the nauseous stuff with some difficulty and much water. Having, by this time, completely lost faith in the power of *hashish*, he went out to spend the evening with some friends in another part of town.

For two hours he sat by the fireside at his friend's house engaged in amiable chitchat without giving so much as a thought to the dark green bolus making its way along the twists and turns of his intestines. As for the bolus, it rolled merrily along, propelled by successive peristaltic waves and, because young Ludlow had for once taken his *hashish* on an empty stomach, it found no obstacles to prevent its absorption. And so the potent ingredients of the *hashish*, after traversing the liver, rose via the ascending carotids toward the brain and young Ludlow paused in his chitchat, suddenly and embarrassingly aware that some exceedingly strange process was taking place within his body. Here, in his own exclamatory language, is his description of that first experience:

Ha! What means this sudden thrill! A shock as of some

unimagined vital force, shoots without warning through my entire frame, leaping to my finger ends, piercing my brain and startling me until I almost spring from my chair.

I could not doubt. I was in the power of the hashish influence. My first emotion was one of uncontrollable terror—no pain anywhere—not a twinge in any fibre—yet a cloud of unutterable strangeness was sitting upon me, and wrapping me impenetrably from all that was natural and familiar. . . .

A question was put to me, and I answered it. I even laughed at a *bon mot*. Yet it was not my voice which spoke; perhaps one which I once had far away in another time and another place. I sat and listened; still the voice kept speaking. Now for the first time I experienced the vast change which hashish makes in all measurements of time. The first word of my reply occupied a period sufficient for the action of a drama; the last left me in complete ignorance of any point far enough back in the past to date the commencement of the sentence. Its enunciation might have occupied years. . . .

And now, with time, space also expanded. . . . I was sitting at a distance of hardly three feet from the centre table around which the members of the family were grouped. Rapidly that distance widened. We were in a vast hall of which my friends and I occupied the extremities. . . . I could not bear it. I should soon be left alone in the midst of infinity of space. And now more and more every moment increased the conviction that I was watched. I did not know then, as I learned afterwards, that suspicion of all earthly things and persons was characteristic of the hashish delirium.

In the midst of my complicated hallucination, I could perceive that I had a dual existence. One part of me was whisked unresistingly along the track of this tremendous experience, the other sat looking down from a height upon its double, observing, reasoning and serenely weighing all the phenomena. . . . I rose to take my leave and advanced towards the centre table. With every step its distance increased. I nerved myself as for a long pedestrian journey. . . . Out in the street the view stretched endlessly away. . . . I was doomed to pass through a merciless stretch of space. A soul disenthralled, setting out for his flight beyond the farthest visible star, could not be more overwhelmed with his newly acquired conception of the sublimity of distance than I was that moment. Solemnly I began my infinite journey.

Before long I walked in entire unconsciousness of all around me. I dwelt in a marvellous inner world. I existed by turns in different places and various states of being. Now I swept my gondola through the moonlit lagoons of Venice. Now Alp on Alp towered above my view, and the glory of the coming sun placed purple light upon the topmost pinnacle. Now in the primaeval silence of some unexplored tropical forest I spread my feathery leaves, a giant fern, and swayed and nodded in the spice gales over a river whose waves at once sent up clouds of music and perfume. My soul changed to a vegetable essence, thrilled with a strange and unimagined ecstasy. . . .

The effects of the hashish had increased mightily. I was bursting with an uncontrollable life; I strode with the thews of a giant. Hotter and faster came my breath; I seemed to pant like some tremendous engine. . . . My sensations began to be terrific—not from any pain I felt, but from the tremendous mystery of all around me and within me. By an appalling introversion, all the operations of vitality which, in our ordinary state, go on unconsciously, came vividly into my experience. Through the thinnest corporeal tissue and the minutest veins I could trace the circulation of the blood along each inch of its progress. I knew when every valve opened and when it shut, every sense was preternaturally awakened. The beating of my heart was clearly audible. Lo, now that heart became a great fountain, whose jet played upward with loud vibrations, and, striking on the roof of my skull as on a gigantic dome, fell back with a splash and echo into its reservoir. Faster and faster came the pulsations and the stream became one continuously pouring flood, whose roar sounded through all my frame. I gave myself up for lost, since judgment, which still sat unimpared above my perverted senses, argued that congestion must take place in a few minutes, and close the drama with my death. . . .

So disturbed did Ludlow become by the prospect of exploding under the impact of his own pounding blood pressure that he set off despite the lateness of the hour to seek a physician. The worthy healer, roused from his slumbers by a frightened youth who stammered out that he had consumed 30 grains of cannabis extract, testily told the lad to go to bed and sleep it off. Ludlow complied with these instructions. After walking through endless eons of space-time he finally reached his bed and flung himself upon it.

The moment that I closed my eyes a vision of celestial glory burst upon me. I stood on the silver strand of a translucent lake across whose bosom I seemed to have been just transported. A short way up the beach, a temple, modelled like the Parthenon, lifted its spotless and gleaming columns of alabaster sublimely into a rosy air—like the Parthenon, yet as much excelling it as the god-like idea of architecture must transcend that ideal realized by man. Unblemished in its purity of whiteness, faultless in the unbroken symmetry of every line and angle, its pediment was draped with

odorous clouds, whose tints outshone the rainbow. It was
the work of an unearthly builder, and my soul stood before
it in a trance of ecstasy. Its folded doors were resplendent
with the glory of a multitude of eyes of glass, which were
inlaid throughout the marble surfaces at the corners of the
diamond figures from the floor of the porch to the topmost
moulding. One of these eyes was golden, like the midday
sun, another emerald, another sapphire, and thus onward
through the whole gamut of hues, all of them set in such
collections as to form most exquisite harmonies, and whirling
upon their axes with the rapidity of thought. At the mere
vestibule of the temple I could have sat and drunk in ecstasy
forever; but lo! I am yet more blessed. On silent hinges the
doors swing open and I pass in.

.I did not seem to be in the interior of the temple. I beheld myself so truly in the open air as if I had never passed
the portals, for whichever way I looked there were no walls,
no roof, no pavement. An atmosphere of fathomless and soul-
satisfying serenity surrounded and transfused me. I stood
upon the bank of a crystal stream, whose waters, as they slid
on, discoursed notes of music which tinkled on the air like
the tones of some exquisite bellglass. The same impression
which such tones produce, of music refined to its ultimate
ethereal spirit and borne from a far distance, characterized
every ripple of those translucent waves. The gently sloping
banks of the stream were luxuriant with a velvety cushion-
ing of grass and moss, so living green that the eye and soul
reposed on them at the same time and drank in peace.
Through this amaranthine herbage strayed the gnarled fantastic roots of the cedars of Lebanon, from whose primaeval
trunks great branches spread above me, and, interlocking,
wove a roof of impenetrable shadow, and wandering down
the still avenues below those grand arboreal arches went

glorious bards, whose snowy beards fell on their breasts beneath countenances of ineffable benignity and nobleness.

They were all clad in flowing robes, like God's high priests, and each one held in his hand a lyre of unearthly workmanship. Presently one steps down a shadowy walk, and, baring his right arm, begins a prelude. While his celestial chords were trembling up into their sublime fulness, another strikes his strings, and now they blend upon my ravished ear in such a symphony as was never heard elsewhere, and I shall never hear again out of the Great Presence. A moment more and three are playing in harmony; now the fourth joins the glorious rapture of his music to their own, and in the completeness of the chord my soul is swallowed up. I can hear no more. But yes, I am sustained, for suddenly the whole throng break forth in a chorus, upon whose wings I am lifted out of the riven walls of sense, and music and spirit thrill in immediate communion. Forever rid of the intervention of pulsing air and vibrating nerve my soul dilates with the swell of that transcendant harmony, and interprets from its arcana a meaning which words can never tell. I am borne aloft upon the glory of sound. I float in a trance among the burning choir of the seraphim. But, as I am melting through the purification of that sublime ecstasy into oneness with the Deity himself, one by one those pealing lyres faint away, and as the last throb dies down along the measureless ether, visionless arms swiftly as lightning carry me far into the profound, and set me down before another portal.

It is hardly surprising, even when one has deducted about fifty per cent of the "sublimity" of the above vision to allow for Ludlow's penchant for exaggeration, that this imaginative, highly impressionable youth could not resist experimenting further with *hashish*. The drug had lived up to his wildest expectations, it had justified all that the Arabian and Persian storytellers had spoken in its praise. So off went Ludlow to the apothecary for another six cents' worth of cannabis extract and soon he was back again in the magic world of *hashish*, glorying in the sense of infinite time and space, in the poignancy with which the drug invested every perception. After a number of these excursions into the *hashish* world he was in a position to generalize about the effects of the drug and some of his conclusions can be given here.

Hashish I called the drug of the traveller. The whole East, from Greece to farthest China, lay within the compass of a township; no outlay was necessary for the journey. For the humble sum of six cents I might purchase an excursion ticket all over the earth.

It was indeed the drug of the traveller, but the trips had a rather fragmentary quality. Like many other students of this curious drug, Ludlow observed that the main effects came in waves.

After the full storm of a vision of intense sublimity has blown past the hashish eater, his next vision is generally of a quiet, relaxing and recreating nature. He comes down from his clouds or up from his abyss into a middle ground of gentle shadows where he may rest his eyes from the splendor of the seraphim or the flames of the fiends. There is a wise philosophy in this arrangement, for otherwise the soul would soon burn out in the excess of its own oxygen.

A further characteristic of *hashish* which has also been

amply confirmed by many other observers is the extreme unreliability of its action.

At two different times, when body and mind are apparently in precisely analogous states, when all circumstances, exterior and interior, do not differ tangibly in the smallest respect, the same dose of the same preparation of hashish will frequently produce diametrically opposite effects. Still further, I have taken at one time a pill of thirty grains, which hardly gave a perceptible phenomenon, and at another, when my dose had been half that quantity, I have suffered the agonies of a martyr or rejoiced in a perfect frenzy. So exceedingly variable are its results, that, long before I abandoned the indulgence, I took each successive bolus with the consciousness that I was daring an uncertainty as tremendous as the equipoise between hell and heaven. Yet the fascination employed Hope as its advocate, and won the suit.

It seems that quite soon after his discovery of *hashish* Ludlow realized that the drug was fully as likely to transport him to the infernal regions as to the fields of Elysium. As he continued to take the drug his trips downward became more numerous and his upward flights increasingly rare. Here is an account of one of his descents into the Inferno:

It was perhaps eight o'clock in the evening when I took the dose of fifty grains. I did not retire until midnight. I awoke suddenly. Beside my bed in the corner of the room stood a bier, from whose corners drooped the folds of a heavy pall; outstretched upon it lay in state a most fearful corpse, whose livid face was distorted with the pangs of assassination. The traces of a great agony were frozen into fixedness in the tense position of every muscle, and the nails of the dead man's fingers pierced his palms with the desperate clench of one who has yielded not without agonizing resistance. . . . A smothered laugh of derision from some invisible watcher ever and anon mocked the corpse, as if triumphant demons were exulting over their prey. I pressed my hands upon my eyeballs till they ached in intensity of desire to shut out the spectacle. I buried my head in the pillow that I might not hear that awful laugh of diabolical sarcasm.

But—oh horror immeasurable! I beheld the walls of the room slowly gliding together, the ceiling coming down, the floor ascending, as of old the lonely captive saw them, whose cell was doomed to be his coffin. Nearer and nearer am I borne towards the corpse. I shrank back from the edge of the bed. I cowered in most abject fear. I tried to cry out but speech was paralysed. The walls came closer and closer together. The stony eyes stared up into my own, and again the maddening peal of fiendish laughter rang close beside my ear. Now I was touched on all sides by the walls of the terrible press; there came a heavy crash, and I felt all sense blotted out in darkness.

Before we take our leave of Fitz Hugh Ludlow, the American *hashish* eater, one further aspect of his observations deserves mention. A strain of mysticism was present in Ludlow's nature and his extensive studies of the writers of antiquity had familiarized him with the theories of the ancient community of Pythagoreans. Though Pythagoras is remembered today mainly for his geometrical theorems, especially that one which relates to the three sides of a triangle, he was in fact far more than merely a mathematician as anyone familiar with the "Golden Sayings" will realize. His school in Crotona imposed on its members very rigid rules of behavior and was pervaded with a strongly mystical element

in which the study of numbers played an important part.
Ludlow was greatly influenced by the concepts of this ancient sage, as is indicated by the full title of his book, *The
Hasheesh Eater; being passages from the life of a Pythagorean*. Under the influence of *hashish* Ludlow found himself
able to understand in an entirely new way the concept of
universal harmony on which was based the teaching of the
old philosopher of Crotona, just as Aldous Huxley, under
the influence of mescaline, comprehended certain otherwise
incomprehensible sayings of the Zen Buddhist teachers. This
passage from Ludlow is of special interest to those who, like
Goethe's Faust, long to penetrate beyond the barriers imposed by our dull uncleansed perceptions, to pass beyond
mere scholasticism and to enter realms of knowledge normally forbidden to mortal man. That a certain psychological danger is involved in such excursions, particularly when
they are made with the assistance of drugs, is evident from
Ludlow's comments. Several takers of mescaline have
written in a similar vein.

> Hashish is no thing to be played with as a bauble. At its
> revealing too dread paths of spiritual life are flung open,
> too tremendous views disclosed of what the soul is capable of
> doing, and being, and suffering for that soul to contemplate,
> till, relieved of the body, it can behold them alone. . . .
> Within our little domain of view, girt by the horizon and
> arched by the dome of heaven, there is enough of sorrow,
> enough of danger, enough of beauty and of mirth to occupy
> the soul. In this world we are but half spirit; we are thus
> able to hold only the perceptions and emotions of half an
> orb. It is this present half-developed state of ours which
> makes the infinitude of the hashish awakening so unendur-
> able, even when its sublimity is the sublimity of delight. The

boundary which was at once our barrier and our fortress is removed, until we almost perish from the inflow of perceptions.

One most powerful realization of this fact occurred to me when hashish had already become a fascination and a habit. The world was horizonless, for earth and sky stretched endlessly onward in parallel planes. Above me the heavens were terrible with the glory of a fathomless depth. I looked up, but my eyes, unopposed, every moment penetrated farther and farther into the immensity, and I turned them downward, lest they should presently intrude into the fatal splendors of the Great Presence. Unable to bear visible objects, I shut my eyes. In one moment a colossal music filled the whole hemisphere above me, and I thrilled upwards through its environment on visionless wings. It was not a song, it was not instruments, but the inexpressible spirit of sublime sound—like nothing I had ever heard—impossible to symbolize, intense yet not loud, the ideal of harmony, yet distinguishable into a multiplicity of exquisite parts.

I opened my eyes but it still continued. I sought around me to detect some natural sound which might be exaggerated into such a semblance; but no, it was of unearthly generation, and it thrilled through the universe in an unexplicable, a beautiful, yet an awful symphony.

My mind grew solemn with the consciousness of a quickened perception. And what a solemnity is that which the hashish eater feels at such a moment. The very beating of his heart is silenced. He stands with his finger on his lip; his eye is fixed and he becomes a very statue of awful veneration. I looked abroad on fields and waters and sky, and read in them a most startling meaning. They were now grand symbols of the sublimest spiritual truths, truths never before even feebly grasped, and utterly unsuspected. Like a map, the arcana of the universe lay bare before me. I saw how every created thing not only typifies, but springs forth from some mighty spiritual law as its offspring.

While that music was pouring through the great heavens above me, I became conscious of a numerical order which ran through it, and in marking this order I beheld it transferred to every movement of the universe. Every sphere wheeled on its orbit, every emotion of the soul rose and fell, every smallest moss and fungus germinated and grew according to some peculiarity of numbers which severally governed them. An exquisite harmony of proportion reigned through space, and I seemed to realize that the music which I heard was but this numerical harmony making itself objective through the development of a grand harmony of tones.

The vividness with which this conception revealed itself to me made it terrible to bear alone. An unutterable ecstasy was carrying me away, but I dared not abandon myself to it. I was no seer who could look back on the unveiling of such glories face to face.

An irrepressible yearning came over me to impart what I beheld, to share with another soul the weight of this colossal revelation. With this purpose I scrutinized the vision; I sought in it for some characteristic which might make it translatable to another mind. There was none. In absolute incommunicableness it stood apart. For it, in spoken language, there was no symbol.

So much for Ludlow, his raptures and his agonies. It is only fair to emphasize that his habit of *hashish* eating did not occupy a very large period in his life. He laments in his book over his dependence on the drug and describes the fearful sufferings he endured in the process of freeing himself from his slavery. This, as was mentioned before, is merely imitative literature, the result of his habit of copying De Quincey, for cannabis does not make slaves of its devotees. Ludlow's dependence on *hashish* was due to his hankering after the curious intellectual and emotional experiences which it afforded. Apparently he felt it morally wrong to indulge his taste for the Infinite in this way. "The soul withers and sinks from the true end of its being beneath the dominance of any sensual indulgence." Furthermore he discovered that, as he continued to use the drug, his unpleasant experiences increased in number whereas his raptures became fewer, "the ecstasy became daily more and more flecked with shadows of an immeasurable pain." So he abandoned *hashish*, nor have we any reason to suppose that he was any the worse, physically or mentally, for his indulgence in the drug.

It is a curious fact that, with the writings of Baudelaire, Gautier, and Ludlow, what might be called the "literature of *hashish*" comes to an end. The drug never became fashionable in literary circles despite the fact that extract of cannabis was available in every drugstore and no legislation had been passed prohibiting its use. No other writer of any note experimented with the drug, or, if he did so, he did not publish his experiences. Scientific interest in this curious plant continued however; physicians, pharmacologists, psychologists, chemists, all at one time or another experimented with cannabis and described their experiences. The French pharmacologist, Pascal Brotteaux, made a particularly detailed study of the drug's effects and his scientific account supplements those given by the more literary devotees of *hashish*.

Following Moreau, Brotteaux divides the *hashish* effects into four stages:

1. A period of nervous excitation.
2. A period of hallucinations and mental instability.
3. A period of ecstasy and profound tranquillity.
4. Deep sleep which terminates the "*hashish* rapture."

Brotteaux, like Baudelaire, warns the would-be *hashish* eater that atmosphere and psychological state are all-important. Calmness, absence of unpleasant preoccupations and anxieties are essential. If you take your *hashish* in company, he warns, be sure that your comrades are congenial. All irritations are enhanced by *hashish,* which enormously increases the sensibilities both pleasant and painful. Prepare an acid drink beforehand, for by such a drink you can dissipate certain unpleasant effects of the intoxication. Be prepared to vomit. This aspect of the *hashish* effect is not mentioned by its literary devotees but, according to Brotteaux, frequently occurs, especially in those taking the drug for the first time.

Schneider, another scientist who experimented with *hashish*, described experiences similar to those of Baudelaire. His dose was 3 milligrams of a fluid extract and in thirty minutes he found himself in a state of extreme apprehension. This initial unpleasant reaction gave way after about an hour to a very different effect:

Quite suddenly there is developed an indescribable feeling of exultation and grandeur. The words "fine," "superfine" and "grand" come to my mind as being applicable to the feeling. This indescribable feeling is purely subjective. Self-consciousness is completely annihilated for the time being. The concepts of time and space have vanished. I say to myself, "If this drug can produce such marvellous effects, I will certainly take it often."

Schneider, like all *hashish* eaters, found that his exaltation came and went in waves and that he suffered from dryness of the mouth and lips. An hour and a half after taking the drug he found himself at the top of that pinnacle of exaltation so vividly described by Baudelaire in "The Man-God."

I am capable of anything and everything. No task would be too great, no problem too difficult. The exalted feeling is wholly indescribable and appears to be general and all-inclusive. [During the next three hours] the feeling of supreme exaltation and grandeur continues in varying degrees. The idea of oneness with all nature and the entire universe seems to take hold. There is no material body or personality. . . . The skin is now moist but the mouth continues dry. I have momentary visions or glimpses of vast beautiful landscapes showing wonderful color effects. . . . I do not visualize persons nor do persons play any part in the mental imagery. . . . There is a marvellous color imagery, blue, purples and old gold predominating with most delicate shading effects. . . . I regret that others cannot share with me this feeling of well-being. . . . Evidently sleep gradually set in and continued undisturbed until the usual rising time. No special sensation on rising. Feeling, if anything, more than usually refreshed. All the sensations recorded above have completely vanished. The recollections of the experiences are, however, very clear and vivid. Mouth continued dry until morning. No aftereffects of any kind. The action of the kidneys is increased but no effects as to the intestinal tract.

But how confusing the picture becomes when one surveys the descriptions published by these experimentalists of their reactions to the drug! Even the same person does not necessarily react in the same way on two successive occasions.

Schneider himself in the course of a second experiment, instead of being exalted, found himself cast into the depths. "Probably for a period of not less than six hours I suffer from nightmare. I am convinced that the end has arrived and that I cannot recover." Duncan experienced both the pains of the damned and the bliss of the redeemed in one session:

I was so giddy that I could not stand still, and the damned in the infernal regions could have felt no more agonizing terrors. My skin was burning up with heat, pulse so fast that I could hardly count it, and a general paralysis taking possession of my whole person, more especially my stomach. . . . The most intense headache accompanied the other symptoms. I was in this condition about three hours having several times concluded I was dying, with not altogether the most comfortable feelings, being decidedly in doubt as to my final destiny, disposed rather to view myself as lost. At the expiration of three hours, the pulse became normal, the skin cool and moist, and the paralysis gradually wore off. Then of all the happy mortals that ever existed I was the most supremely so. I saw the most beatific visions, the most beautiful women, angelic in their mental and physical configurations. If all the gold of Solomon's Temple had been offered me I would not then have relinquished my perfect happiness and mutual repose counterbalancing the exciting experience of the previous three hours. These mental hallucinations lasted, I suppose, four to five hours. Then came the reactionary feeling, dull heavy headache for forty-eight hours, uncertain in gait and terrible mental confusion. . . . While I would not be without the experience gained, relative to its action, I would not for the same length of time undergo similar doubts and fears, to say nothing of the unpleasant after effects.

Burr, who took 60 minims of Parke, Davis tincture, found himself in convulsions. The convulsions were quite deliberate. He "willed to convulse." He knew that he was throwing his arms about, writhing like a snake, acting like a clown, making silly grimaces. He could not will to do otherwise. Sex ideas were entirely absent and "Venus herself could not have tempted" him. But though the sexual appetite was depressed, the appetite for food was sharpened. After the first convulsion he devoured a whole cold chicken, a large loaf of bread, and some butter. He had a hallucination of himself sitting in a boat floating through the sky amid pink clouds. At four in the morning he went to bed, woke five hours later comfortable but tired, passed large volumes of dilute urine, and went to work none the worse for his experience. A friend of his who took the same dose of the same drug from the same bottle was seized by a sense of death by suffocation and suffered similar seizures every twenty minutes for about three hours.

Every aspect of the *hashish* effect seems to be subject to amazing variation, as if the impish genie in the plant gloried in his capacity to change his manifestations at will. In the above passage the absence of any aphrodisiac effect has been described: "Venus herself could not have tempted me." And yet this drug has been regarded for centuries in the East as the aphrodisiac *par excellence*. Burton, translator of *The Arabian Nights*, declares that Orientals used it both to prolong coition and to increase the intensity of the sensations. His words are echoed by those of Hector France: "Hashish is of course a positive aphrodisiac, the length of the venereal act being at once reinforced and repeated." Wood, one of the first American students of the drug, found that "at no time were there any aphrodisiac feelings produced" but a friend of his, after taking a preparation of the resin, not only became so ravenous that his Gargantuan appetite evoked comment but also was roused to a state of "venereal excitement" accompanied by priapism which lasted for several days. Walton does not consider the drug itself an aphrodisiac but believes that it may produce such an effect by exerting a paralytic action on the higher structures of the brain, releasing the lower, more primitive structures which are normally restrained and controlled by the cerebral cortex. This view is in agreement with that expressed by Drs. Allentuck and Bowman: ". . . Marihuana is no more aphrodisiac than is alcohol. Unlike damiana, yohimbin, testosterone propionate, etc., which produces genital engorgement directly, marihuana, like alcohol, acts only indirectly through the cerebral cortex in this respect."

This quotation raises a further question. What is the effect on society of widespread indulgence in cannabis? Is the drug dangerous? Should it be outlawed? Is its use associated with crimes of violence? Does it lead its devotees to the madhouse? These questions are rather difficult to answer. In countries like Egypt and India there does seem to be a certain form of insanity associated with excessive use of *hashish*, nor can one deny that its consumption in some regions of the Middle East reaches such a point that it poses a public health problem. Just why it poses such a problem is brought out in a very recent account given by that intrepid journalist, John Roy Carlson, whose book *Cairo to Damascus* gives a vivid picture of the forces at work within the Islamic nations in one of the world's most dangerous trouble spots. Carlson mentions that very large amounts of *hashish* are consumed in Egypt and that the drug is produced mainly in

Lebanon. Unlike wine, *hashish* was never forbidden to his followers by Mahomet, and they therefore feel perfectly at liberty to indulge in the drug. The conditions under which they indulge are depicted in Carlson's account, which also furnishes a description of the effect produced by *hashish* when it is smoked rather than swallowed. He took the drug in a *hashish* salon in Beirut, the floor of which was thickly encrusted with sputum deposited by the ceaseless spitting of the habitués. In the center of the room stood a *josie* or water-pipe to which was attached a long bamboo stem. Seated round the *josie* were six customers eager for the drug, which the proprieter introduced into the bowl of the pipe in the form of pale green pellets mixed with charcoal. Carlson hesitated to smoke a pipe used by countless habitués but finally placed his fate in the hands of God, seized the bamboo stem, and inhaled deeply.

The hashish seared my throat, and burned my lungs choking me. I thought my eyes would pop out, so intense and scorching were its effects on nasal passages. I coughed violently. Then I began to hawk and spit. My eyes watered as I alternately coughed and spat. Everything about hashish is violent. . . .

Still coughing and spitting I saw the *josie* passed around to the Arab next to me. My neighbor took the reed like a starving infant at his mother's breast, and sucked in the hashish with a desperate craving. He took two, three long puffs, holding the last inhalation long and dreamily in his nostrils, leaning his head backward so that the smoke penetrated lungs, throat and nose. Then came the reaction—as violent as mine. He doubled over, coughing spasmodically, his eyes rolling. He spat and coughed, coughed and spat again and wiped the water from his eyes with the back of his hand.

The *josie* kept making the rounds, from man to man, each inhaling the fumes, each series of inhalations followed by the same rocking explosion. . . . It was my turn again. Though more than half its strength had by this time become dissipated, it was still powerful enough for me and I reacted with even greater violence.

"Fill the *josie* again," Hagop said to the waiting proprietor.

The Arab went into the kitchen and reappeared with the pipe and I went through the same torture over again. My head reeled, my throat was aflame. I had had enough for one sitting and wanted to leave. I motioned to Hagop. But one of our friends offered to treat the group. We couldn't turn it down without offending those present. So I stayed and got a third dose of the drug in my nostrils, lungs and into my quivering body. After this we left.

In a second dive to which they went Carlson and his friend found a larger salon.

In the room were half a dozen small groups of men. Smoking, coughing and spitting went on all about me; some were coughing so violently they seemed to be shaken by a cataleptic fit. . . . The attendant arrived with the *josie*. I found it even stronger than before and underwent the same ordeal, and the same violent convulsive seizures. The floor was filthy with sputum. Later, I learned, an attendant would sprinkle dried earth. The next morning, when the place was empty, the blood-stained sputum of the tubercular would be swept along with the others.

Hagop said, "How do you feel?"

"Stimulated and hungry, very hungry."

"Still don't feel sick to your stomach?"

"How could I eat all this food if I did?"

"Well," he said. "At least I know how the stuff affects you."

"As a matter of fact, it's not only hunger I feel—I feel supercharged with strength. Here . . ." I took Hagop's hand and gripped it. He let out a howl of pain.

"You've turned into a savage," he bellowed.

I put him in a taxi. Sleep was out of the question for me. I felt more energetic than I had ever been before. My mind was keen, my senses alert. I knew, now, why the miserable fellaheen consumed it. Hasheesh first made gods of them— then it enslaved and destroyed them.

I walked on, voraciously hungry again . . . found a restaurant and gorged myself. I couldn't sleep, apparently the stimulating effect of the hasheesh hadn't worn off yet. I had eaten six times during the day. I stayed up all night; and by morning was still full of energy. I suspected that some sort of reaction would come, but I did not worry about it. . . . We taxied down the runway and took off. As the magnificently beautiful landscape faded from view, and the Mediterranean spread below us, I fell into a heavy sleep, a drugged sleep. I woke, still half conscious, only after the stewardess had shaken me by the shoulder repeatedly.

It can be seen from the above account that *hashish* smoking in the Middle East is a far from elevating occupation, indeed its effect on the population of these countries is so unfortunate that the Central Narcotics Intelligence Bureau of the Egyptian government has lavished some of its most violent abuse on the hemp plant and all its derivatives: ". . . the prepared product of the Cannabis sativa plant, while having very limited medicinal use, is capable of profoundly disturbing the brain cells and of inducing acts of violence, even murder; it is in fact a thoroughly vicious and dangerous thing of no value whatever to humanity and deserving of nothing but the odium and contempt of civilised people." Commenting on this outburst, Goodman and Gilman observe, "Almost everyone in the United States is agreed that marihuana is a nuisance and that trafficking in it should be strictly suppressed by the adequately stringent laws now in force but few in this country would entirely agree with the conclusion of the Central Narcotics Intelligence Bureau of the Egyptian Government."

These very different attitudes toward cannabis, one defining it as "a thoroughly vicious and dangerous thing" and the other dismissing it as merely "a nuisance," underline the great differences of opinion that exist regarding the social effects of this drug. It seems desirable at this point to describe a few of the studies which have been made in the United States on the use of *marihuana* and its effects.

Marihuana is a cheap and very crude preparation of hemp consisting of the flowering tops of the female plant in various stages of development. In relation to refined preparations such as *charas*, it stands as *vin ordinaire* does to fine champagne. The *marihuana* habit is of quite recent development and the problems it has brought result more from the types of people indulging in the drug than from the effects of the drug itself. Clearly there was no "menace to society" as long as a few literati, physicians, and scientists indulged in *hashish* eating for interest or pleasure. *Marihuana*, however, was enjoyed by members of a very different stratum of society. Introduced into the southern parts of the United States by laborers from Mexico the habit of smoking *marihuana* took hold in New Orleans and soon it was estimated that thousands of pounds of the weed were being smuggled into the port.

The habit of *marihuana* smoking spread and made its appearance in practically every state in the Union. Lurid stories were published in the press concerning the effect of this drug on those who consumed it. Instances were described in which drugged individuals had completely lost control over their actions and committed unpremeditated acts of violence. A youth in Tampa, Florida, seized an ax and killed his father, mother, two brothers, and a sister. Armed criminals were using the drug to give them reckless courage. Newspapers and magazines began to feature sensational articles on the "*marihuana* menace" and state legislatures hastened to pass laws to regulate the evil. So terrible did the menace seem to the sovereign state of Oregon that prison sentences up to ten years were imposed on those possessing or trafficking in the drug.

These shrieks of alarm and dismay were accompanied here and there by derisive voices which declared that the whole uproar was uncalled for, that *marihuana* never hurt anybody and that the Narcotics Bureau would do better to devote its time and energies to the control of the really dangerous drugs, morphine, heroin and cocaine, instead of chasing after a relatively innocuous weed. Thus in an editorial in *The Military Surgeon* entitled "The Marihuana Bugaboo," there appeared the statement, ". . . the smoking of the leaves, flowers and seeds of *Cannabis sativa* is no more harmful than the smoking of tobacco or mullein or sumac leaves . . . the legislation in relation to marihuana was ill advised. . . . It branded as a menace and a crime a matter of trivial importance. . . . It is hoped that no witch hunt will be instituted in the military service over a problem which does not exist. . . ."

The cries of alarm continued nonetheless, particularly in the region of New York City, and so strident did the clamor become that some action seemed necessary. This action was taken by one of New York's best-loved and most colorful mayors, Fiorello La Guardia, who sensibly concluded that his first duty was to discover the facts concerning the use of *marihuana* in the city and, on the basis of those facts, to take whatever steps seemed necessary. He accordingly requested assistance from the New York Academy of Medicine, which appointed a committee to obtain those facts of which the mayor was in need.

The report of the Mayor's Committee on Marihuana, which was published in 1944, is a mine of valuable information, sociological, psychological, and pharmacological, concerning *marihuana* and its effects. The results are worthy of careful study because they place the whole phenomenon of *marihuana* smoking in the correct perspective and reveal the so-called "*marihuana* problem" as a minor nuisance rather than a major menace. In his foreword to the report Mayor La Guardia himself remarked, "I am glad that the sociological, psychological, and medical ills commonly attributed to marihuana have been found to be exaggerated as far as the City of New York is concerned," but observed that he would continue to enforce the laws prohibiting the use of *marihuana* "until and if complete findings may justify an amendment to existing laws." As regards these "complete findings," the more important can be summarized as follows:

Marihuana is generally used in New York City in the form of cigarettes commonly called muggles or reefers. The cheapest brand is known as *sass-frass*, retails at three for about fifty cents (these are 1944 prices), and is made from hemp grown in the United States. Smokers do not consider such *marihuana* very potent. A more potent brand of cigarette is the *panatella,* made from hemp grown in Central or South America; it retails for twenty-five cents. Still more potent is *gungeon,* which is considered to be the highest grade of *marihuana* and is said to be imported from Africa, though the name strongly suggests the Indian name of the drug, *gangha. Gungeon* retails for about a dollar per cigarette. Confirmed *marihuana* users can distinguish the quality and potency of various brands just as the habitual cigarette smoker is able to differentiate between the qualities of tobacco.

In New York City most of the *marihuana* smoking appears to take place in the predominantly Negro section of Harlem. The investigators estimated that, at that time, there were about five hundred of these "tea-pads" in Harlem. They were, in most cases, comfortably furnished rooms with a radio, phonograph or a rented juke box. The lighting was more or less uniformly dim, with blue predominating, and an incense burner was considered a natural part of the furnishings. Many of the "tea-pads" were decorated with pictures of nude subjects suggestive of perverted sexual practices. These characteristic furnishings are believed to be essential as a setting for those participating in smoking *marihuana.*

The *marihuana* smoker appears to derive greater satisfaction if he smokes in the presence of others. Within the "tea-pad" his attitude is that of a relaxed individual, freed from the anxieties and cares of the realities of life. "The tea-pad takes on the atmosphere of a very congenial social club. The smoker readily engages in conversation with strangers, discussing freely his pleasant reactions to the drug and philosophizing on subjects pertaining to life in a manner which, at times, appears to be out of keeping with his intellectual level." A boisterous, rowdy atmosphere did not prevail and on the rare occasions when there appeared signs of belligerency in one of the smokers he was either ejected or forced to become quieter. One of the more unorthodox "tea-pads" took the form of a series of pup tents arranged on a rooftop in Harlem. Those present smoked their cigarettes in the tents. When the desired effect of the drug had been obtained they emerged into the open to admire the stars and the beauties of nature.

The confirmed *marihuana* smoker described in this study consumed perhaps from six to ten cigarettes per day. He appeared to be quite aware of the quantity needed to produce the effect called "high." Just what constitutes this condition apparently varies with the individual. There was general agreement that a feeling of adequacy and efficiency was induced by the use of *marihuana* and that current mental conflicts were allayed. Once a *marihuana* smoker has obtained the effect he desires he cannot be persuaded to consume any more of the drug. He knows when he has had enough. (Would that this applied with equal force to consumers of alcohol!) It appears that as soon as too much of the drug has been smoked the pleasant feelings associated with being "high" become transformed into their opposites. Anxiety is experienced, associated with uneasiness of the stomach which may culminate in vomiting. Smokers who find themselves "too high" immediately institute measures so that they can "come down." This is accomplished by the use of beverages such as beer or sweet soda. A cold shower is also said to be effective. Smokers will not drink whisky when using the "weed" because it appears to prevent the drug from taking its effect. They consume large quantities of sweet wine, however, and most *marihuana* smokers insist that the appetite is increased as the result of smoking.

The method of smoking *marihuana* as practiced by experienced users is interestingly described in the mayor's report. Such a one selects his cigarettes in the manner of a connoisseur, opening the end to examine the *marihuana*. Smoking takes on the form of a ritualistic ceremony, varying slightly from user to user. First the cigarette is wetted by being inserted into the mouth, a procedure which prevents the paper from burning too rapidly. After the cigarette has been ignited the smoker takes several short puffs, at the same time inhaling as much air as possible. The smoke is retained as long as possible and often causes severe paroxysms of coughing. As the cigarette burns, the active resins on which its effect depends are distilled toward the end. This makes the butt of the cigarette especially potent and the experienced smoker supports the butt in a cleft stick or "crutch" to enable him to absorb the maximum amount of the potent distillate. Though eager to become "high," the user is careful not to smoke so much that he "blows his top."

The practice of *marihuana* smoking was not observed to lead to addiction in the medical sense of the word. Members of the investigating committee frequently found themselves with *marihuana* smokers who, on seeking a "tea-pad" and finding it closed, would calmly resume their previous activity such as the discussion of life in general or the playing of pool. The fact that they could not gratify their desire for the drug produced no signs of frustration in the smokers. This behavior is highly significant because it is so unlike that of a real narcotic addict. Such a one, unable to obtain his drug, swiftly becomes an anguished, obsessed being, driven by an implacable physical need to obtain the poison at all costs. The investigating committee could not find any evidence suggesting that *marihuana* smoking is the first step toward the use of such drugs as cocaine, morphine, and heroin. "The instances are extremely rare where the habit of marihuana smoking is associated with addiction to these other narcotics."

We have mentioned already that cannabis has a reputation in some parts of the world as a powerful aphrodisiac. It is said to arouse such lust in those that take it that they cannot even be satisfied with one woman but needs must have two. This picturesque notion of the lust-maddened *hashish* eater was very much in the minds of the investigators, who no doubt expected to witness scenes in the "tea-pads" of Harlem rivaling those of an ancient Roman bacchanal. In this respect, however, they were disappointed. True it was that lewd pictures, often representing perverted forms of sexual activity, frequently decorated the "tea-pad" walls. These pictures, however, seemed to attract little attention from the clientele. In fact one of the investigators who was concentrating his attention on the relation between *marihuana* and eroticism found himself embarrassed because he was the only one who examined the pictures on the wall. Numerous conversations with smokers of *marihuana* revealed only occasional instances in which there was any relation between the drug and eroticism. One investigator who succeeded in securing the position of doorman at a very intimate social gathering in a Harlem apartment noted that the dancing was of the most abandoned type. It was highly suggestive and appeared to be associated with erotic activity. Careful observation, however, did not suggest that those who were smoking "reefers" behaved in a more abandoned fashion than those who were not. Visits to brothels which also served as "tea-pads" revealed that the use of *marihuana* was not linked to sexuality. "These observations allow us to come to the conclusion that in the main marihuana was not used for direct sexual stimulation."

No direct relationship could be demonstrated between

marihuana smoking and crime, nor was the practice wide-spread among school children. Juvenile delinquency was not associated with the practice of smoking *marihuana* and the report on the sociological aspects of *marihuana* indulgence concludes with the words, "The publicity concerning the catastrophic effects of marihuana smoking in New York City is unfounded."

Needless to say, this calm report was not at all welcome to sensation-hungry journalists who saw themselves deprived of a valuable source of material for headlines. So after the publication of the mayor's report there was much stormy correspondence, some of which invaded the pages of the medical press. Even the austere *Journal of the American Medical Association* abandoned its customary restraint and voiced its editorial wrath in scolding tones. So fierce was the editorial that one might suppose the learned members of the mayor's committee—appointed, incidentally, by the New York Academy of Medicine—had formed some unhallowed league with the "tea-pad" proprietors to undermine the city's health by deliberately misrepresenting the facts about *marihuana*.

The book states unqualifiedly that the use of this narcotic does not lead to physical, mental or moral degeneration and that permanent deleterious effects from its continued use were not observed on 77 prisoners. This statement has already done great harm to the cause of law enforcement. Public officials will do well to disregard this unscientific uncritical study and continue to regard marihuana as a menace wherever it is purveyed.

This outburst was followed by letters from several individuals well qualified to speak on the subject who pointed out that, before blasting the report, the editors would do well to read it more carefully. None could conclude from the report that *marihuana* is harmless. There are dangers involved in its use as there are in the use of alcohol. Individuals already unbalanced may become temporarily insane under the influence of the drug. "Given the potential personality make-up and the right time and environment marihuana may bring on a true psychotic state" (S. Allentuck in *Medical Aspects*). As for the supposed association of the effects of the drug and crime, this was defined in an earlier statement by Bromberg: "The antisocial, aggressive and sadistic elements of the personality uncovered by the drug are responsible for the crime, rather than any specific crime producing properties of marihuana. . . . It is probable that alcohol is more responsible as an agent in crime than marihuana." "All serious opinions," wrote Walton, "have branded it [marihuana] an undoubted nuisance." It is, however, a nuisance and not a menace. To place it, for legislative purposes, in the same category with really dangerous drugs such as heroin and morphine is unrealistic.

In view of the powerful effects which cannabis exerts on the mind of man, it is logical to wonder whether it might not be used in the treatment of certain forms of mental illness. Consider, for instance, that condition described in the older literature as melancholia and now more generally referred to as a depression. Might not the celebrated "*hashish* rapture" lighten the darkness of individuals in this state? Tayleur Stockings, using not cannabis itself but a synthetic preparation of its active principle called Synhexyl, answers this question with an enthusiastic "yes." Out of fifty individuals suffering from depression, thirty-six showed definite improvement after receiving 15 to 90 milligrams of the drug. The quiet, apathetic type of patient seemed to do best;

the tense, overanxious types also showed good response but required higher doses. He defined the compound as a "promising therapeutic agent for the treatment of the chronic and intractable depressive states." Parker and Wrigley were less enthusiastic, though they conceded that "further work on Synhexyl and allied substances is justified, especially since we feel that a drug of this type might be very useful for tiding over depressions and would help in keeping cases out of mental hospitals."

One very interesting cure brought about by the use of cannabis was recently described by Drs. Rolls and Stafford-Clark. The condition which they treated goes under the name of depetsonalization. It is a peculiar form of mental illness in which the patient loses his feeling of his own identity. The sense we have of identification with and control over our own bodies, so much a part of our over-all sensation that we normally take it completely for granted, is lost by these people so that they neither know who or what they are. The same aura of unreality comes to pervade their perception of the outside world. Space has no depth, objects have no reality. Everything appears crude and meaningless like stage settings prepared for a display of amateur theatricals.

In the case these doctors describe a young woman, under the stress of a prolonged and anxious labor, developed the typical symptoms of depersonalization. She said, "I felt cut off from everything. Nothing seemed real. I had no sense of time." This unreality enveloped all her relationships, including that between her and her newly born child. "I feel I don't know him. I haven't any mother love for him." At home she was unable to undertake the normal responsibilities of wife and mother. Her sexual relations with her husband, which before her illness had been in every way ideal, became for her as meaningless and unreal as everything else.

This young woman was treated with methedrine and "Pentothal," two drugs whose effects will be described in a later chapter. As no improvement was noted the physicians decided to try cannabis, administering a dose of four grains of the freshly prepared tincture in alcohol. The patient first experienced the reactions usually ascribed to this drug, a succession of transient but gradually increasing periods of euphoria with slowing of the time sense, accompanied by sweating and palpitations. As the effect developed she became aware of increasing feelings of anxiety and apprehension which, as they reached their climax, led her suddenly to begin to re-enact her labor. She complained of no pain during the re-enactment but behaved in every other way as though it were taking place. The experience culminated in the delivery of the imaginary child, after which she claimed happily and triumphantly that she had managed to have the baby at last. She said, "I'm all right now. . . ." She then fell asleep.

When she awoke from this sleep she had complete insight into her condition and had regained normal contact to a remarkable extent. One further treatment with cannabis was given during which she remained cheerful and dreamy for several hours. Returning home, she found that she had become her old self again, was able to take full interest in the house and baby, and was, as far as she could judge, completely recovered. Commenting on this cure, the authors write as follows:

Characteristic effects of *Cannabis indica* include euphoria with disturbances of time and space perception, sometimes accompanied by erotic visual imagery and usually followed by profound relaxation and sleep. A striking feature may be the vivid recall or re-experience of feelings long since past and formerly forgotten. This drug thus seemed particularly suited to our requirements in the treatment of this case of depersonalization, and proved in fact empirically to be highly successful.

Yawger has also commented on the extraordinary power of cannabis to summon up remembrance of things past. "John Stuart Mill, philosopher, wrote of its power to revive forgotten memories, and in my enquiries, smokers have frequently informed me that while under its influence, they are able to recall things long forgotten. If through such use the unconscious mind could be rendered more accessible, possibilities as an aid in psychoanalysis and psychotherapy are shown." Several medical writers have praised the drug as an analgesic (pain reliever). The *Journal of the American Medical Association* comments favorably on its effect on the pains of childbirth: ". . . the sensation of pain is distinctly lessened or entirely absent and the sense of touch is less acute than normally. Hence a woman in labor may have a more or less painless labor. If a sufficient amount of the drug is taken, the patient may fall into a tranquil sleep from which she will awaken refreshed." This comment also indicates that cannabis has rather valuable sedative properties, the sleep it induces being particularly tranquil and natural. Unfortunately this sleep is generally preceded by a period of excitement during which the visions, etcetera, previously described take place. One who wishes to journey to the land of Morpheus on the chariot of cannabis is liable to see some curious sights on the way. The drug, however, is an excellent sedative for horses; even the most neurotic thoroughbred sinks into a presumably dreamless slumber which may last up to twenty-four hours. One other rather unusual use for this drug is mentioned by Allentuck, who declares that it greatly relieves the miseries experienced by morphine and heroin addicts when their drug is withdrawn.

What is the nature of that substance which gives to cannabis its peculiar activity? This question has proved exceedingly difficult to answer. In most plant drugs the active principle belongs to that very mixed group of chemical compounds which are collectively known as alkaloids. Morphine, heroin, atropine, scopolamine, mescaline, bulbocapnine, reserpine, and yohimbine are all alkaloids, and caffein and theobromine, though not included among the alkaloids by such a leading authority as Henry, have at least much in common with these substances and contain, as do the alkaloids, one or more atoms of nitrogen in their molecules. But the active material from cannabis has this peculiarity: it contains no nitrogen in the molecule nor does it form with acids those convenient salts which make the task of crystallizing alkaloids so relatively easy. So baffling was the behavior of the active material that, although several attempts were made from 1895 on to isolate a chemical substance having the pharmacological properties of cannabis, it was not until the 1940s that any real light was shed on the nature of the active principle. Several groups of workers both in England and in America contributed to our understanding of this elusive principle. For a detailed summary of this research the reader should consult Adams or the section, "The Approaches to the Discovery of the Active Principle of Marihuana," by S. Loewe in *The Marihuana Problem*. Here it is sufficient to say that the activity of cannabis preparations appears to depend mainly on a group of substances called tetrahydrocannibinols, the structure of which is shown in the Appendix.

The preparation of these active materials represented a

prodigious amount of work on the part of the chemists, but for some strange reason practically all work on the drug has now been abandoned. We have no idea what happens to this potent substance, tetrahydrocannibinol, after it enters the body. We cannot tell in what form it enters the brain or in what manner it affects the chemistry of the brain cells. Despite the tremendous recent interest in psychochemistry this important group of compounds has been ignored and we know as little about the mode of action of the hemp drug on the brain as did Hasan-i-Sabbah when he fed it to his followers nearly a thousand years ago.

Addicts and Addictions

Already in our chapter on *marihuana* we have touched on the problem of drug addiction. Baudelaire, well qualified to speak on this subject, has been quoted at length. The "Taste of the Infinite" in his opinion provides the reason for all guilty excesses "from the solitary and concentrated intoxication of the man of letters who, obliged to turn to opium for relief of some physical suffering, little by little makes it the sun of his spiritual life, to the drunkard who, his brain aflame with glory, hideously wallows in the filth of a Paris street." Baudelaire's concept of the cause of addiction is altogether too poetic and will not stand up to a moment of scientific scrutiny. The quotation, however, serves to focus attention on the two substances with which this chapter will be mainly concerned: opium, with its derivatives, heroin and morphine; and alcohol.

"Addiction" is a word that is given rather varied meanings. Some authorities use it only in connection with such drugs as morphine, heroin, and the barbiturates whose hold on the addict is such that he cannot stop taking them without going through a very unpleasant illness. Others include

alcohol and cocaine in the class of addicting drugs, though
neither of these substances binds its victim with such chains
as do the opiates. The reader will understand this problem
more readily if he bears in mind the useful term "physical
dependence." Physical dependence has nothing to do with
mere habit or with the satisfaction of some vague emotional
craving. It is as real and as material as man's physical dependence on food, air, water, or the essential vitamins which
his body cannot manufacture for itself. The morphine or
heroin addict is physically dependent on a continuous supply of the drug just as a normal man is dependent on a continuous supply of vitamins. If a normal man's vitamins are
cut off he becomes sick. If a heroin addict's drug is cut off he
also becomes sick. There is nothing imaginary or mental
about this sickness. It is a physicochemical reality. Monkeys
can be addicted to heroin just as readily as can men and they
go through much the same misery when the drug is withdrawn. After a certain amount of morphine or heroin has
circulated in the body for a certain time it actually changes
the chemistry of the body in such a way that normal function becomes impossible unless the drug is present. This is
the chemical basis of physical dependence.

We might limit our use of the word "addiction" to those
drugs that produce physical dependence, in which case we
could correctly speak of a heroin addict or of a barbiturate
addict, but not of an alcohol addict or cocaine addict. This
may seem merely an unnecessary play on words but the fact
remains that there are very great differences between drugs
that are truly addicting and drugs that are only habit-forming. A habit is largely mental and emotional—the smoker's
desire for a cigarette, the drinker's desire for a cocktail. But
addiction is as physical, as urgent, and as implacable as a

thirsty man's need for water. It is a phenomenon of an entirely different order.

It is sufficient if the reader will simply bear these differences in mind while reading this chapter, for it will happen inevitably that the word "addiction" will be somewhat loosely used. Alcohol, though not strictly a drug of addiction, nonetheless can exert a very powerful hold on one who particularly craves this substance, as any confirmed alcoholic will testify. This particular drug, one of the most ancient, most widely enjoyed, and most extensively misused of all drugs known to man, will be considered first. Its immensely long and somewhat sordid history will be briefly sketched, its effects on the mind and emotions will be portrayed, and the consequences of its abuse, that distressing condition formerly crudely referred to as drunkenness but now more often defined as alcoholism, will be described.

However deeply we may probe into the mists of antiquity we shall never discover at what point man first discovered the virtues and drawbacks of alcohol. Of all the drugs that affect the mind and emotions it has the longest history. It was known, we can surmise with reasonable certainty, to Neolithic man and it is not unreasonable to assume that even Paleolithic man, far older and far more primitive, also knew of the solace afforded by wine. That man became so early acquainted with alcohol is due to the fact that any fruit juice if left open to the air infallibly undergoes a change known as fermentation. This fermentation is the work of a group of insignificant one-celled fungi, the yeasts, which are present on the skins of fruit and whose tiny spores float in millions in the air about us. The yeasts are eaters of sugar, but their eating habits are rather inefficient, for instead of burning the whole sugar molecule to carbon dioxide and water they merely bite off a part of the molecule, leaving the residue in the form of an alcohol. This particular alcohol which the yeasts produce is known to the chemists as ethyl alcohol and the structure of this potent substance is shown in the Appendix. The alcohols from the chemist's point of view constitute a very large family of substances which range from liquids to solids and include such materials as glycerine. Closely related to ethyl alcohol is methyl or wood alcohol. whose effects on man's organism are most unsettling as those in the habit of drinking methylated spirits can testify

The fermentation of sugary juices is the basic process from which all alcoholic liquors arise. Different races at different periods have used an almost infinite number of starting materials from which to prepare the brews they so greatly desired. The ancient Egyptians and the Sumerians appear to have favored an extract of sprouted grain and thus to have laid the foundations of the brewers art. The ancient He brews. or their forebears, to judge by the unedifying story of Noah learned soon after the flood that no fruit of the earth yields a juice better suited to fermentation than does the grape and prepared from it that wine "which maketh glad the heart of man ' Tribes dwelling on the steppes of Cen tral Asia brew *koumiss* from mare s milk In Mexico the potent *pulque* is made from the sugary juice of the agave Date wine is enjoyed in Morocco rice wine in Japan dande lion elderberry and cowslip wine have been known to gladden the hearts of English herbalists The apple yields cider the pear pomace the scented honey suitably diluted gives rise to that mead so esteemed by the roving Viking But however diverse the starting materials may be these brews, if they possess any potency at all owe it to the single substance ethyl alcohol

All this brewing and bubbling that went on through countless millennia placed at man's disposal wines or beers whose alcohol content was comparatively low. It was not until the art of wine maker and brewer was supplemented with that of the distiller that really potent alcoholic liquors began to be available. The distiller's art was unknown to the older civilizations. The Greeks had no word for it. The Romans knew nothing about it. This was just as well. Considering what pigs the old Romans made of themselves with wine, one shudders to think what would have happened had they had access to brandy In the days of Nero, brandy, whisky, gin, and all their spirituous relatives lay safely folded in the womb of time, out of reach alike of emperor and slave. It was not until considerably later that some obscure alchemist, probably seeking the elixir of youth, placed wine in an alembic and produced a fiery distillate of which a mere thimbleful contained the intoxicating potency of a glassful of wine. Thus was mankind launched on the sea of spirit in which so many have since drowned not only their sorrows but themselves.

The whole basis of the distiller's art rests on the simple fact that alcohol boils at a lower temperature than does water Thus, by heating wine or beer and condensing the vapors, one first obtains the alcohol, then the water This alcohol is flavored by a variety of volatile substances which give to whisky and brandy their characteristic aromas.

Since it was first discovered the art of the distiller has flourished greatly In the United States, during the fiscal year ending June 1955, there poured forth from distilleries all over the land a total of 593,982,000 gallons of whisky brandy, rum. gin. vodka. and spirits. Add to this the alcoholic content of 86,000,000 barrels and 6.3 billion cans of beer and 140,000,000 gallons of wine and one obtains a

sizable ocean of ethyl alcohol. On this rather crude protoplasmic poison—and no conscientious pharmacologist would
dignify alcohol with any better title—the people of the
United States spend more than they do on the education of
their children, the care of their sick, or the glorification of
their God.

During the countless centuries of man's acquaintance
with this drug several hymns have been sung in praise of its
effects. Wine-purpled Bacchus, deified by the Greeks,
crowned with a wreath of vine leaves and waving the thyr-
sus, was once an object of fervent adoration and his festivals,
the Bacchanalia, provided occasions for collective indulgence
in every form of physical excess. Wine has been praised by
the wise as well as the foolish. "It seems to me, O friends, to
be right to drink," says Socrates. "Wine comforts the soul,
soothes the sorrow of man like mandragora, and arouses joy
as oil the flame." Even the abstemious St. Paul had no quarrel with wine, advising Timothy to "drink no longer water
but use a little wine for thy stomach's sake."

But for every hymn in praise of alcohol there is a corresponding lamentation, detailing the horrid effects of excessive indulgence in this poison. Here, for example, is an
inscription on an old Greek tomb which doubtless applied
to many others besides the man whose bones reposed beneath it.

> Wanderer, hear the warnings of Orthon of Syracuse,
> Don't travel at night when drunk, especially in winter!
> Such was my luckless destiny. Not at home
> But here I lie under an alien soil.

So great was the abhorrence with which Mahomet regarded wine that he absolutely forbade his followers to

drink it. Gautama Siddartha, the Buddha, imposed upon his disciples a similar rule. The course of history, on more than one occasion, has been changed by the destructive effects of alcohol. Alexander of Macedon, who was frequently drunk for three days on end, would almost certainly not have died prematurely, with his empire still unstabilized, had not the fever which he contracted in Asia been aggravated in its effects by a prolonged orgy of drunkenness.

Let us now consider the effects which this time-honored drug, ethyl alcohol, exerts on the mind and body of man. Concerning these effects there are many misconceptions, the chief of which is that alcohol is a stimulant. This is quite untrue. Alcohol is a protoplasmic poison with a purely depressant effect on the human nervous system. Its depressant effect is so strong that, taken in sufficient amount, it will render a man unconscious, functioning in this respect as a general anesthetic. It could, in fact, be used as an anesthetic and in the past frequently was, but the dose of alcohol which renders a man insensible is dangerously near to the dose that puts him to sleep once and for all. In view of all this it is indeed surprising to find that Hesse in his *Narcotics and Drug Addiction* has placed alcohol among the stimulants. Goodman and Gilman have laid down the law in this matter: "It may be stated categorically that alcohol is not a stimulant but rather a primary and continuous depressant of the nervous system."

How did this widespread misconception arise? It arose, we may safely guess, because alcohol affects the nervous system selectively. After alcohol has passed from the blood into the brain it acts first on that area of the cerebral cortex which exerts a restraining action on our more native impulses, the censorious, restricting, critical entity to which Freudians have given the name of the Super-ego. Alco-

hol's first effect is to put the Super-ego more or less to sleep.
While that cold-eyed critic snores our other natures manifest more freely. The tongue-tied become eloquent, the shy
grow bold, the awkward become graceful. It is not surprising that one who finds himself thus released from his inward
fetters feels as if he has escaped from a prison and acts accordingly. It should be noted that ether, which has much in
common with alcohol, also appears to be stimulating when
taken in small doses. Hence the "ether frolicks" popular
during the last century, in the course of which the anesthetic
properties of this substance were discovered. Actually, of
course, both substances are depressants.

The second reason why alcohol has been erroneously considered a stimulant is that, by dilating the blood vessels in
the skin, it gives an impression of warmth to one who takes
it. This glow in throat and stomach, this warmth in the
skin, led to the assumption that alcohol was a warmth-giving
substance, particularly suitable for reviving chilly travelers.
This belief has its most picturesque expression in the little
barrels of brandy carried by the St. Bernard dogs sent to rescue snowbound wanderers in the Alps. Actually, far from
warming the unfortunate traveler, alcohol dissipates such
warmth as he has left by sending a flow of blood to the surface blood vessels previously contracted by the wisdom of nature for the very purpose of conserving warmth in the vital
organs. The noble beast in the Alps would serve the interests
of the snowbound traveler best if it threw away its picturesque brandy barrel and substituted for it a prosaic thermos
of hot coffee. There is little real warmth to be gained from
brandy or from any other form of alcohol, concentrated or
otherwise.

As a euphoriant alcohol has a limited value. It is freely
available, fairly cheap, and, in moderation, does not harm

the body. In fact it even has a certain food value, being burnt up in the blood to liberate a modest number of calories. It is not, in normal people, a habit-forming drug and its effects are not cumulative if the body is given sufficient time to eliminate it. Although no one with any knowledge of the subject could ever claim that alcohol is the ideal euphoriant it does possess some rather valuable properties as a sort of catalyst in social gatherings, promoting friendly and lively interchange of ideas and removing awkwardness and unnecessary restraint. To parties which might otherwise prove gray and dreary it may lend a certain sparkle and vivacity, nor could one find much fault with the drug if its effects were confined to the gentle liberation of the timid from the restraints of an over-rigid Super-ego.

The effect which the consumption of alcohol produces depends very greatly on the *type* of individual who takes it. That great American scientist, William Sheldon, has shed much light on this problem, as on many others, by his fundamental studies on human body build (somatotype). Consider the type which is high in *endomorphy,* the roly-poly, baby-faced, full-gutted *viscerotonic,* of whom Sir John Falstaff must remain the eternal prototype. Such a one can and commonly does consume large amounts of alcohol without suffering any particular inconvenience.

"Oh monstrous!" cries Prince Henry in disgust. "But one half-pennyworth of bread to this intolerable deal of sack!" But Falstaff, being *viscerotonic,* could not only stomach his sack but also metabolize it. The *viscerotonic* is normally warmly sociable and under the influence of alcohol this trait is exaggerated. He is apt to become maudlin and sentimental under the influence of the drug but he does not become aggressive.

The muscular *mesomorph,* leathery of face and hard of

body, is often a heavy drinker. He loves his alcohol, tends to drink his whisky neat, and so specific is his reaction to the drug that Sheldon recommends the use of whisky to determine the variety of temperament. "In temperament study an ounce of alcohol is sometimes worth hours of the shrewdest inquiry." The muscular *mesomorph* with his *somatotonic* personality reacts to the drug with exaggerated manifestations of his chief characteristics. He becomes more openly and noisily aggressive, more expansive, filled with a sense of power. He envisages vast undertakings and adventures. His energies seem unlimited. His voice and his laugh, noisy at the best of times, rise to new achievements in volume. Inhibitions crumble, candor is complete, the sense of being important holds full sway. The *mesomorph,* primed with alcohol, feels very definitely on top of the world.

People of this body type often become "problem drinkers." The reason for this is not difficult to see. A body type high in *mesomorphy* goes hand in hand with an aggressive *somatotonic* temperament. This aggression, in our civilized world, has to be restrained and the need for this restraint imposes considerable stress on the individual. Alcohol, which relaxes this inward tension, is thus a euphoriant for such people and they tend for this reason to consume it both more frequently and more freely than is good for them. It is this type of individual who becomes troublesome when drunk, is apt to pick fights and to start throwing his weight around. His aggressive tendencies, released from their inhibitions, run wild like wolves and are liable to lead to violence. While the *viscerotonic* becomes slobbery and sentimental under the influence of alcohol, the *somatotonic* becomes ferocious and may be dangerous.

For people of the *ectomorphic* body type, slender, small-boned, thin-skinned, "nervous" and tense, alcohol has an essentially unpleasant effect. It functions simply as a depressant. Often it increases rather than decreases their feeling of strain and produces a sense of dizziness and fatigue. For this reason people of this type rarely become heavy drinkers and are frequently teetotalers. Owing to the popular approval given to high consumption of alcohol in certain circles of society, the individual of this variety of temperament (*cerebrotonic*) often pretends to a liking for the drug which he does not actually feel. Sheldon describes the situation with wry humor. ". . . only the hardiest or the stupidest of the cerebrotonics are likely to confess openly a distaste for this drug. In the politer and more intellectual circles, such a confession now places an individual in a position similar to that of a Czarist in Soviet Russia."

We will now consider in more detail the effect of this widely used drug on the body. When a man drinks a glass of whisky on an empty stomach he offers a chemical insult to an important organ which, properly treated, should last him for a lifetime. The stomach, wiser than its owner, takes immediate steps to protect its walls from this poison, secreting protective mucus and large amounts of gastric juice to dilute the alcohol to a tolerable concentration. Of course, if the man is a wise drinker and prefers to live on good terms with his stomach he will take the precaution either of lining it with food before he drinks or of diluting his liquor, for, apart from any intoxicating effects which alcohol may produce after it has been absorbed, it exerts on the walls of the unprotected stomach an action which is both irritating and inflaming. Strong alcoholic beverages such as whisky which contain forty per cent alcohol or more produce chronic stomach disorders in approximately one out of three individuals who make a regular habit of pouring them into an unprotected stomach. Dilute alcohol (10 per cent or less, as in beers or light wines) stimulates the stomach to produce a secretion rich in acid though poor in pepsin. This action may be responsible for the widespread idea that alcoholic drinks are good aperitifs. Because of the acid secretion which the stomach generates under the influence of alcohol, those whose stomach walls are already ulcerated do well to regard the drug with particular suspicion.

After the drug has been received by the stomach and that long-suffering organ has made necessary adjustments to protect its vital interests, the alcohol is absorbed more or less rapidly into the blood. The rate at which it is absorbed is influenced by several factors, chiefly the fullness of the stomach and the rate at which drinks are taken. If a man swallows his drinks fast enough and their alcohol content is high enough he may so insult his stomach that a violent spasm will occur and the injured organ, swiftly and decisively, will hurl out the poison by the shortest route so that the debauch comes to an end before it has properly begun.

Alcohol passes rapidly into the blood stream and is quickly distributed to every organ in the body. This includes the baby in the case of expectant mothers and the milk in the case of nursing mothers, who may, if they indulge to excess, offer their infants breast milk spiked with gin. Signs of intoxication begin to be seen as soon as the alcohol has entered the brain. First comes the inhibition of the function of the cerebral cortex produced by a drink of two to three ounces of whisky and corresponding to 0.05 per cent of alcohol in the blood. At this stage the drinker is freed from many of his inhibitions and acquires that sense of liberty already described. When the concentration of alcohol in the blood rises to about .1 per cent (from five to six ounces of whisky) the depressant influence spreads to those centers in the brain which regulate movements. The drinker walks unsteadily; he has difficulty in putting on his overcoat, fumbles with his door key, slurs his words. At a concentration of .2 per cent of alcohol in the blood (from ten ounces of whisky) the entire motor area of the brain is affected and the depressant effect of the drug spreads to those centers in the midbrain which control the emotional manifestations of men. At this stage our boozer may be called "beastly drunk," though such an epithet is really an insult to the beasts. He is not only almost unable to stand upright but is also prone to ridiculous displays of emotion in which he alternates between senseless rage and equally senseless tears. With .3 per cent of alcohol in his blood (from about a pint of whisky) the drinker's brain becomes affected in that area which is concerned with sensory perception. Although still vaguely conscious, he is stuporous and has little comprehension of what he sees or hears. At a level of .4 per cent or .5 per cent in the blood, alcohol depresses the whole perception area in the brain and the drinker becomes comatose. Finally, with .6 per cent to .7 per cent of alcohol in the blood, our drinker dies a swift and painless death, his breathing and the beating of his heart arrested by paralysis of the centers that control these vital functions.

Throughout this sequence the concentration of alcohol remains much too low to cause any serious damage to the major organs of the body. All the observed effects are due to the fact that ethyl alcohol interferes with nerve function and up to the last stage the effect is reversible. Some may claim that the drug exerts other effects besides those described. They may believe, for example, that it especially stimulates sexual desire. In this connection Shakespeare, whose insight into the action of drugs was often surprisingly acute, has probably offered the most revealing comment.

MACDUFF. What three things does drink especially provoke?

PORTER. Marry, sir, nose-painting, sleep and urine. Lechery, sir, it provokes and it unprovokes; it provokes the desire, but it takes away the performance.

The abuse of alcohol, however, has other effects not noted by Shakespeare's Porter, for it appears to interfere with the liver's handling of fat. After severe alcoholic intoxication this organ is often swollen and yellow with fat. Probably this impairment of the liver's handling of fat is responsible for the development of cirrhosis of the liver, a serious disease which occurs with particularly high incidence among alcoholics.

Paradoxically enough, the most serious ailments which afflict the alcoholic are not due to alcohol at all. It is perhaps unfortunate for those who tend to consume large amounts of it that alcohol is a food. It is a food in the sense that it liberates calories, for an ounce of whisky can supply as much energy as four and a half teaspoons of sugar, one and a half pats of butter, or a large slice of bread. This fact tends to cause the heavy drinker to drink his meals instead of eating them. From a pint of whisky he can obtain 1200 calories per day, fully half of his total requirements. Man, however, is more than a simple heat engine and cannot live on calories alone. What the alcoholic cannot get from his whisky bottle is the protein needed to replace his worn-out tissue, the mineral elements, and above all the vitamins, thiamin, niacin, pyridoxine, essential for the normal working of his nervous system.

It is the lack of vitamins in his diet far more than the direct effect of alcohol on the tissues that causes the most dangerous afflictions that plague the alcoholic. All of these afflictions may be seen in the alcoholic ward of any big city hospital. Here, for example, is Mike, picked up on the streets by the police on a freezing December night. Mike is not merely drunk, he is obviously a very sick man. In the hospital to which Mike is taken the doctor notes a familiar group of symptoms. Mike's legs are swollen and edematous. His grossly enlarged liver can be felt well below the last rib. The fingers are tremulous, the eyes are curiously fixed, the walk, when Mike is asked to walk along a line, has a weaving, unsteady quality that suggests more than temporary alcoholic inco-ordination. The doctor writes in his notes "Wernicke's syndrome?" and looks for confirmatory evidence—the smooth reddened tongue, the dry, loosely hanging skin. These symptoms are not the results of too much alcohol but of too little thiamin (vitamin B_1). Mike, living on the bottle, eating little, his food uptake impaired by the inflammation which alcohol has produced in his stomach and intestines, has been receiving so little of this substance, vital for the normal working of the nerves, that those organs may well have been damaged irreparably.

As it turns out Mike can still be saved. Dosed intravenously with the needed vitamin, quietened with chlorpromazine, his vitality renewed by a suitably nourishing diet, he is fairly quickly restored to a reasonably good state of health, released from the hospital, restored to society and to the company of the whisky bottle. Nothing can be done for Mike. He belongs to that group of alcoholics in whom the capacity for self-criticism has died. He will do nothing about his condition because he refuses to face it. Ask him about it and he dismisses it with a laugh—just a social drinker, no harm in that. Soon he will be back in hospital in a condition slightly worse than before. The combined resources of modern medicine will be exerted at considerable expense to salvage him again, for which he will show no gratitude whatever. Finally a time will come when the outraged nervous system will stand no more abuse. The inner world of Mike will crumble into ruins and his demented remains will be transferred to a mental hospital. To the words "Wernicke's syndrome" the examining physician will add a more serious piece of medical jargon, "Korsakoff's psychosis."

Mike might think more seriously about his "social drinking" if he could see the plight of Mrs. S., picked up by the police that morning wandering in a city park, talking incoherently to the empty air. Mrs. S. in a fine mink coat, with all the marks of wealth about her person, was identified as a rich widow with an apartment on Park Avenue. She was over fifty, gray, undernourished, and insane. A study of her personal history revealed a long series of alcoholic episodes, of expensive "cures" in high-class private institutions, of resolutions to reform which were sooner or later broken. After the death of her husband Mrs. S., alone in her luxurious apartment and conscious of an emptiness which threatened to become unbearable, finally ceased to struggle with her taste for alcohol. She drank more or less constantly. Gin was her favorite and she practically lived on it: gin for breakfast, gin for lunch, gin for supper, for elevenses, for tea, for snacks. All of which Mrs. S. might possibly have survived had the makers of gin merely taken the trouble to add to their product enough thiamin to keep the good lady's nervous system functioning. Indeed it is astonishing that makers of hard liquor have still not tumbled to the simple fact that they could save many valued customers from premature death simply by supplementing their products with vitamins at the cost of a few cents per bottle. This they might do if only for selfish reasons, for it obviously is not in their interests to drive rich alcoholics like Mrs. S. into mental hospitals in which their consumption of alcohol will be reduced to zero. Owing to this oversight on the part of the gin maker, Mrs. S. so deranged the chemistry of her nervous system that neither wealth nor skill could repair the damage. She could remember nothing; knew neither who she was nor where she was, what time of year it was, whether it was morning or afternoon. She was worth just over a million dollars and died insane for lack of a few cents' worth of thiamin. Such is "Korsakoff's psychosis."

Better known and more alarming is the condition known as *delirium tremens,* to which all chronic alcoholics are liable. Here, for example, is Caroline, an unsuccessful actress who tried to take refuge from the stresses and strains of existence in Hollywood by blunting her sensibilities with alcohol. It was the same old story, drunk in the morning, drunk at midday, drunk at night; not enough food, not enough vitamins, not enough protein, not enough calcium or phosphorus. Caroline had been sick for days. Tormented with vague anxieties, restless, fearful, she was vaguely aware of the approach of the coming storm. The slightest noise or movement was enough to frighten her. She dared not go out, dared not leave her apartment. Sitting in her chair with a dressing gown wrapped about her shoulders, she sweated with unreasoning terror. Her sleep was broken with nightmares from which she awakened scarcely able to stifle her screams. Finally, unable any longer to fight off the terrible hallucinations closing in upon her, she screamed aloud, thus calling the attention of her neighbors to her condition. She was removed in an ambulance to the alcoholic ward in one of the large hospitals where she was restrained by being strapped to the bed. Convinced that snakes were crawling over her body, she screamed constantly and tried to fight off the reptiles. Crazy with fear her body shaken with constant tremors, disoriented, dehydrated, malnourished, and vomiting, the unfortunate girl presented a singularly unglamorous picture. Fortunately for her, the new tranquilizing drug, chlorpromazine, was available to quiet her terrors at the same time as large amounts of B vitamins were pushed into her system to repair her damaged nerve cells. After forty-eight hours the rats and snakes retreated. The normal functioning of Caroline's psyche was slowly restored. She left the hospital somewhat shattered but not permanently damaged. She was luckier than some. Even under the best conditions a 4 to 5 per cent mortality goes with *delirium tremens*. Under less favorable conditions it may rise far higher.

One other form of alcoholism which should be mentioned is so-called "dipsomania," which differs from chronic alcoholism in being a cyclic condition. The dipsomaniac may not touch alcohol for weeks, then quite abruptly, on account of some mysterious change that takes place within him, he is overwhelmed by an irresistible urge to drink. And drink he does, ceaselessly and steadily, with a single-minded devotion worthy of a better cause. For a period of several days or several weeks he continues to saturate his system with alcohol until, shaken, worn out, and quite possibly penniless, he reaches a point where his mysterious need is satisfied and he can, for a while at least, do without the poison. Such is the process illustrated in the novel *Lost Week End,* but what is lost is more than a week end. Happiness, self-respect, even a man's means of livelihood may all be transformed into alcohol and lost without a trace in the course of a single Gargantuan debauch.

In the United States alcoholism is a major public health problem. The Yale University Center of Alcohol Studies estimates the number of alcoholics in the country at around 4,500,000. "Problem drinkers," to use a phrase that has recently become popular, are commonest in California, the city of San Francisco leading with 16,760 alcoholics per 100,000 adult population. The yearly cost of this ailment has been estimated at $432,000,000 in lost wages alone. Jobs are lost, marriages wrecked, children's lives distorted and ruined, innocent pedestrians or motorists mown down on the roads by drivers whose reactions have been slowed by alcohol. The poison is really a major menace, nor can one wonder that so many attempts have been made to outlaw its use. But, as Hirsch points out in his book, *The Problem Drinker*, to place the blame on alcohol is absurd. The fault lies with those who insist on misusing this drug. It is useful in this connection to bear in mind a passage from St. John Chrysostom's "Homilies" which the above writer quotes:

> I hear many cry when deplorable excesses happen, "Would there were no wine! O folly! O madness!" Is it the wine that causes this abuse? No. It is the intemperance of those who take an evil delight in it. . . . If you say, "Would there were no wine!" because of drunkards, then you must say, going on by degrees, "Would there were no night!" because of the thieves. "Would there were no light!" because of the informers, and "Would there were no women!" because of adultery.

The cause of alcoholism lies not in the whisky bottle but in the psyche of those unfortunates who swallow its contents too freely. The alcoholic is sick mentally and emotionally. He belongs, according to Dr. Lolli, director of the Yale Plan Clinic, to that group of disturbed individuals who are labeled "impulsive neurotics." He is an insecure, emotionally immature individual who seeks in alcohol a crutch to support him in his journey through life. Often he is more sensitive than his fellow men and is thus more prone to injury life inflicts. For this reason creative artists often become alcoholics. Painters, poets, writers too numerous to mention have sought to deaden their sensibilities with this poison. As recently as 1953 the finest of contemporary lyric poets, that incomparable Welshman, Dylan Thomas, died of acute alcoholic poisoning in a Manhattan hospital, only one of many creative spirits whose genius was prematurely blighted by this crude depressant of the nervous system.

What can be done to help the alcoholic? The answer is, absolutely nothing until he has reached a fixed decision to help himself. Only when he has grown utterly disgusted with his dependence, when he has sunk to the bottom of the pit and come to loathe his self-inflicted degradation can he be helped to help himself. Without doubt he needs help. He is a lonely being, insecure and unstable. He needs love, support, understanding, and a certain amount of protection from himself, for his resolution to abstain stands like a sheep amongst the wolves of his own cravings and, if left unprotected, may be devoured by a single impulse. So, being in need of a spiritual shepherd, he will naturally seek the aid of those best able to understand his problems, people who have been through the same hell and reached the same resolve—in short, rehabilitated alcoholics. This is the logical basis for that organization, Alcoholics Anonymous, whose immense achievements reflect the soundness of its methods and the correctness of its underlying philosophy.

Besides the help offered by such an organization as Alcoholics Anonymous the alcoholic can obtain a certain amount of additional help from the chemist In 1948 two Danish physicians, J. Held and E. Jacobsen, dosed themselves with a chemical called tetraethylthiuram disulphide to determine its value as a remedy for worms. With this chemical inside them they proceeded to a cocktail party at which they both became acutely ill. They were perspicacious enough to blame this illness not on their hostess' canapés but on the worm remedy they had tried, which had evidently rendered them hypersensitive to alcohol. Quick to realize the possibilities of such a substance, they started a series of studies which laid the basis for the use of this substance as a protective chemical device for chronic alcoholics.

Tetraethylthiuram disulphide was thus launched on its career and has since accumulated an impressive collection of fancy names such as "Antabuse," "Aversan," "Abstinyl," "Refusal." In the United States it is generally called "Antabuse." Taken alone, it is harmless, but when alcohol is introduced into the body it interferes with the process by which alcohol is burned and eliminated. This results in the accumulation in the blood of a very poisonous substance known as acetaldehyde. The unfortunate alcoholic develops a set of symptoms drastic enough to make him an enemy of the bottle ever afterward. His eyes bulge and grow red, his face flushes, he becomes nauseated, vomits copiously, develops pains in the chest, dizziness, weakness, and confusion. All of which should convince the reader that "Antabuse" is not a drug to be played with. It should be taken only under medical supervision. Those who do drink while they have "Antabuse" in their systems are likely never to repeat the experiment.

Leaving now the subject of alcohol, we pass to the consideration of a second drug, the origins of which are also lost in the mists of antiquity. This drug is opium. It is easy to see how mankind discovered alcohol; the prevalence of fermentation made this almost inevitable. It is much less easy to understand how he first found opium, yet find it he did and at a remarkably early period. Opium almost certainly was the active principle of the drug *nepenthe* described by Homer as the "potent destroyer of grief." He attributed its discovery to the ancient Egyptians, but whether they actually discovered this drug or merely learned about it from some other race we shall never know. Opium was widely used in the ancient world. The poppy played its part in the mysteries of Ceres, who drank of its milk to gain "oblivion from grief." Among both Greeks and Romans it was universally employed. Theophrastus, Pliny, and Dioscorides were all familiar with its effects. We can safely assume that opium addiction was a very common phenomenon in those days, and both Diagoras of Melos and Erasistrates recommended, on account of its addicting properties, complete avoidance of the use of the drug.

Opium is a product of the opium poppy, the very name of which, *Papaver somniferum*, links it inseparably with sleep and dreams. Its wrinkled paperlike petals, white or pale purple, are folded tightly within a two-membered calyx like a pearl within an oyster. The nodding heads of the flower symbolize Morpheus, heavy-eyed god of dreams. The shapely seed capsule, finely proportioned as a Grecian urn, is so designed by nature that the seeds it contains are shaken out from holes beneath the starlike top which gives them protection from injurious rain. These seeds are as innocent as unborn babes, containing a bland oil and several fragrant essences which impart a distinctive flavor to various cakes and confections. But the green unripened capsule contains a spirit more potent than any genie ever imprisoned in a bottle by the imagination of an Arabian storyteller. That capsule is the dwelling place of opium.

The opium poppy will grow in many climates but its cultivation for purposes of opium manufacture is confined to a few countries. India, Persia, Turkey, Yugoslavia, Macedonia, Bulgaria, and China are the main producers. Though eighteen hundred years have elapsed since Dioscorides, a Greek physician in the days of Nero, described the method by which opium was collected, few changes have taken place in the procedure. It is a slow and tedious operation and is economically feasible only in countries where labor costs are low. For this reason, though it would be perfectly possible to cultivate the poppy for opium in the United States, it would never be commercially feasible to do so. In the early morning, when the dew has barely dried from the poppy heads, bands of women and older children make their way into the fields. The gray-green capsules from which the petals fell but a few days previously are delicately cut with many-bladed knives. The merest scratch is all that is required; a deeper incision, penetrating the capsule wall, is fatal to the seeds, which are themselves a valuable crop. From the parallel wounds there gushes a droplet of white milk which dries on the surface of the capsule. Twenty-four hours later the opium gatherers return to the fields. The droplets of brown dried gum are scraped from the capsule with broad-bladed knives and deposited on poppy leaves. Very slowly the lump of brown opium enlarges as the little dried tears are scraped from the capsule and added to the mass. The product reaches the world markets in lumps weighing a half to two pounds. Turkish opium is most esteemed on account of its high morphine content, but Macedonian, Persian, and Indian opium also find their way into the world markets. Most of the opium produced in China is consumed in that country.

This brownish gum is extremely rich in alkaloids, of

which no less than twenty-five have been described. Morphine, thebaine, codeine, narcotine, and papaverine are the better known of these substances. Heroin, of ill repute on account of its addicting properties, does not occur in opium. It is manufactured from morphine by a relatively simple chemical procedure and is known chemically as diacetylmorphine. Its manufacture in the United States is forbidden by federal law. All of the heroin that gains entry into the country and keeps the members of the Narcotics Bureau so busy is manufactured elsewhere and smuggled across the border or brought in through the ports of New York or San Francisco.

Opium in the past has had many devotees who, taking it first to relieve some physical pain, came gradually to rely upon it and ultimately became its slave. Best known of its devotees are the English writers, Coleridge and De Quincey. Baudelaire indulged in the drug and Jean Cocteau, a member of the Académie Française, has also written an account of his use of opium. De Quincey's work, *Confessions of an English Opium-Eater*, has long been regarded as a classic, though it is difficult to account for the veneration that has been bestowed upon this work in literary circles, it being for the most part diffuse, disorganized, and dull. Certain passages, however, do have a curious brilliance and, as they deal with the effect of opium on the mind, will be quoted in full.

De Quincey describes his first acquaintance with opium as follows:

I awoke with excruciating rheumatic pains of the head and face from which I had hardly any respite for about twenty days. On the twenty-first day I think it was, and on a Sunday, that I went out into the streets; rather to run away if possible from my torments, than with any distinct purpose of relief. By accident I met a college acquaintance who recommended opium. Opium! dread agent of unimaginable pleasure and pain! I had heard of it as I had heard of manna or of ambrosia, but no further. How unmeaning a sound was opium at that time! What solemn chords does it now strike upon my heart! . . . Arrived at my lodgings, it may be supposed that I lost not a moment in taking the quantity prescribed. I was necessarily ignorant of the whole art and mystery of opium taking; and what I took I took under every disadvantage. But I took it and in an hour O heavens! what a revulsion! What a resurrection from its lowest depths of the inner spirit! What an apocalypse of the world within me! That my pains had vanished was now a trifle in my eyes; this negative effect was swallowed up in the immensity of those positive effects which had opened before me, in the abyss of divine enjoyment thus suddenly revealed. Here was a panacea, a *pharmakon nepenthes* for all human woes; here was the secret of happiness, about which philosophers had disputed for so many ages, at once discovered; happiness might now be bought for a penny, and carried in the waistcoat pocket; portable ecstasies might be corked up in a pint bottle, and peace of mind could be sent down by the mail.

In passages which follow De Quincey compares the effects of alcohol and opium and loudly sings his praises of the latter drug.

Crude opium, I affirm peremptorily, is incapable of producing any state of body at all resembling that which is produced by alcohol; and not in *degree* only incapable but even in *kind*: it is not in the quantity of its effects merely.

but in the quality, that it differs altogether. The pleasure
given by wine is always rapidly mounting, and tending to a
crisis, after which as rapidly it declines; that from opium,
when once generated, is stationary for eight or ten hours;
the one is a flickering flame, the other a steady and equable
glow. But the main distinction lies in this—that whereas wine
disorders the mental faculties, opium, on the contrary, (if
taken in the proper manner,) introduces amongst them the
most exquisite order, legislation and harmony. Wine robs a
man of his self-possession; opium sustains and reinforces it.
Wine unsettles the judgment, and gives a preternatural
brightness and a vivid exaltation to the contempts and the
admirations, to the loves and the hatreds, of the drinker;
opium, on the contrary, communicates serenity and equipoise
of all the faculties, active and passive, and, with respect to
the temper and moral feelings in general, it gives simply that
sort of vital warmth which is approved by the judgment and
would probably always accompany a bodily constitution of
primaeval or antediluvian health.

Just as Ludlow gained mystical experiences from *hashish*
and Aldous Huxley from mescaline, so De Quincey obtained new insights from opium.

More than once it has happened to me, on a summer
night, when I have been at an open window, in a room from
which I could overlook the sea at a mile below me, and could
command a view of the great town of L——, at about the
same distance, that I have sat from sunset to sunrise, motionless, and without wishing to move.
I shall be charged with mysticism, Behmenism, quietism,
etc., but that shall not alarm me. . . . The town of L——
represented the earth, with its sorrows and its graves left

behind, yet not out of sight, nor wholly forgotten. The ocean, in everlasting but gentle agitation, and brooded over by dovelike calm, might not unfitly typify the mind and the mood which then swayed it. For it seemed to me as if then first I stood at a distance, and aloof from the uproar of life; as if the tumult, the fever, and the strife, were suspended; a respite granted from the secret burdens of the heart, a sabbath of repose; a resting from human labors. Here were the hopes which blossom in the paths of life, reconciled with the peace which is in the grave; motions of the intellect as unwearied as the heavens, yet for all anxieties a halcyon calm; a tranquility that seemed no product of inertia, but as if resulting from mighty and equal antagonisms; infinite activities, infinite repose.

De Quincey concludes this account of "the Pleasures of Opium" with the following paean of praise in honor of the drug:

O just, subtle, and all-conquering opium! that, to the hearts of rich and poor alike, for the wounds that will never heal, and for the pangs of grief that "tempt the spirit to rebel" bringest an assuaging balm; eloquent opium! that with thy potent rhetoric stealest away the purposes of wrath; pleadest effectually for relenting pity, and through one night's heavenly sleep callest back to the guilty man the visions of his infancy, and hands washed pure from blood. O just and righteous opium! that to the chancery of dreams summonest for the triumphs of despairing innocence, false witnesses; and confoundest perjury; and dost reverse the sentences of unrighteous judges:—thou buildest upon the bosom of darkness, out of the fantastic imagery of the brain, cities and temples beyond the art of Phidias and Praxiteles;

and, "from the anarchy of dreaming sleep," callest into sunny light the faces of long buried beauties, and the blessed household countenances, cleansed from the "dishonours of the grave." Thou only givest these gifts to man; and thou hast the keys of Paradise, O just, subtle and mighty opium!

The "fantastic imagery of the brain" which, for De Quincey, was evoked by opium was described by him in considerable detail and, because it is relevant to our subject, his account will be quoted at some length. It must be observed, however, that De Quincey and Coleridge, both of whom saw visions under the influence of opium, were the exception rather than the rule in this respect. They were both of them unusual individuals, endowed with imaginations of peculiar brilliance. Opium seems in some way to have stimulated this image-making faculty. In general, however, opium is not regarded as a fantasy-provoking drug, as is cannabis or mescaline. It would appear to have this effect only in certain types of whom both Coleridge and De Quincey were examples. The strange spectacles which opium presented to him came to De Quincey mainly at night in the form of dreams or those curious experiences which come between sleeping and waking and go by the name of hypnagogic hallucinations.

A theatre suddenly opened and lighted up within my brain, which presented nightly spectacles of more than earthly splendor. And the four following facts may be mentioned, as noticeable at this time:—

I. That, as the creative state of the eye increased, a sympathy seemed to arise between the waking and the dreaming states of the brain in one point—that whatsoever I happened to call up and to trace by a voluntary act upon the darkness was very apt to transfer itself to my dreams; so that I feared to exercise this faculty; for, as Midas turned all things to gold, that yet baffled his hopes and defrauded his human desires, so whatsoever things capable of being visually represented I did but think of in the darkness, immediately shaped themselves into phantoms of the eye; and, by a process apparently no less inevitable, when thus once traced in faint and visionary colors, like writings in sympathetic ink, they were drawn out by the fierce chemistry of my dreams, into insufferable splendor that fretted my heart.

II. For this, and all other changes in my dreams, were accompanied by deep seated anxiety and gloomy melancholy, such as are wholly incommunicable by words. I seemed every night to descend, not metaphorically, but literally to descend, into chasms and sunless abysses, depths below depths, from which it seemed hopeless that I could ever reascend.* Nor did I, by waking, feel that I had reascended. This I do not dwell upon; because the state of gloom which attended these gorgeous spectacles, amounting at least to utter darkness, as of some suicidal despondency, cannot be approached by words.

III. The sense of space, and in the end, the sense of time, were both powerfully affected. Buildings, landscapes, etc., were exhibited in proportions so vast as the bodily eye is not fitted to receive. Space swelled, and was amplified to an extent of unutterable infinity. This, however, did not disturb me so much as the vast expansion of time; I sometimes

---

* This is reminiscent of the experience of another English opium eater, Samuel Taylor Coleridge, whose *Kubla Khan* is said to have been written under the influence of opium:

> Where Alph, the sacred river, ran
> Through caverns measureless to man,
> Down to a sunless sea.

seemed to have lived for seventy or one hundred years in one night; nay, sometimes had feelings representative of a millennium passed in that time, or, however, of a duration far beyond the limits of any human experience.

IV. The minutest incidents of childhood, or forgotten scenes of later years, were often revived: I could not be said to recollect them; for if I had been told of them when waking, I should not have been able to acknowledge them as parts of my past experience. But placed as they were before me, in dreams like intuitions, and clothed in all their evanescent circumstances and accompanying feelings, I recognized them instantaneously. I was once told by a near relative of mine, that having in her childhood fallen into a river, and being on the very verge of death but for the critical assistance which reached her, she saw in a moment her whole life, in its minutest incidents, arrayed before her simultaneously as in a mirror; and she had a faculty developed as suddenly for comprehending the whole and every part. This, from some opium experiences of mine, I can believe; I have, indeed, seen the same thing asserted twice in modern books, and accompanied by a remark which I am convinced is true; viz., that the dread book of account, which the scriptures speak of, is, in fact, the mind itself of each individual. Of this, at least, I feel assured, that there is no such thing as forgetting possible to the mind; a thousand accidents may, and will, interpose a veil between our present consciousness and the secret inscriptions on the mind; accidents of the same sort will also rend away this veil; but alike, whether veiled or unveiled, the inscription remains forever; just as the stars seem to withdraw before the common light of day, whereas in fact we all know that it is the light which is drawn over them as a veil—and that they are waiting to be revealed, when the obscuring daylight shall have withdrawn.

Such were the visions which De Quincey obtained from
opium and which, no doubt, were in part responsible for the
fascination this drug held for him. It is important at this
point to consider more carefully the whole question of the
"Pleasures of Opium," because, but for such pleasures,
there would not be any addicts. Dr. Lawrence Kolb, one of
the world's leading authorities on opiate addiction, thoroughly investigated this question and published his findings
in a classic paper entitled "Pleasure and Deterioration from
Narcotic Addiction." The chief fact to emerge from this
paper is that normal people do not derive any pleasure from
opium or morphine. If they are in pain their pain is relieved, but in such cases the pleasure they feel is not due to
the euphoriant action of the drug but merely to the removal of former discomfort. Pleasure is derived from opiates
only by psychopaths:

> . . . the intensity of pleasure produced by opiates is in
> direct proportion to the degree of psychopathy of the person
> who becomes an addict . . . the subsequent depression re-
> sulting from long continued use of the drugs carries him as
> far below his normal emotional plane as the first exaltation
> carried him above it.

Kolb's observations have been fully substantiated by
recent experiments of Dr. Louis Lasagna and his coworkers
at the Harvard Medical School. These scientists actually
administered drugs to healthy, normal individuals and recorded their reactions. The human guinea pigs in this experiment had no idea whether the pill they were given
contained morphine, heroin, amphetamine ("Benzedrine"),
or no drug whatever. In this way the effects of imagination
were eliminated and a completely objective appraisal of the

drug's effect was obtained. The results were most interesting. Of eleven subjects who received 15 milligrams of morphine, eight described its effect as predominantly unpleasant. Heroin, which is commonly supposed to afford such rapture that one who takes it can scarcely resist the temptation to become addicted for life, fared not a whit better. Seven of those who took it found its effects unpleasant, two found them neutral. This, then, is all a normal individual can expect from De Quincey's "just, subtle, all-conquering opium" into whose keeping he confides the keys of paradise.

With the psychopath, however, the situation is different. He derives pleasure from morphine or heroin for much the same reason that an alcoholic receives pleasure from alcohol. It relaxes his inner tensions and enables him to live at peace with his conflicts.

"It makes my troubles roll off my mind."
"I do not have a care in the world."
"You have a contented feeling and nothing worries you."
"It makes you drowsy and feel normal."

Such were the descriptions of their reactions given by addicts studied by Dr. Kolb. ". . . Opium produces in these cases a feeling of mental peace and calm to which they are not accustomed and which they cannot normally achieve." One highly educated addict had a reaction more in line with that described by De Quincey. ". . . It caused a buoyancy of spirits, increased imagination, temporarily enlarged the brainpower, and made him think of things he otherwise would not have thought of."

Some addicts described a purely physical thrill which immediately followed an injection of heroin or morphine.

It took the form of a feeling of warmth in the region of the abdomen. One psychopath with a low intelligence quotient described the sensation as a thrill through the body lasting seven or eight minutes and resembling the sexual orgasm. The brother of this individual also experienced the thrill and, though he derived intense pleasure from it, said it did not in any way resemble the sexual feeling. This curious reaction seems not to occur at all in normal people, but those psychopaths who experience it are rapidly led into addiction by its allurements. As their bodies grow accustomed to the drug they find they can no longer obtain the reaction. They increase the dose and start the pernicious practice of injecting the drug directly into their veins, a practice known as "main-lining." Probably it is this physical reaction that underlies the term "joy popping," a slang term for the occasional use of heroin.

Those who imagine that addiction to heroin or morphine is a short cut to the grave and that, if it does not lead to premature death, it certainly brings about moral and intellectual ruin, may find some of Dr. Kolb's conclusions rather enlightening.

That individuals may take morphine or some other opiate for 20 years or more without showing intellectual or moral deterioration is a common experience of every physician who has studied the subject. . . . We think it must be accepted that a man is mentally and morally normal who graduates in medicine, marries and raises a family of useful children, practices medicine for 30 or 40 years, never becomes involved in questionable transactions, takes a part in the affairs of the community, and is looked upon as one of its leading citizens. The same applies to a lawyer who worked himself up from a poor boy to one of the leading attorneys in his country, who became addicted to morphine following a severe abdominal disease with recurrence and two operations, and who continued to practice his profession with undiminished vigor in spite of his physical malady and the addiction.

Such cases as are cited above, and they are not uncommon, have taken as much as 15 grains of morphine daily for years without losing one day's work because of the morphine. Such addicts, however, are under the necessity of concealing a practice which is disapproved by the public and proscribed by law. To this demoralizing situation is added the shame most of them feel at finding themselves slaves to a habit from which they would like to be free. This combination of furtive concealment and shameful regret cannot help but bring about some change for the worse in any personality, but the change produced in mature individuals is usually so slight that it cannot be demonstrated or cannot be classed as "moral deterioration."

It should also interest those who speak of "murder on the installment plan" in connection with opiate addiction to know that Dr. Kolb, in his testimony before Senator Daniel's committee, made the following statement. "There is . . . a certain type of shrinking neurotic individual who can't meet the demands of life, afraid to meet people, has anxieties and fears, who if they took small amounts of narcotics—and I have examined quite a few of them—would be better and more efficient people than they would be without it." Describing two physicians who were morphine addicts and who, on being withdrawn from the drug, became hopeless problems to themselves and their families, Dr. Kolb states, "These two physicians that I am talking about didn't get cured, they should have it forever, because it would not mean anything but an insane asylum for them, and they were doing a pretty good job of work as physicians when they were on the drug and regularly taking it." Another statement of Dr. Kolb's should give food for thought to those who suppose that opium is a more destructive drug than alcohol. "Some of the inebriates had good industrial records, and the history presented by a few of them seemed to indicate that had they not changed from alcohol to opium, they would have been useless drunkards."

These quotations should not be interpreted as meaning that either Dr. Kolb or any other responsible physician approves of opiate addiction. Addiction of any kind is undesirable, whether to alcohol, morphine, heroin, "Benzedrine," or barbiturates. But the concept of what opiate addiction actually involves has become very gravely distorted in the public mind and the above statements by an experienced physician, whose knowledge of this subject is unexcelled, should help to bring the problem into the correct perspective. The narcotics addict is not a criminal, though the criminal may become a narcotics addict. Heroin and morphine do not necessarily destroy life or impair intellect. They do reduce ambition, reduce sexual desire almost to vanishing point, produce a feeling of lethargy and encourage idleness. Above all they enslave, and the slavery they impose is absolute. No tyrant, ancient or modern, exerts a more absolute control over his subjects than do heroin and morphine over the individual addicted to these drugs. Over the heads of all addicts these drugs hold the threat of torture and misery if they ever dare to attempt to break their fetters. Few, for this reason, ever make the attempt and the threat of this torture fills the life of the addict with fear, compelling him, whether he wishes to do so or not, to associate with criminals and commit crime himself in his ceaseless quest for a drug which he cannot get legally and cannot do without.

People become addicted to opiates for a variety of reasons. Association with addicts in the slum areas of the great cities is the commonest cause of addiction among adolescents, a growing problem in the United States. The youth or girl who encounters such addicts is commonly offered the drug free and exposed to the scorn of his companions if he refuses to try it. One injection of course does not make an addict. The state of physical dependence is the result of frequent injections, but soon the habit of "joy popping" leads to addiction and the young person is "hooked," as the saying is. It is to stop this kind of spread of addiction that such savage punishments are now incorporated into the United States legislation, threatening one who illegally provides a minor with heroin with twenty years' imprisonment or death.

Addiction, however, may also take place in perfectly normal people as a result of some painful illness or accident for which opiates had to be used to give relief from suffering. An example of this kind of addiction is described in Dr. John A. Hawkins's book, *Opium: Addicts and Addictions*, a contribution to the subject which is of special value because Dr. Hawkins himself was for a time an addict. His addiction dated from a day in February 1936 when he made the terrible discovery that some experiments he had been making had resulted in X-ray burns on both his feet. "Hard" X rays, or gamma rays, to give them their modern name, do not merely burn the surface of the skin as do those infrared or ultraviolet rays which inflict ordinary burns. Being ex-

ceedingly penetrating, they burn the deep tissues as well as
the superficial ones and the pain they inflict is unbelievable.

> From February until the last of June 1936 [writes Dr.
> Hawkins] I learned from long continuous suffering just how
> severe burns of this character can be. To undertake to de-
> scribe, with any degree of efficiency, the severity or persistence
> of this pain is a task for which I feel myself unqualified.
> Suffice it to say that what Dante described I actually felt, and
> I am convinced that I know in part what "hell" must be
> like, and I only hope that Satan never discovers the efficiency
> of ray burns as a means of torture.

Being himself a physician, he recognized at once the
seriousness of his condition and the hopelessness of any form
of treatment. Repeatedly he pleaded for the amputation of
both his feet to end the severe pain and to avoid the necessity of continuous doses of morphine. His pleas were ignored. The plastic surgeon in charge of the case insisted
that he could graft new skin onto the injured feet, but
because of the damage to the deeper layers none of the
grafts took, so that good skin taken from the thighs merely
followed the bad skin from the feet into the incinerator. At
last the surgeon consented to amputate so that Dr. Hawkins,
after more than four months of intense agony, left the hospital with two stumps extending not quite six inches below
his knees. In place of the feet he had lost he was left with a
"definite appetite for and dependency upon morphine."

His descriptions of his reactions to morphine entirely con-
firm those published by Lasagna and his colleagues. The
drug gave him neither mental satisfaction nor emotional
thrills. The only pleasure he derived from it was the fact
that it blunted his pain. He resented his dependence on the

drug and longed to be free. As soon as he was out of hospital he determined once and for all to liberate himself from his bondage.

God forbid that any reader of this book should ever know from direct experience what he suffered. "Withdrawal sickness" in one with a well-developed physical dependence on opiates is a shattering experience and even a physician, accustomed to the sight of suffering, finds it an ordeal to watch the agonies of patients in this condition. About twelve hours after the last dose of morphine or heroin the addict begins to grow uneasy. A sense of weakness overcomes him, he yawns, shivers, and sweats all at the same time while a watery discharge pours from the eyes and inside the nose which he compares to "hot water running up into the mouth." For a few hours he falls into an abnormal tossing, restless sleep known among addicts as the "yen sleep." On awakening, eighteen to twenty-four hours after his last dose of the drug, the addict begins to enter the lower depths of his personal hell. The yawning may be so violent as to dislocate the jaw, watery mucus pours from the nose and copious tears from the eyes. The pupils are widely dilated, the hair on the skin stands up and the skin itself is cold and shows that typical goose flesh which in the parlance of the addict is called "cold turkey," a name also applied to the treatment of addiction by means of abrupt withdrawal.

Now to add further to the addict's miseries his bowels begin to act with fantastic violence; great waves of contraction pass over the walls of the stomach, causing explosive vomiting, the vomit being frequently stained with blood. So extreme are the contractions of the intestines that the surface of the abdomen appears corrugated and knotted as if a tangle of snakes were fighting beneath the skin. The abdominal pain is severe and rapidly increases. Constant purging takes place and as many as sixty large watery stools may be passed in a day.

Thirty-six hours after his last dose of the drug the addict presents a truly dreadful spectacle. In a desperate effort to gain comfort from the chills that rack his body he covers himself with every blanket he can find. His whole body is shaken by twitchings and his feet kick involuntarily, the origin of the addict's term, "kicking the habit."

Throughout this period of the withdrawal the unfortunate addict obtains neither sleep nor rest. His painful muscular cramps keep him ceaselessly tossing on his bed. Now he rises and walks about. Now he lies down on the floor. Unless he is an exceptionally stoical individual (few addicts are, for stoics do not normally indulge in opiates) he fills the air with cries of misery. The quantity of watery secretion from eyes and nose is enormous, the amount of fluid expelled from stomach and intestines unbelievable. Profuse sweating alone is enough to keep both bedding and mattress soaked. Filthy, unshaven, disheveled, befouled with his own vomit and feces, the addict at this stage presents an almost subhuman appearance. As he neither eats nor drinks he rapidly becomes emaciated and may lose as much as ten pounds in twenty-four hours. His weakness may become so great that he literally cannot raise his head. No wonder many physicians fear for the very lives of their patients at this stage and give them an injection of the drug which almost at once removes the dreadful symptoms. "It is a dramatic experience," writes Dr. Harris Isbell, "to observe a miserably ill person receive an intravenous injection of morphine, and to see him thirty minutes later shaved, clean, laughing and joking." But this holiday from hell is of short duration and unless the drug is administered again all the symptoms start afresh within eight to twelve hours.* If no additional drug is given the symptoms begin to subside of themselves by the sixth or seventh day, but the patient is left desperately weak, nervous, restless, and often suffers from stubborn colitis.

Such is the nature of "withdrawal sickness," nor should anyone be surprised, reading this account, that the addict is prepared to do almost anything to assure a continued supply of his drug, not so much to give him pleasure as to save him from such torments. How greatly, then, one must admire the fortitude of a man like Dr. Hawkins, addicted through no fault of his own, who, even though he had morphine within easy reach, refused to avail himself of its comforts and endured his agonies until he had finally liberated himself from his bondage. It must be emphasized, however, that such suffering is not necessary. The so-called "cold turkey" treatment—i.e., sudden and complete withdrawal of the addicting drug without any other medication—is unnecessarily cruel and may on occasion be fatal. One such case is described by a witness before the Daniel Committee: a wretched woman imprisoned for possessing heroin, left in a bare cell to "kick the habit" without medical attention or even spiritual consolation. "I personally saw this girl lying on the floor . . . she was throwing up and it was actually black. . . . The doctor in charge said she didn't like drug addicts anyway, she used to say right to our faces that we were the lowest type of humanity." In the end, after going through all the torments of the damned, the wretched

* These symptoms relate to morphine or heroin. It should be emphasized that synthetic drugs having a morphine-like action, such as meperidine ("Demerol"), also give rise to addiction. The withdrawal symptoms are somewhat different. Addiction to "Demerol" is particularly common among doctors and nurses and is, according to Isbell, more harmful in its effects than addiction to morphine.

woman died. One might ask, as the legislators are so fond of talking about "murder on the installment plan," who in this case was the murderer. Shall we bring these authorities to trial who locked up this wretched woman and left her to die of her withdrawal symptoms? But no. The woman was a "dope fiend," beyond the reach of human sympathy. No one is expected to care whether such "fiends" survive or perish.

Actually the common practice of locking up addicts and leaving them untreated to fight their miseries in a bare police cell is an inexcusable piece of barbarism. A few injections of reserpine or chlorpromazine, those precious "tranquilizing" drugs of which more will be said later, will greatly reduce the suffering of such people. In properly equipped hospitals such as the one at Lexington, Kentucky, the addict is not deprived of the drug at once but weaned from it gradually, morphine or heroin being replaced with methadon ("Dilaudid"). The "Dilaudid" is given in sufficient quantities to prevent the appearance of anything but mild withdrawal symptoms. This drug is then withdrawn gradually over a period of from three to fourteen days. In this way the devastating miseries of the "cold turkey" treatment are avoided and the physical condition of the patient does not deteriorate so seriously. "Whatever method of withdrawal is used, addicts will complain," writes Dr. Isbell. If the withdrawal is intelligently managed, however, there does not seem very much cause for dissatisfaction.

Such are the effects of opiates. As pain relievers they are unequaled; as euphoriants, "givers of happiness," they have nothing to offer the normal man or woman. The "abyss of divine enjoyment" which De Quincey discovered in opium is evidently open only to psychopaths, and that De Quincey was a psychopath cannot be doubted by anyone who has read the story of his life. Meanwhile, because psychopaths are always with us, as also are criminals who dearly love to get rich with little effort, we are faced today with a social problem of opiate addiction. The addict is determined to get his drug; society, at least in the United States, is determined that he shall do without it. The result is a rather expensive civil war with the addict on the one hand paying an estimated $400,000,000 per year for contraband heroin while a sizable sum of the taxpayers' money is spent (a) to stop the drug entering the country; (b) to throw opiate addicts into jail and keep them there; (c) to provide facilities for the treatment of addicts at such institutions as the hospital for addicts at Lexington, Kentucky.

An enormous amount has been written about the war on opiate addiction, in fact the subject commands an interest out of all proportion to its social importance. To judge by statements one sometimes sees in the press, one might suppose that the whole country was on the verge of being engulfed in a cloud of heroin, specially manufactured by those dreadful Communists in China. One might think that "dope fiends" wandered in American cities by the million and that the very Constitution of the United States was on the point of being undermined by these heroin-crazed addicts. Actually the problem is a minor one. Dr. Harris Isbell, director of the Addiction Research Center at Lexington, is certainly well qualified to speak on this subject. "Opiate addiction," he states, "is a relatively small problem in the United States as compared with tuberculosis, alcoholism and schizophrenia." The number of addicts has declined from between 100,000 and 150,000, which was the figure in 1924, to something in the order of 60,000 at the present time. These 60,000 addicts are concentrated in the slum areas of a few large cities. The majority are Negroes and there are more male addicts than female.

So much for the "menace." Like the "*marihuana* bugaboo," the problem of heroin addiction has been blown up into a monster of terrifying proportions. This is largely the work of sensation-mongers who insist on speaking of "dope fiends" as if heroin addicts developed horns and tails and went around spearing their fellow men with red-hot pitchforks. The concept is picturesque but not accurate. One can scarcely imagine any character less suited to the role of fiend than the opiate addict. Timid, insecure, psychologically inadequate, plagued by inward conflicts and tensions which he cannot resolve, the addict is a sick being who has sought to smother his problems in heroin, just as the alcoholic has sought to drown his in liquor. The one is no more of a fiend than the other, yet for some strange reason contemporary American society insists on treating one as a criminal and the other as a sick man. This is an injustice. Both are equally sick and the alcoholic, because the drug affects his co-ordination and his ability to work, is actually more of a danger to society than the opiate addict. If one is a criminal so is the other. If we are going to jail one we should jail the other. This is quite a large order. With alcoholics running at a figure around 4,000,000, the jails would be kept pretty full.

Just why the alcoholic is tolerated as a sick man while the opiate addict is persecuted as a criminal is hard to understand. There is, in the present attitude of society in the United States toward opiate addicts, much the same hysteria, superstition, and plain cruelty as characterized the attitude of our forefathers toward witches. Legislation reflects this cruelty and superstition. Prison sentences up to 40 years are now being imposed and the death sentence has been introduced. Perhaps one should feel thankful that the legislators have not yet reached the point of burning addicts alive. If one insists on relying on terrorism to cope with a problem which is essentially medical one may as well be logical and "go the whole hog."

The entire problem has been recently reviewed in a report by the New York Academy of Medicine in which it is pointed out that laws now in force more or less compel the addict to take to crime because they regard him as a criminal. If he has the drug in his possession he is automatically guilty. No provision has been made for the treatment of incurable addicts. Their physicians may not treat them. The clinics once established to provide legal medication were long ago closed by the Narcotics Bureau. So they go in and out of jail with monotonous regularity. In this process the addict becomes thoroughly indocrinated in crime, the criminal receives an education in where to obtain narcotics and how to use them. Society gets the worst of both worlds, for the addicts become criminals and the criminals become addicts. Now and again, to vary the monotony, the addict goes to the federal hospital at Lexington to take "the cure" at a cost to the taxpayers of about $4000. He has in most instances no intention of remaining off opiates and in about 75 per cent of cases is back on the drug again soon after release. Even if he does want to stay off drugs the attitude of society makes this very difficult. He is labeled a "dope fiend," he cannot get a job, everyone turns away from him in self-righteous loathing. One must remember that he is never very spiritually robust but generally a neurotic individual unable to cope with life's difficulties. Even a spiritually healthy man might find it hard to make an adjustment in the face of such universal disapproval. The addict cannot do so and back he goes to his "chemical crutch." No wonder the New York Academy of Medicine, contemplating the sorry situation, concludes that "the punitive approach is no deterrent to the non-addict dealer or to the addict."

And the solution? It seems simple enough if society and the legislators will stop confusing sickness with sin and creating crime where crime does not exist. "There should be a change in attitude towards the addict," states the Academy of Medicine report.

> He is a sick person, not a criminal. That he may commit criminal acts to maintain his drug supply is recognized, but it is unjust to consider him criminal simply because he uses narcotic drugs. . . . The addict should be able to obtain his drugs at low cost under Federal control, in conjunction with efforts to have him undergo withdrawal. Under this plan these addicts, as sick persons, would apply for medical care and supervision. Criminal acts would no longer be necessary in order to obtain a supply of the drugs and there would be no incentive to create new addicts. Agents and black markets would disappear from lack of patronage. Since about eighty-five percent of the "pushers" on the streets are said to be addicts, they would be glad to forgo this dangerous occupation if they were furnished with their needed drug. Thus the bulk of the traffic would substantially disappear. . . . By a change in social attitude which would regard them as sick persons, and by relieving them of the economic oppression of attempting to obtain their supply of the drug at an exorbitant price, it will be possible to reach existing addicts in an orderly dignified way, not as probationed persons or sentenced criminals. They would come under supervision in the interest of health, not because of entanglement with the law. Thereafter, on a larger scale and in a humanitarian atmosphere, there would be an opportunity to apply persuasion to

undergo rehabilitation. It is reasonable to expect that more might accept the opportunity.

The report goes on to detail exactly how, through properly supervised clinics, the addict could be injected with the minimum amount of drug needed to keep him free of withdrawal symptoms.

. . . All the while unrelenting attempts would be made to persuade the resistant addict to undergo therapy to break the habit. It will be seen that this recommendation is a humane, reasonable, and promisingly effective method of distribution. . . . Every addict will get his drug. Under the present law to do that he must "push," rob, steal, burglarize or commit forgery. For he is desperate when he is without drugs.

To prevent the spread of addiction among adolescents, an educational program is proposed to give these innocents some idea of what addiction to opiates really involves.

Such are the recommendations of the New York Academy of Medicine. They have been debated widely in medical circles but there is no real agreement among physicians as to the value of the kind of narcotics clinic suggested. Critics of the idea point out that such clinics were in fact tried some thirty years ago and proved ineffectual. Advocates of the clinics declare that they were never given a fair trial, that the proper safeguards were not used, that, defective as they were, they still accomplished their end of bringing the addicts into the open, making possible their treatment by regular means. The legislators have emphatically rejected the clinics but have increased drastically the severity of the punishments to be inflicted on those found illegally in possession of heroin or morphine. The penalties are terrific: a minimum of two years' imprisonment for the first offense, up to forty years for a third. Sale of heroin to juveniles can be punished by a fine of not more than $20,000 and imprisonment for life, "except that the offender shall suffer death if the jury in its discretion shall so direct." A curious development, this. While many civilized countries have abolished the death penalty even for murder, the United States has introduced it for the violation of a tax act!

No one, of course, can quarrel with the aim of this legislation. The spread of heroin addiction among teen-agers in New York City has become a problem and has necessitated the setting up of a special hospital on North Brother Island devoted entirely to the treatment of addicts of less than twenty-one years of age. The rate of spread of addiction among these boys and girls can be estimated from the figures for arrests on narcotics charges which, in the under-twenty-one age group, rose from 560 in 952 to 749 in 1954. Treatment of these misguided juveniles at Riverside Hospital costs the overburdened New York taxpayer over $1,000,000 per year. Obviously something drastic needs to be done to prevent this bad state of affairs from becoming worse.

The aim of the narcotics legislation is to make life so dangerous for the "dope peddler" that he will decide to abandon this activity in favor of some less hazardous way of making a living. Unfortunately the peddler is usually himself an addict and has to sell the drug to others in order to maintain his own supply. He has, in most cases, what is known as a psychopathic personality, which means that he is unable to understand the consequences of his own actions and has a habitual contempt for the process of law. For this reason even the most drastic legislation fails to scare him as much as it should. He simply has not enough intelligence to understand the nature of the risk he takes. The new law regards this individual as so great a menace that society is even justified in taking his life. This attitude is certainly debatable. Some eminent jurists, among them Mr. Rufus King, consider this whole approach to the problem to be basically unsound:

> All the billions our society has spent enforcing criminal measures against the addict have had the sole practical result of protecting the peddler's market, artificially inflating his prices and keeping his profits fantastically high. No other nation hounds its addicts as we do and no other nation faces anything remotely resembling our problem.

Leaving the opiates, we will now consider a recent arrival among the group of addicting drugs, the barbiturates. Barbiturates constitute a rather large family of chemical substances, all of which are derived from barbituric acid. The oldest is barbital or "Veronal," the structure of which, so legend relates, was dreamed up by the great German chemist, Emil Fischer, as the train on which he was traveling in Italy stopped in the station at Verona. Next came phenobarbital or "Luminal" and, in the years that followed, so great was the interest in this class of drugs that twenty-five hundred barbiturates were synthesized, of which fifty were marketed for clinical use. They are extremely valuable compounds which, by their action on the higher centers of the brain, bring on sleep similar to, though not quite the same as, natural sleep. They are also used as anesthetics and, to a limited extent, in the method of psychoanalysis known as narcoanalysis, of which more will be said later. It is, however, as bringers of sleep that these drugs are most esteemed, and such are the difficulties people in the United States experience in drifting into the land of dreams that they consumed in 1954 almost three hundred tons of barbiturates to assist them. As instruments of suicide these agents are also enjoying a vogue. In 1949, the peak year so far, 1140 perished from barbiturate poisoning, of which 674 were adjudged to be suicides.

Like the opiates, the barbiturates calm and soothe and are for this reason liable to be abused by neurotic individuals who take them first on medical advice as aids to sleep and later continue to take them in increasing amounts until addiction results. Such excessive amounts of barbiturates are obtained in the black market, where they are available under such fanciful names as "red birds" or "yellow jackets" and are known collectively as "goof balls." Here we should mention that to become a barbiturate addict one must take a very excessive dose of the drug for quite a long time. The doses normally prescribed by a physician will never lead to addiction. Those who do become addicted, however, are worse off than the morphine or heroin addict. Their mental processes are seriously retarded. They seem dull, stupid, slow, disoriented and half asleep. Deprived of the drug, they rapidly become very ill and have violent epileptic convulsions. Between the third and seventh day of withdrawal they are plagued with hallucinations and suffer much the same horrors as afflict an alcoholic in the grip of *delirium tremens*. So violent does their agitation become that it sometimes leads to death from exhaustion. Normally the delirium ends after five days. A wise physician, however, will see that this extreme symptom does not develop by withdrawing barbiturates very slowly and cautiously. Sudden withdrawal of barbiturates from an addict is extremely dangerous and may result in his death.

A certain amount of publicity has been given recently to the abuse of a drug having an effect on the nervous system exactly opposite to that of the barbiturates. This drug is amphetamine, more commonly known by its trade name "Benzedrine." It is used in nasal inhalers to contract mucous membranes swollen by colds. Taken internally, it has a stimulating effect on the nervous system and gives the taker a feeling of liveliness and energy. It wards off sleep and is frequently consumed by truck drivers to keep them awake during long hauls across the continent. Unfortunately this practice often results in dizziness, hallucinations, and mental confusion and the truck driver, instead of reaching his destination, takes a short cut to the morgue. There is a case on record of a driver who became so confused under the influence of "Benzedrine" that he was convinced that "Benny" was driving the truck. Under the influence of this delusion he crawled into his sleeping berth to rest, leaving the truck to steer itself! Surprisingly enough the driver survived to tell the tale. The truck did not.

Similar to "Benzedrine" in its effects is another much-abused drug, cocaine. The plant from which this substance is obtained (*Erythroxylon coca*) was endowed with divine properties by the people of Peru. At the time of the Incas it was worshiped as a god. The children of the sun, so ran the legend, had presented man with the coca leaf to "satisfy the hungry, provide the weary and fainting with new vigor, and cause the unhappy to forget their misery." It was recognized, in fact, as a typical euphoriant, and, like so many euphoriants, was employed in various religious ceremonies. The royal family used it as a symbol of royalty and the idols of the time, as a sign of divinity, were represented with one cheek stuffed with coca leaves. Then as now the leaves were mixed with lime or vegetable ashes, which aided in the extraction of the active principle, and chewed. The habit of chewing coca leaves is still widespread among the poorer Indians of Peru and northwestern Brazil, who consume the leaves in astonishing quantities. The civilized world, however, has rejected the chewing of coca just as it has rejected the eating of opium, preferring to take the purified alkaloid cocaine, which can be injected into the blood stream by means of a hypodermic syringe and which, being rapidly absorbed, takes effect more swiftly.

Cocaine is a stimulant that acts first on the higher levels of the brain. It was employed as such by that prototype of all fictional sleuths, the great Sherlock Holmes. Under its influence men grow talkative, restless, and excited, they are filled with an ecstatic sensation of great physical and mental power, and feelings of fatigue and hunger are abolished. But these sensations, delightful though they may be, pass very rapidly and are succeeded by a depression fully as dark as the ecstasy was brilliant. The remedy, of course, is to take more cocaine, and as the drug is really very poisonous, one who misuses it in this way soon pays the penalty for his folly. The mind, under the influence of the poison, becomes crowded with delusions. The cocainist has the feeling that insects are crawling over his body. Soon he becomes convinced that people are discussing him, that detectives are watching him, that someone is planning to kill him. Often the cocainist carries a weapon and, under the influence of his delusions, is quite capable of using it. Probably the idea of the "dope fiend," so incorrectly applied to heroin addicts, originated from some violent acts committed by cocainists. Cocaine may make a man dangerous whereas opiates do not. Unlike the opiates, however, cocaine is not an addicting drug and can be withdrawn without provoking serious symptoms. It is very destructive to health and definitely leads to criminal or violent acts. Misuse of this drug, however, has steadily declined and the cocainist is now a rarity, at least in the United States.

Such is the situation regarding drug addiction. It is certainly a tragic comment on human frailty that such drugs as opium, the "potent destroyer of grief" extolled by Homer, should be misused and converted into creators of grief rather than its destroyers. There can of course be no doubt that any sort of addiction, whether to opiates, barbiturates, or alcohol, is always an evil and always involves slavery. Society, however, when it shoulders responsibility for preventing such abuse, treads on very slippery ground. The real situation tends to become clouded by misconceptions, and legislation is often enacted which tends to aggravate the very evils it was intended to prevent.

The Chemistry of Madness

The greatest public health problem at the present time is mental illness. It fills more hospital beds than cancer, heart disease, and tuberculosis combined; and for every totally disabled inmate of a mental hospital at least two others are living in the outer world, not sick enough to be institutionalized, not well enough to live healthy, happy lives. This huge population of mentally sick individuals imposes a burden on the healthy segment of the population whose size is appalling to contemplate: In terms of cost, no other form of illness is more expensive. In terms of suffering, no other affliction is more devastating. Anyone who has had the experience of watching a close relative or dear friend go mad will certainly testify that there is no experience more harrowing. Death one can accept. It is inevitable that all must die. But the spectacle of madness is a daily and hourly affront to man's faith in a just and benevolent Providence, for the mad do not die, nor can they live. They inhabit a shadowy borderland between life and death and neither love nor pity will enable the sane to enter that strange region. Madness severs the strongest bonds that hold human beings together

It separates husband from wife, mother from child. It is death without death's finality and without death's dignity.

A few figures will not be out of place to acquaint the reader with the magnitude of this health problem. According to the National Committee for Mental Health, 9,000,000 people in the United States have some form of mental disorder. New patients are being admitted to mental hospitals at the appalling rate of a quarter of a million per year and thousands more need treatment that is not available. The cost of this treatment in 1954 alone was $2,867,877,000, of which the Veterans Administration hospitals accounted for $200,000,000. In New York State 36 per cent of the entire state budget of $460,000,000 went to the Department of Mental Hygiene. In most other civilized countries the situation is equally serious.

By far the most widespread as well as the most tragic form of mental illness is schizophrenia. It is the most tragic because it is particularly liable to develop in young people and was formerly called *dementia praecox* ("precocious dementia") to distinguish it from "senile dementia," the insanity of old age. Schizophrenia often develops at adolescence or in the early twenties. It may even afflict children, though childhood schizophrenia is rather rare. To gain an idea of what the illness means we must visit the iron-barred wards in some of our larger mental hospitals, where, behind carefully locked doors, the more violently disturbed patients pass their lives, often herded together under conditions which would be judged unsuitable even for animals.

Consider the case of Mary, now twenty-eight years old, an inhabitant of the "disturbed ward" for the past eight years. We find her huddled in a corner of a wooden bench, completely motionless, her knees drawn up under her chin and her thin arms clasped about her legs. Her short cropped hair is in disorder, her body so thin that the bones are visible through the flesh. She is wearing nothing but a shabby nightgown made of a heavy coarse material, for in her occasional fits of violence she is liable to strip off her clothing and tear it to pieces. Most of the time, however, she remains motionless, not moving even to satisfy the calls of nature or to take food. If you move her arm it remains in any position in which you happen to place it, a condition known as "waxy flexibility." Her strangely immobile state is called "catatonia" and her illness diagnosed as "catatonic schizophrenia," one of the four subdivisions of the disease.

Mary's history is characteristic of that of many schizophrenics. She was an only child brought up in a household dominated by a short-tempered and tyrannical father, with a mother who at times made a great fuss over her and at other times ignored or rejected her. A dreamy, fragile, solitary child, she loved above all to wander by herself in the woods or to sit doing nothing in the garden, indulging in all sorts of fantastic daydreams. Whenever her feelings were hurt, whenever she was rejected by her unstable mother or abused by her domineering father, she would retreat into that imaginary world which by degrees became for her more real than reality. She grew up into a slender fair-haired woman, pretty enough in her own rather fragile fashion, with the dreamy, other-worldly expression on her face with which Dante Gabriel Rossetti loved to endow his long-necked beauties. The approach of maturity placed an additional strain upon her. Her parents, still dominated by the pruderies of a previous generation, told her nothing of the changes that would take place in her body at the time of puberty. Her menstrual periods seemed to her something shameful and terrible. Her awakening sexual impulses filled her with fear and self-loathing.

At sixteen she had what was euphemistically called a "nervous breakdown." The characters from her fantasy world invaded her real world. She actually began to see them. She heard their voices whispering in her ear. Her increasing dreaminess brought down upon her the wrath of her intolerant father and the dislike of her mother, who withdrew from the girl what little support and affection she had previously given. One day Mary left home and was discovered wandering in the woods, talking in the most animated fashion to a being who was visible to her alone. Her frightened parents called in the family doctor, who packed her off to a nursing home to avoid the "stigma" of having her admitted to a mental hospital. There, without any special treatment save a change of scene, the girl made what appeared to be a good recovery.

Mary did not return home but launched out on a life of her own, met her husband-to-be, married, and bore her children. Then the burden of her duties as wife and mother began to prove too much for her. Once again the fantasy world started to intrude. She grew more dreamy, more incapable of attending to those countless daily tasks that are the lot of every housewife. As she grew more inefficient her husband grew more critical. As he grew more critical she became more withdrawn. Then, quite abruptly, she crossed the border line that separates the sane from the mad. He came back from work to find her seated motionless in a chair. The house was in confusion, the children had not been put to bed. When he spoke to her she did not answer. When he lifted her hand it stayed lifted as if she had been a waxen image. She was removed to a mental hospital and there she remains, a catatonic, seemingly dead to the world. As she will not eat, food has to be introduced into her stomach by means of a nasal tube. As she will not attend to her needs, she has to be changed like a baby. The attendants have come to regard her as virtually an inanimate object, like a piece of furniture. Every now and then, however, her catatonic immobility gives way to fits of murderous rage. At such times the attendants appear to her as devils and she fights against them with all the strength of which her skinny body is capable. Then once again immobility descends on her.

Thus she lives on, alive only in the sense that she still breathes. All her contacts with the outer world have been severed. Her husband has moved to a state in which insanity constitutes valid grounds for divorce, has freed himself from the burden, and married again. Her children do not remember her. The stream of life, with all its bustle and sparkle, flows past her without touching her. There she sits, her knees drawn up under her chin, gazing motionless at nothing, fed, clothed, cleansed by the overworked attendants, who regard her, when passive, as a nuisance and, when violent, as a menace. Her illness began when she was twenty. She may live on into her sixties. For all those forty years she must be cared for—a living corpse denied even the privilege of burial.

Or consider the case of George, in the men's section of the same hospital. George is a paranoid schizophrenic. He is about the same age as Mary but does not sit motionless as she does. George, in fact, is very active, but his activity has no connection with the realities of this world, for within the labyrinth of George's mind is a distorting mirror which prevents even the simplest impression from reaching his brain unaltered. Everything he sees, everything he hears, the things he touches, even the food he eats becomes endowed, through the action of this distorting agent, with sinister, malignant significance. The words of one of the physicians, the glance of an attendant, even a casual gesture by one of his fellow inmates is interpreted as a threat. The radio broadcasts the plottings of some foreign power disguised to resemble ordinary news or music. The scent of a flower is really a poisoned gas being secretly brewed by the "enemy" under the floor boards. Often his food seems to have a strange metallic taste. Again it is "the enemy" attempting to poison him. He pushes the food away and refuses to eat for several days. When they try to feed him by force he fights and screams and struggles, knowing that he has fallen into the hands of "the enemy" and that they are about to kill him. One might suppose, surrounded as he is by terrors, that George would welcome death, and indeed he did, on one occasion, attempt to release himself by thrusting his head through a glass door and endeavoring to cut his throat on the jagged edges. He was rescued and his wounds were sewn up, since which time he has been carefully watched and housed in a special cell where suicide is virtually impossible. So he must live with his terrors until natural death at last relieves him of his burden. Like Mary, he may live for another forty years, alone as only the mad can be alone, a curse to himself, a burden to those who must care for him.

A few further observations should be added to these descriptions. Schizophrenia is an illness of the body as well as the mind and its physical manifestations are as important as its mental ones. The delicate inner balance of the body is in some way upset. The hands and feet of the schizophrenic are cold, clammy and blue, indicating some derangement in the workings of the autonomic nervous system through the agency of which the blood vessels in the skin are expanded or contracted according to the needs of the moment. The perception of pain may be completely destroyed by this condition. Students of those horrible procedures, the trials of

witches, have often been astonished to read that the witch
would frequently frustrate her tormentors by singing or
even going to sleep while the cruelest tortures were being
applied to her body, thus terrifying her judges by demonstrating the powers of the Evil One. What she was actually
demonstrating was the effect of schizophrenia on pain perception. Shattuck describes a case of a female schizophrenic
who, having wrapped herself in a blanket, set the blanket on
fire: ". . . when found two hours later she was sitting con-
tentedly on the floor, her legs badly burned, her charred
tibiae exposed. Third degree burns also covered her chest,
abdominal wall, back and hands. She spoke pleasantly, begging to be left where she was, exculpated everybody and discussed philosophically whether the absence of religious be-
liefs was a matter of importance in her present condition.
The patient denied repeatedly that she was in any pain and
remained cheerful and argumentative for half an hour,
while her body was lifted with difficulty from the burning
floor boards. She then complained of pain in her shoulders,
the only part of her body which was not burned, and a few
minutes later collapsed and died."

Such is schizophrenia. The illness does not always manifest itself in the extreme forms described above. There are
degrees of schizophrenia which range from a mild illness
that may not even necessitate hospitalization to the totally
incapacitating condition seen in the disturbed wards of large
mental hospitals. In all its forms this illness constitutes, like
cancer, one of the great unsolved medical mysteries of the
mid-twentieth century. New methods and medicaments,
shortly to be described, have improved the prospects of cure
enormously, but though it is no longer regarded as a rather
hopeless condition its cause remains as much of a mystery as

ever. The words of Strecker and Ebaugh, published twenty years ago, are still true today.

"Its etiology is unsettled, its pathology unknown, and its clinical limits in dispute and yet it is a more serious problem than either tuberculosis or cancer. Each year not less than 30,000 to 40,000 individuals soon after adolescence or in the first flush of manhood or womanhood fall victim to this condition. They are condemned to a living death, devoid of emotional life as others savour it, and barred from participating in the normal activities and affairs of the living."

Despite the fact that schizophrenia is the greatest of all public health problems, for all these thousands of crippled individuals must be fed, clothed, and housed in special institutions, the sums spent on research into the causes and cure of the disease are scarcely equal to the cost of a single jet bomber. No other major ailment is so totally ignored. Every victim of poliomyelitis receives the benefit of $28.20 worth of research funds per year, every victim of cancer $27.70, every victim of tuberculosis $26.80. But the schizophrenic, despised and rejected by the public, has spent upon him a mere $4.15 of research money. Thirty-seven thousand patients in twenty-nine public mental hospitals receive no psychiatric treatment at all. Not a single state mental hospital meets, as yet, the personnel standards defined by the American Psychiatric Association. And yet the schizophrenic's need for treatment is as urgent as the cancer victim's. Left untreated, the illness swiftly becomes untreatable. "In the first year in a mental hospital patients have a fifty-fifty chance of release, in two years, the odds against being released alive rise to sixteen to one and by the time the patient has been hospitalized for eight years the odds are more than ninety-nine to one." The mental hospital, which should be a place of intensive treatment where the ravages wrought by illness can be arrested and their effects repaired, is more often merely a sordid prison in which the last glimmerings of sanity are extinguished by the combined effects of boredom, idleness, association with other mad people, and absolute lack of proper medical care. The message that might be carved above its gates is all too often the one Dante envisaged at the lowest levels of the Inferno: "Abandon hope, all ye that enter here." An idea of the utter contempt with which society regards the mentally ill can be gathered by comparing the money spent, per day, in New York State to maintain a criminal ($4.40) with that spent on a mentally ill patient ($3.70).

The fact is that, although our attitude toward mental illness is infinitely more enlightened than was that of our ancestors, who frequently burned schizophrenics alive as witches, we still tend to regard the mad with fear and horror and to consider them in some way to blame for their condition. Madness, in its various forms, is not yet accepted simply as an illness, for contracting which the sufferer is no more to blame than is the individual with coronary thrombosis or diabetes. We suffer, in this respect, from the aftereffect of centuries of Judeo-Christian superstition, which defined madness in terms of demonic possession and which justified cruel treatment of the insane on the theory that cruelty would drive out the devil. Why so foul a theory should have taken hold in so-called Christian countries is hard to understand, for it is certain that Christ himself, who had many dealings with the mad, never recommended that they should be chained or flogged or otherwise tormented. Chained and flogged they were, however, and these centuries of cruelty still color our attitude today, for which reason campaigns are conducted to raise funds for research on almost any illness except schizophrenia, which may, without exaggeration, be called the scourge of the twentieth century.

Concerning the cause of schizophrenia there have been many theories and we will have occasion, in the course of this chapter, to mention several of them. From the standpoint of this book, however, one theory is of especial importance. This theory suggests that the schizophrenic is the victim of a poison brewed within his own body. He has, as it were, a Borgia in his system and the workings of this hidden poisoner affect the functioning of both his mind and his emotions. So his whole awareness of the outside world becomes distorted. Sights which seem perfectly normal to the healthy individual become, for the schizophrenic, distorted, weird, and terrifying. Sounds become endowed with strange significance. Perfectly harmless remarks are interpreted as threats. Every impression that reaches the schizophrenic is twisted into a sinister experience through the action of the poison.

There is much experimental evidence to support this theory that schizophrenia results from the workings of a poison produced in the body as the result of what is called an "error in metabolism." We know that such errors in metabolism do occur and that they can profoundly affect the mind. There is a condition known as "phenylpyruvic idiocy" caused by a hereditary defect as a result of which the body is unable to metabolize the amino acid, phenylalanine, whose toxic products cause permanent damage to the brain.

The defect in the schizophrenic is nothing so obvious and easily demonstrated as this. His poisoner works more subtly and the poison itself, whatever its identity, has varied effects, producing in some paranoia, in others catatonia, in some violent excitement, in others withdrawn immobility.

We do not, however, have any great difficulty in finding a poison that produces all these varied effects. Ever since Beringer performed his monumental study, *Der Meskalin-rausch,* psychiatrists have realized that a close resemblance exists between mescaline intoxication and schizophrenia. Both Guttman and Tayleur Stockings have enumerated the similarities of the two conditions. The following account is taken from the latter's paper:

> Mescaline intoxication is indeed a true "schizophrenia" if we use the word in its literal sense of "split mind," for the characteristic effect of mescaline is a molecular fragmentation of the entire personality, exactly similar to that found in schizophrenic patients. . . . The change consists of a radical alteration of the mind and body. Thus the subject may feel that he is being several different persons at once. . . . More characteristic still is the feeling that he is divided into two separate beings—one a purely intellectual and emotionless creature, the other a fantastic being of delusion and fantasy, the first being able to observe the other in an extraordinary detached and unemotional fashion. . . . The feeling of unreality, both as regards the self and the external world, so often found in schizophrenics, is one of the typical features of the mescaline psychosis. One of the most common descriptions given to the writer by his subjects of their feelings was that of living in a world of one's own. "I am living in a private world" and "Other people cannot understand me because I am living in a different world from them," were actual descriptions obtained in these experiments.

Precisely similar descriptions were obtained from recovered schizophrenic patients studied by the writer who were asked to give, as far as they were able, a description of their experiences during the period of their acute illness. In both cases, those of the schizophrenic and the mescaline subject, the impossibility of putting their feelings and experiences during the acute stage of the psychosis into ordinary language was a striking feature.

Even more remarkable are the self-descriptions of their mental experiences by schizophrenic patients under sodium amytal. As is well known, this drug, when administered intravenously, has the property of temporarily producing a lucid interval in a psychotic subject previously inaccessible and incoherent. Under this drug, the writer has obtained from schizophrenic patients accounts of their mental experiences which bear a remarkable resemblance to those of mescaline intoxication. For instance, the bizarre hallucinations of color and distorted appearance of external objects and of other persons have been described by patients given sodium amytal by the author. The resemblance to the mescaline psychosis is even closer in the case of the confusional states, especially as regards visual hallucinations.

A further feature of the personality changes must be mentioned before leaving this subject, namely, the symptom of transformation of the personality—that is, the belief that the patient has been changed into someone else. Thus the subject of the mescaline psychosis may believe that he has become transformed into some great personage, such as a god or a legendary character, or a being from another world. This is a well-known symptom found in states such as paraphrenia and paranoia. As found in the mescaline psychosis, it appears to be due partly to the abnormal bodily feelings referred to in the discussion of the delusions of grandeur. Another mechanism, observed by the writer as occurring in his own case, was a process of identification of the subject's self with the stupendous beings of the mescaline fantasies. This process, in which the subject sometimes appears to lose the power of being able to distinguish between the self and the outside world, is strikingly reminiscent of the introjection processes of childhood.

According to Stockings, both paranoia and catatonia can be produced by mescaline. Concerning paranoia, he makes the following statements:

Taking first the delusions of persecution, we find that one of the characteristic actions of mescaline is that of sensitization of the auditory centres. Sounds appear to be either unnaturally loud, or distorted, and to have acquired strange qualities. They appear to the subject to rush upon him in an extraordinary purposive and deliberate way, and to have a reference for him which they would not have in the normal state. Thus, to quote actual examples, seen in the writer's experiments, the sound of a typewriter being used in the next room seemed to vibrate and reverberate through the walls and into the subject's body; thus, the typewriter became an infernal machine persecuting him with rays of electricity. In another case a group of people talking in the next room becomes a gang of enemies plotting against him or interfering with him. Similarly, the announcer's voice is sending messages over the wireless specially meant for him.

In the visual sphere, the strange distorted appearance of people's faces, their movements and conversation all seem to be directed against him, so that he feels as if he was being watched, spied upon or otherwise interfered with.

Similarly, the strange bodily paraesthesiae readily produce ideas of influence, electrical interference, or bodily changes produced by the machinations of other persons.

The sinister changes which seem to take place in the faces of others would seem to be particularly disturbing.

The features appeared to become intensely vivid, and all the peculiarities of their physiognomy to be greatly exaggerated; at a later stage the faces appeared monstrously distorted, with huge eyes, enormous foreheads, and grim and menacing expressions. This illusion often leads to ideas on the part of the subject that faces are being made at him, that others are mocking him, or that he is being hypnotized or influenced in similar ways. The writer has obtained descriptions of exactly similar experiences from schizophrenic patients under sodium amytal narcosis. This phenomenon is apparently the principal exciting cause of the impulsive attacks on others which frequently occur in these conditions.

[Stockings] was able to observe in himself the catatonic state, which is a most remarkable experience. The feeling is that of a delightful laziness and disinclination for active movement, resulting partly from extreme self-absorption and preoccupation with fantasy and indifference to the outer world, two characteristic symptoms of the intoxication. There is a peculiar inability to make up one's mind to a course of action. . . . Attitudes of religious ecstasy, similar to those found in some acute schizophrenic cases, may be assumed as a result of vivid hallucinations with a religious context. Suicidal impulses, secondary to the terrifying feelings of unreality experienced in the early stages of the intoxication, and homicidal impulses . . . are also found. . . . Negativism, with an attitude of hostility and stubbornness, and refusal of food with neglect of the ordinary bodily functions, were encountered in nearly all the subjects studied. The refusal of food and drink during the acute stage was partly due to the ideas that such food might be poisoned. . . . In subjects who had passed into the state of catatonic stupor, painful stimuli, such as pricking with a pin, were often completely disregarded, although pain was still felt.

All the above descriptions make one thing clear. There is practically no aspect of schizophrenia that mescaline intoxication does not reproduce. As Aldous Huxley puts it, "The schizophrenic is like a man permanently under the influence of mescaline." It is logical therefore to ask oneself this question: May not the "metabolic error" which seems to occur within the body of the schizophrenic result in the production either of mescaline itself or of some substance having similar properties? Exactly this thought presented itself to two Canadian students of mental illness, Humphrey Osmond and John Smythies, who had the courage, rare in these prosaic days when anything in the nature of creative thinking is regarded with suspicion in scientific circles, to publish a purely speculative paper entitled "Schizophrenia —A New Approach." What made this paper significant was the fact that it drew attention to a chemical resemblance between mescaline and those potent hormones, adrenalin and nor-adrenalin, so intimately associated with the response to stress in man. One small failure in the body's chemistry could result in the production not of adrenalin but of an analogous but poisonous "M" substance having properties similar to those of mescaline. Stress is generally concerned in the production of schizophrenia and adrenalin production has an important bearing on the individual's reaction to stress. In the potential schizophrenic we may assume that, besides adrenalin, the "M" substance is produced. The effects to which it gives rise—the hallucinations, the feelings of unreality—naturally impose further stresses on the patient, who, caught up in a vicious circle, reacts to the situation with the production of more "M" substance and so becomes yet more hallucinated, catatonic and, in general, schizophrenic. The doors opening onto the real world close behind him and he becomes imprisoned in a world of unreality cut off from the healthy by a barrier through which neither he nor they can penetrate.

This theory of Osmond and Smythies formed the basis of a series of researches whose aim was to identify the "M" substance. In this quest they were joined by Abram Hoffer and at the end of a year's research these three workers published their findings. Their attention, logically enough was directed to adrenalin and its possible breakdown products, nor did they need to seek for very long before clues were discovered as to the possible identity of the "M" factors. Several individuals who had been in the habit of taking adrenalin to control their asthma declared that they sometimes suffered from hallucinations after taking larger doses of this material. Most often these hallucinations took place when adrenalin was used which had begun to deteriorate, as a result of which process the normally colorless solution of adrenalin turns pink.

At our first meeting in Saskatoon with our colleagues in the research, Professors Hutcheon, MacArthur and Woodford, we raised the question of "pink adrenalin" and put forward a suggestion about its composition. Hutcheon pointed out that "pink adrenalin" certainly contained among other things adrenochrome. In the exciting ten minute discussion which followed after Hutcheon drew the spatial formula of adrenochrome, it was shown that this substance is related chemically to every hallucinogen whose chemical composition has been determined.

It is evident that we had stumbled on a compound which has an indole nucleus in common with the hallucinogens; which is readily derived from adrenalin in the body and which can be fitted into a logical scheme relating to stress. Under stress the quantity of adrenalin in the body will increase and this might be turned into adrenochrome in the schizophrenic individual.

The next step in this research was obvious enough. Adrenochrome was prepared synthetically and the research workers, using themselves and their wives as guinea pigs, set out to determine just what effect the substance had on the mind and the emotions. The following account was given by Osmond of his own reactions to an intravenous injection of adrenochrome:

After the purple red liquid was injected into my right forearm I had a good deal of pain. I did not expect that we would get any results from a preliminary trial and so was not. as far as I can judge, in a state of heightened expectancy The fact that my blood pressure did not rise suggests that I was not unduly tense. After about ten minutes, while I was lying on a couch looking up at the ceiling, I found that it had changed color It seemed that the lighting had become brighter I asked Abe and Neil if they had noticed anything but they had not. I looked across the room and it seemed to have changed in some not easily definable way I wondered if I could have suggested these things to myself. I closed my eyes and a brightly colored pattern of dots appeared. The colors were not as brilliant as those which I have seen under mescal. but were of the same type. The patterns of dots gradually resolved themselves into fishlike shapes. I felt that I was at the bottom of the sea or in an aquarium among a shoal of brilliant fishes At one moment I concluded that I was a sea anemone in this pool Abe and Neil kept pestering me to tell them what was happening, which annoyed me They brought me a Van Gogh self-portrait to look at I have never seen a picture so plastic and alive Van Gogh gazed at me from the paper, crop headed, with hurt, mad eyes and seemed to be three dimensional. I felt that I could stroke the cloth of his coat and that he might turn around in his frame. Neil showed me the Rorschach cards. Their texture, their bas-relief appearance, and the strange and amusing shapes which I had never before seen in the cards were extraordinary.

My experiences in the laboratory were, on the whole, pleasant but when I left I found the corridors outside sinister and unfriendly. I wondered what the cracks in the floor meant and why there were so many of them. Once we got out of doors the hospital buildings, which I know well, seemed sharp and unfamiliar. As we drove through the streets the houses appeared to have some special meaning, but I couldn't tell what it was. In one window I saw a lamp burning and I was astonished by its grace and brilliance. I drew my friends' attention to it but they were unimpressed.

We reached Abe's home where I felt cut off from people but not unhappy. I knew that I should be discussing the experience with Abe and his wife but could not be bothered to do so. I felt no special interest in our experiment and had no satisfaction at our success, although I told myself that it was very important. Before I got to sleep I noticed that the colored visions returned when I shut my eyes. (Normally I have hypnagogic visions after several minutes in a darkened room when I am tired.) I slept well.

Next morning, although I had only slept a few hours, life seemed good. Colours were bright and my appetite keen. I was completely aware of the possibilities arising from the experiment. Colour had extra meaning for me. Voices, typewriting, any sound was very clear. With those whom I felt did not appreciate the importance of the new discovery I could have easily become irritable, but I was able to control myself.

A second experience with adrenochrome brought more curious observations.

I saw only a few visual patterns with my eyes closed. I had the feeling that there was something wonderful waiting to be seen but somehow I couldn't see it. However, in the outside world everything seemed sharper and the Van Gogh was three dimensional. I began to feel that I was losing touch with everything. My sister telephoned and, although I am usually glad to hear her voice, I couldn't feel warmth or happiness. I watched a group of patients dancing and, although I enjoy watching dancing with the envious interest of one who is clumsy on his feet, I didn't have a flicker of feeling.

As we drove back to Abe's house a pedestrian walked across the road in front of us. I thought we might run him down, and watched with detached curiosity. I had no concern for the victim. We did not knock him down.

I began to wonder whether I was a person any more and to think that I might be a plant or a stone. As my feeling for these inanimate objects increased my feeling for and my interest in humans diminished. I felt indifferent towards humans and had to curb myself from making unpleasant personal remarks about them. I had no inclination to say more or less than I observed. If I was asked if I liked a picture I said what I felt and disregarded the owner's feeling.

I did not wish to talk and found it most comfortable to gaze at the floor or a lamp. Time seemed to be of no importance I slept well that night and awoke feeling lively but although I had to attend a meeting that morning, I did not hurry myself. Eventually I had to be more or less dragged out of the house by Abe. I had to get my car from a garage where it was being repaired. There was some trouble about finding it in the garage. When at last I was seated in the driver's seat I realized that I couldn't drive it through traffic, although quite able to do so usually. I did not, however, feel anxious or distressed by this but persuaded the garage proprietor to drive me to my destination. I would, I believe, have normally found this a humiliating situation, I did not feel humiliated.

I attended the scientific meeting, and during it I wrote this note: "Dear Abe, this damn stuff is still working. The odd thing is that stress brings it on, after about 15 minutes. I have this 'glass wall other side of the barrier' feeling. It is fluctuant, almost intangible, but I know it is there. It wasn't there three quarters of an hour ago; the stress was the minor one of getting the car. I have a feeling that I don't know anyone here; absurd but unpleasant. Also some slight ideas of reference arising from my sensation of oddness. I have just begun to wonder if my hands are writing this, crazy of course."

I fluctuated for the rest of the day. While being driven home by my psychologist colleague, Mr. B. Stefaniuk, I discovered that I could not relate distance and time. I would see a vehicle far away on the long straight, prairie roads, but would be uncertain whether we might not be about to collide with it. We had coffee at a wayside halt and here I became disturbed by the covert glances of a sinister looking man. I could not be sure whether he was "really" doing this or not, I went out to look at two wrecked cars which had been brought in to a nearby garage. I became deeply preoccupied with them and the fate of their occupants. I could only tear myself away from them with an effort. I seemed in some way to be involved in them.

Later in the day when I reached home the telephone rang. I took no notice of it and allowed it to ring itself out. Normally, no matter how tired I am, I respond to it.

By the morning of 19.x.52 I felt that I was my usual self again.

Some time before this work on adrenochrome was started in Canada a chance observation by a chemist in Basle offered another approach to this problem of the chemistry of madness. Dr. A. Hofman of the Sandoz Chemical Works had been working with a substance, lysergic acid, derived from a black fungus called ergot, which sometimes develops in place of the seed in rye and other grasses. In the Middle Ages this fungus was responsible for horrible outbursts of a form of poisoning called "St. Anthony's Fire" in which whole limbs became blue and gangrenous and crumbled away. Ergot of rye is a source of several valuable drugs, one of which is used to prevent excessive bleeding after childbirth, another to relieve the distressing symptoms of migraine. Lysergic acid, with which Hofman was working, was not, in itself, of any special medicinal interest but Hofman had added to the molecule an extra "tail" in the form of a diethylamine group, the resulting chemical having the full name d-lysergic acid diethylamide tartrate, referred to in laboratory shorthand as LSD-25.

Last Friday, April 16th, [wrote Hofman in his laboratory report], in the midst of my afternoon work in the laboratory I had to give up working. I had to go home because I experienced a very peculiar restlessness which was associated with a slight attack of dizziness. At home I went to bed and got into a not unpleasant state of drunkenness which was characterized by an extremely stimulating fantasy. When I closed my eyes (the day light was most unpleasant to me) I experienced fantastic images of an extraordinary plasticity. They were associated with an intense kaleidoscopic play of colors. After about two hours this condition disappeared.

Hofman was puzzled by these extraordinary symptoms. He was forced to the conclusion that somehow he had either swallowed or absorbed through his skin a little of the chemical with which he had been working. To test this hypothesis he returned to the laboratory and swallowed 250 micrograms * of LSD. This was a very minute dose of material; there are few drugs, apart from vitamins or hormones, which exert an observable effect when taken by mouth in such small amounts. What Hofman did not realize was that he had prepared a substance since shown to be the most potent hallucinogen ever discovered and that his tiny dose actually represented over *ten times* the amount (20 micrograms) now known to be quite adequate to produce hallucinations.

This astounding discovery of a chemical substance which, in the merest traces (20 micrograms of LSD represents $\frac{1}{700,000,000}$ of the weight of an average man), produces very definite mental symptoms, aroused the interest of psychiatrists throughout the world. At the Boston Psychopathic Hospital, one of the most advanced mental hospitals in the United States, extensive studies were undertaken to determine how this strange drug affects both the sane and the mad. This work was carried out by Drs. H. C. Solomon, M. Rinkel, H. J. De Shon, and R. W. Hyde and their find-

* A microgram or gamma is the smallest unit of weight, being one millionth of a gram.

ings have recently been summarized in an illustrated article in the *Scientific American*.

The sequence of events in individuals who had taken LSD was similar to that which follows mescaline. Physical symptoms, restlessness, tremor, weakness, sweating, were accompanied by mental and emotional changes. Within one hour after taking the drug the subject began to display irritation, hostility, or anxiety. In the second hour he began to lose touch with reality, withdrawing into himself, over-come with apathy, lethargy, and confusion. Then came the illusions, extraordinary sensations of non-existence, a feeling that parts of the body had vanished (one subject felt that there was nothing between his hip and his foot), illusions of taste, of smell, visual illusions, the feeling of being "out of time," familiar to those who have worked with mescaline or *hashish*. The subjects became more or less inarticulate, unable to put into words the unfamiliar ideas and strange sensations they were experiencing. They were able, how-ever, to portray their experiences pictorially and were en-couraged to do so. One of these representations of the weird world of LSD shows first a jolly little figure dancing against a green background, portraying, in the subject's account, a sense of supreme joy. "The figure is happy and, above all, free. He has thrown off all cares, problems, ugliness, anger and fear. The world around him is bright and beautiful. Beyond the next rise in the field is that which he wishes more than all else. He feels liberated and unlocked within, integrated, realised." The next picture shows an empty masklike face with tears streaming from the eyes, its top sliced off like the top of a boiled egg to reveal an empty space in which, minute as a mosquito, the jolly little figure is still performing its dance. Above the open head roll threatening storm clouds. "The image of the dancing figure is retained as a memory only, and one about to disappear. The feeling is one of loss. A loss of perfection, a departure from Eden. The intensity of the feeling is extreme and expressed through the lack of any environment. The enveloping storm is one of overwhelming feeling, at first nostalgia, then grief, then sheer feeling with no describable content. All this takes place within. The face is a mere mask which has little meaning. The eyes are closed for this reason. The head is a dead shell, the environment does not exist, the feeling comes from without as well as within and replaces the environment." In the third and last drawing the little black figure has returned, but now its head is bowed, its shoulders hunched, its hands hang helplessly, all its jollity is gone. "The figure is walking in an infinitely narrow walk, with an abyss on either side. The sun is a meaningless glare. The feeling is emptiness, apathy. The blotch (at upper left) indicates that the figure is aware of the sun, but unable to grasp it."

Such are the strange effects on mind and emotion of an almost invisible quantity of this most potent of hallucinogens. The question must now be asked, how does LSD produce these extraordinary effects? What is its relationship to that hypothetical poison, the so-called "M" substance from the working of which the madness of the schizophrenic may result? It is highly improbable that LSD itself is the "M" substance. More probably, as the Boston workers suggest, LSD interferes with the body's use of adrenalin and, by blocking some system of enzymes, leads to the production of substances related to adrenalin and having the property of producing hallucinations. The Boston workers do not agree with the Canadians that adrenochrome is hallucinogenic. They attribute the strange experiences described by Osmond after injecting himself with "homemade adrenochrome" to the fact that the solution contained other sub-stances besides adrenochrome, in particular adrenoxine, another breakdown product of adrenalin. The final proof of the theory that adrenoxine is the secret poisoner of the schizophrenic will, of course, depend on the isolation of this substance from the blood of those suffering from this disease.

Quite recently a rather different chemical substance has attracted the attention of some of those scientists interested in the chemical aspects of schizophrenia. This substance is called serotonin or enteramine and its chemical name is 5-hydroxytryptamine. Serotonin occurs naturally in the body and is present in the brain. Musing on its significance, two workers at the Rockefeller Institute for Medical Research, Drs. D. W. Wooley and E. Shaw, have suggested that sero-tonin in the brain plays a role in maintaining normal men-tal processes and that a deficiency of this substance may con-tribute to the production of certain mental disorders. From this standpoint we would have to regard schizophrenia not as the result of the action of a poison but rather as the con-sequence of a deficiency of a vital substance, like the various nervous disorders which develop in individuals with inade-quate supplies of vitamin B_1. There is some evidence to sup-port this theory of Wooley and Shaw. The amazing new "tranquilizing agent" reserpine, whose virtues will be ex-tolled in the next chapter, appears to cause the liberation of extra serotonin in the brain and may exert its beneficial effect by this means. On the other hand the potent "brain poison" LSD seems to interfere with the action of serotonin and some have suggested that LSD exerts its hallucinogenic effect in this way, though the evidence is questionable.

An entirely opposite conception of the function of sero-tonin in schizophrenia has been put forward by the Italian scientist, Dr. Alfredo Poloni who finds, in the blood of schizophrenics, an excess of serotonin which he can detect by its action on the specially prepared muscle of the leech. According to Poloni schizophrenia results from the combined action of a poisonous substance probably derived from adrenalin and an excess of serotonin which accentuates the ill effects of the poison. This question, whether schizophrenia is connected with an excess or a deficiency of serotonin, can only be settled by further biochemical research.

Stress of one kind or another is usually involved in the development of schizophrenia. Several research workers have sought for the cause of this condition among those mechanisms which have to do with the body's response to stress. Under stressful conditions a chain of nervous and chemical reactions is initiated. The hypothalamus, at the base of the brain, sends its message to the pituitary. This master gland pours out a hormone, ACTH (adrenocorticotropic hormone) which, carried by the blood, acts on the cortex of the adrenals. These, in their turn, secrete cortisone and its chemical relatives, substances concerned in the body's struggle with adverse conditions, whether these originate from within or without. Drs. H. Hoagland and G. Pincus at the Worcester Institute have paid special attention to this stress response in a long term study they have made of the origins of schizophrenia. There is, in the schizophrenic, some defect in the chemical machinery that enables the body to cope with stress. The pituitary appears to secrete ACTH but the adrenals do not seem to respond normally to this substance.

That the schizophrenic is the victim of a poison brewed in his own body is only a theory at the present time. Scientists search for the poison but have not found it. They make various guesses, implicating breakdown products of adrenalin, faulty metabolism of serotonin, "in-born errors of metabolism." At the moment there are more guesses tlian certainties. The puzzle has many pieces; we are not in possession of more than a few. Until we have more we cannot hope to put them all together.

If the "M" substance can be identified and its production blocked by chemical means the psychiatrist will then have a weapon as effective in the treatment of schizophrenia as is penicillin in the treatment of streptococcal infections. The prospects are encouraging. Surprisingly good results are being obtained with several new drugs, as will be shown in the next chapter. It must be admitted, however, that these new drugs do not always restore their sanity to the mad. The ideal pharmacological agent has yet to be discovered, nor is it clear at the moment in which direction the chemist should look for this agent. Meanwhile, for those cases which fail to respond to drug therapy, the psychiatrist must continue to use three curative agents whose efficacy has been well established by years of use but whose mode of action is still obscure. The first of these is electroconvulsive therapy, or E.C.T. The second is insulin coma. The third is prefrontal leucotomy or lobotomy.

A brief account of these treatments is offered here because, although they fall somewhat outside the scope of this book, they do have effects which are often very dramatic, and any theory as to the cause of schizophrenia must take these effects into account. Insulin coma is a condition which is justly feared by diabetics and results from a lowering of the sugar in the blood to such a point that the brain cells are starved of their chief food. The result of this starvation is loss of consciousness, in some instances accompanied by convulsions. Nobody knows why such a condition, which ought, theoretically, to be quite damaging to the brain, actually proves beneficial in certain types of schizophrenia.

The treatment arose out of a chance observation by Dr. M. Sakel, a Viennese psychiatrist, who was using insulin to arouse appetite in mental patients who refused to eat. Often in these patients the insulin produced coma, an effect considered both dangerous and undesirable until Sakel made the extraordinary observation that, after such comas, a great improvement was frequently to be seen in the patient's mental state. With wonderful care and thoroughness he proceeded to work out the new method of treatment, using gradually increasing doses of insulin until coma was produced, leaving the patient in this state for about an hour, then terminating the coma by giving the patient a drink of some material rich in sugar. Fifty or sixty comas are commonly needed to produce the desired effect. The treatment is not without its hazards, the chief of which is "prolonged coma" when the patient fails to respond even to direct injections of glucose solutions. This complication can be expected about once in 1877 individuals treated and the death rate is around 0.33% of all cases.

Electroconvulsive therapy (E.C.T.) resulted from an observation by Dr. J. L. Meduna that schizophrenia and epilepsy rarely occur together and that, when they do, the schizophrenic symptoms often become less marked after an epileptic fit. Several authorities now question the correctness of this theory but, correct or not, it resulted in the development of a potent new weapon now widely used by psychiatrists. Convulsions were produced in the early days of this therapy by injecting as rapidly as possible into the veins a camphorlike chemical called metrazol or cardiazol. Such an injection was usually followed by convulsions within thirty seconds, the patient uttering that peculiar cry which always precedes a major epileptic fit, then becoming rigid and ceasing to breathe and finally twitching in what are known as clonic convulsions. Metrazol injections, however, had several drawbacks, the chief of which was the extreme terror experienced by the patient during the period before the convulsions set in, at which point he always became unconscious. So great was this terror that patients often refused to continue the treatment. Soon the use of metrazol was virtually abandoned when it was shown by two Italian doctors, U. Cerletti and L. Bini, that a shock of alternating current (70 to 130 volts for 0.1 to 0.5 seconds) passed through the brain will also produce convulsions and that such a procedure produces immediate unconsciousness with none of the preliminary terrors generated by injections of metrazole.

Electroconvulsive therapy, because of its simplicity and relative safety, has gained very wide use. It is not as effective as insulin coma against certain types of schizophrenia but has the advantage of being a far simpler procedure which does not even necessitate hospitalization of the patient. On those states of gloom once known as melancholia and now lumped together as depressions, E.C.T. often acts like a charm. After as few as three or four treatments the melancholy, sorrowful patient for whom all life has become one long tragic episode, who frequently echoes Hamlet's sentiments concerning the general staleness of life, and who openly or secretly is planning suicide, suddenly finds new confidence and enthusiasm as if the violence of his convulsions had reawakened his slumbering will to live. The efficacy of E.C.T. in such depressions is remarkable. The treatment is not entirely without its hazards. Bones may sometimes be broken by the violence of the muscular contractions; the arrow poison, curare, is sometimes injected to soften the violence of the contractions by interfering with the transmission of impulses from nerves to muscles. Curare and similar drugs introduce their own hazards, however, and modern methods of applying E.C.T. have greatly reduced the dangers of fractures. Loss of memory may also follow this treatment but this complication generally disappears fairly rapidly.

The third new method of treating schizophrenia, which is more drastic than either insulin coma or E.C.T., consists in operating on the brain in such a way that certain nervous connections within it are severed. This operation takes various forms but the most widely used procedure severs the connection between the frontal lobes, which occupy that part of the skull immediately behind the brow, and the structures of the "old brain," the thalamus and the hypothalamus, which appear to be the spawning grounds of our emotions. The operation, though it has nothing to do with drugs, needs to be considered in connection with our subject because of the light it throws on the workings of the mind. It was devised originally by a Portuguese surgeon, Egaz Moniz, but the observation on which the operation was based was made in America by C. F. Jacobsen. Working with a highly emotional chimpanzee, Jacobsen noticed that, whenever the animal made an error in the psychological tests he was using, she developed violent temper tantrums, rolling on the floor, urinating, and defecating. The more the animal was persuaded to attempt the problem the more outlandish did her behavior become. She finally developed a serious emotional illness which caused her to react with violent display to any frustrating situation. At this point Jacobsen operated on the ape, severing the connection between the frontal lobes and the rest of the brain. An astonishing change came over the animal's behavior. Temper tantrums disappeared. Frustrating situations were met with a placid indifference. Mistakes made in psychological tests no longer drove the creature to a fury. "It was," in Jacobsen's words, "as if the animal . . . had placed its burdens on the Lord."

Dr. Moniz, reading of this work, reflected that if some of the hagridden, tormented schizophrenics who fill the disturbed wards in mental hospitals could also be persuaded to place their cares on the Lord life would become much more agreeable for all concerned. Accordingly, with a boldness which few surgeons would be willing to emulate, he operated, and the procedure now known as leucotomy in England and lobotomy in the United States was introduced to the medical world. It was received by some with cries of protest, by others with approval, and controversy still centers about the procedure. The operation has been so simplified that any psychiatrist with a mallet in one hand and an ice pick in the other can, if he has a taste for this kind of interference, drive the one by means of the other into the frontal lobes of his more troublesome patients, thereby severing, with greater or less efficiency, the nerve fibers connecting the frontal lobes and the thalamus. The charm of this operation lies in its extreme simplicity, for the bony plate immediately above the eyeball provides a path of entry straight into the brain. One good hard tap and a wiggle or two and presto! the infinitely complex network of fibers built up during untold millennia of evolution is churned into a structureless porridge and the patient emerges with nothing worse than a couple of black eyes, plus, of course, a brain defect that will never heal.

The ice-pick-and-mallet approach—"transorbital lobotomy," to give it its more dignified name—is of course rather a crude procedure and several eminent surgeons prefer to use more refined methods when mutilating their patients' brains. They drill holes in the side of the skull and use a blunt knife neatly marked off in centimeters with which much more extensive cutting can be done than with an ice

pick blindly driven through the orbit. The outcome, however, is much the same: an irreparable injury to the fine
structure of the brain. Needless to say, it is an operation by
no means universally approved by the medical profession,
particularly the psychoanalysts. "The psychoanalyst believes
in the power of love and reason. . . . He is fundamentally
a strategist and feels about the more violent forms of physical treatment as a highly trained military strategist must
feel about atomic warfare" (E. Stengel). To this Jan Frank
adds, "The cavalier-like fashion in which psychosurgical
enthusiasts mutilate healthy brains in patients with personality disorders justifiably fills a psychoanalyst with horror."

Why, then, is the operation used at all? Why does the
medical profession, bound by the terms of the Hippocratic
oath to protect the patient from harm, tolerate a procedure
of such dubious value? No simple answer can be given to
this question. Prefrontal leucotomy is mutilation. It creates
a defect that can never be repaired. It places the patient
once and for all beyond the reach of psychotherapy. It in-
variably "down-grades" the individual, coarsening his behavior, destroying his insight, blunting his ambitions, dull-
ing his appreciations. All that is highest in the life of man
in the realm of art, science, philosophy, and religion is
placed, to a large extent, out of reach of the lobotomized
individual. The role of the frontal lobes in the spiritual life
of man is a vital one. This "silent" region of the brain enables us to reach out into the future, to plan, to aspire, to
dream, to create. With this or through this we gain those
intuitions that to many a poet have seemed more precious
than life itself.

> Not for thee I raise
> The song of thanks and praise;

> But for those obstinate questionings
> Of sense and outward things,
> Fallings from us, vanishings;
> Blank misgivings of a Creature
> Moving about in worlds not realised,
> High instincts before which our mortal Nature
> Did tremble like a guilty Thing surprised.

From this and from all that goes with this, the highest, the deepest, the most profound aspects of human experience, the lobotomy patient is cut off by a few strokes of a surgeon's knife.

To these objections, however, that section of medical opinion which approves mutilation of the brains of the mentally ill might offer a very caustic rebuttal. Consider, they might say, the type of patient on whom we operate. Terrorized night and day by vivid hallucinations, obsessed by agonizing thoughts of guilt and shame, violent, aggressive, dirty, undernourished, what have such beings as these to lose by the operation? Would they not gladly swap their "Intimations of Immortality" for placid freedom from their haunting terrors? True it is that the operation may leave them coarsened, that they may become tactless, primitive, crude, lazy, without ambitions, without insight, of small value to society. But look at them now. Of what use are these raging miserable beings to society in their present state? At least if we operate we will expect them to grow more placid. At least they will need less nursing care, less restraint, will be less likely to harm themselves or others. Though we may not cure them we can hope at least that they will graduate from the disturbed ward to the quiet ward. Better still, they may so improve that they can be sent home, not their old selves, it is true, but capable, with encouragement, guidance, and considerable pushing, of making themselves useful in a humble capacity. Is not this a gain rather than a loss?

All this is true, and it is precisely for this reason that the operation is tolerated in some countries, though not in all. Here we are interested not so much in its moral aspects as in the light it throws on the chemistry of madness. If a knife thrust in the brain can cure mental illness, what becomes of our "M" substance? Do the effects of lobotomy make this theory untenable?

We can attempt to answer this question. Lobotomy does not necessarily cure mental illness. Hallucinated schizophrenics may continue to hear and see the voices, devils, et cetera, which haunted them before. What lobotomy achieves is to remove the element of terror from these experiences. In the words of Watts and Freeman, it "draws the sting of the psychosis." "I still hear voices," the lobotomized patient will often say, "but they don't bother me." The root of the disturbance has not been removed but the patient reacts to it in a different way. Lobotomy therefore does not necessarily make the theory of the "M" substance untenable. The poison may still be produced but its effect on the mind is altered by the severing of the connection between the emotional and the thinking brain.

Can the effects of prefrontal lobotomy be duplicated by a drug? Is there any chemical that will temporarily sever the connection between frontal lobes and thalamus without inflicting that irreparable injury which follows the path of the surgeon's knife? The quest for such an agent is occupying the time of many a chemist and pharmacologist. We have very good reason to suppose that such a drug can be found, indeed some of our newer chemopsychiatric agents show promise of producing exactly this effect. In fact we may soon be able to give an affirmative answer to that question which the agonized Macbeth addressed to his physician:

> Canst thou not minister to the mind diseased,
> Pluck from the memory a rooted sorrow,
> Raze out the written troubles of the brain;
> And with some sweet oblivious antidote
> Cleanse the stuffed bosom of that perilous stuff
> Which weighs upon the heart?

At that time the best reply the doctor could offer was "therein the patient must minister to himself," nor can one blame Macbeth for his impatient rejoinder: "Throw physic to the dogs—I'll none of it." Today, however, we are in a position to offer a more hopeful answer and the substance of this answer is contained in the next chapter.

Sick Minds, New Medicines

Mental illness takes many forms. A *psychosis* draws a veil between its victim and the outer world, clouds the mind with hallucinations which make purposive action difficult or impossible. The psychotic individual can play no active part in life. He must, for his own good and that of others, be separated from his normal surroundings and cared for in a special hospital until he re-establishes contact with reality.

A *neurotic,* on the other hand, does not lose contact with reality. He can continue his work and deal with most of the situations that confront him. Nonetheless he is sick emotionally and mentally and his sickness colors his waking and possibly also his sleeping hours. Because of it he can never really enjoy his existence. His neurosis hovers over him like the mythological harpy and whatever choice morsel life offers him in the way of pleasure it swoops upon and carries off. It distorts his every feeling and colors his every impression, poisoning with suspicion, fear, guilt, apprehension, envy, or malice the very fountainhead of his existence. The psychiatrists spend much time delving into the subconscious of such a one to discover the old griefs, traumas, repressions, complexes which set this poison flowing. The chemist pre-fers to leave the complexes alone and to pin his faith on the dictum, "All is chemical." He believes that the sufferings of these hapless neurotics have a chemical basis, that there can be neither guilt, anxiety, depression, nor agitation without some sort of chemical unbalance within the body.

Where should we seek the basis for such unbalance? If we consider the mental and emotional life of man we see that it changes its tone from day to day and from hour to hour. Today he is elated, tomorrow depressed; in the morn-ing an optimist, in the afternoon a pessimist; a lover after lunch, a misanthrope before it. And on what do these cease-less variations of mood depend? They depend on an endless sequence of minor changes in the outpourings of those glands whose blended secretions make up the chords of man's inner symphony. From pituitary and adrenals, from thyroids and gonads flows the stuff of which man's feelings are created, partially regulated by processes in the brain which, like a conductor struggling through a difficult sym-phony, does not always produce a very distinguished per-formance. Neurosis and psychosis alike must be the result of a breakdown in glandular harmony: too much adrenalin here, too little thyroxine there, a shade too much testo-sterone or too little progesterone, a shortage of ACTH, an insufficiency of cortisone, too little serotonin or perhaps too much. Why should we enmesh ourselves in a tangle of complexes when the root of all evil lies in chemical dis-harmony? Let us take as our motto the dictum of R. W. Gerard: "There can be no twisted thought without a twisted molecule."

So, from this standpoint, to use a slightly different anal-ogy, we can depict the ever changing moods of man as a more or less continuous spectrum composed of many colors.

From hour to hour man's ego, that which he feels to be himself, moves to and fro across this spectrum under the influence of inward and outward events. At one end of the spectrum lies the infrared of melancholia or depression. At the opposite end lies the ultraviolet of mania or extreme agitation. A normal, balanced man remains for the most part in the middle region of the spectrum and strays into the extreme regions only rarely. If he does enter those regions he can, without too much difficulty, remove himself from them. The dark or the frenzied mood passes. The needed chemical adjustments are carried out. Harmony is restored, the inward symphony trips along smoothly again, *allegro ma non troppo*.

In the mentally sick individual, however, this healthy chemical adjustment does not take place. Such a one may become permanently stuck at one end or the other of the psychological spectrum. If stuck at one end he is said to be suffering from depression or melancholia; if stuck at the other he is said to be suffering from agitation or mania. Quite commonly such a sick individual fluctuates between the two extremes in a condition known as a manic-depressive psychosis. Now like a god he strides on the clouds above Olympus, feeling himself to be capable of anything and everything; a few hours later, falling with a crash from the heights, he creeps through the glooms of the infernal regions, feeling lower than a worm. There is, in this case, an obvious effort on the part of the ruling chemical mechanism to correct the unbalance which has arisen among the lesser hormones. The correction, however, is always overdone, so that the mood of such an unfortunate swings from one extreme to the other and his personal symphony fluctuates between a frenzied *presto agitato* and an almost unendurably dreary *largo*.

To treat conditions such as these the physician will seek a remedy among two very different classes of drugs. The patient at one end of the spectrum, overactive, agitated, tense, nerves "frayed" with anxiety, requires a medicament that will soothe and tranquilize. But the patient at the opposite end of the spectrum, whose load of depression is so heavy that he can scarcely raise his head, whose life is an empty, meaningless, valueless void, and whose pale apathetic face gazes indifferently alike at the prizes and penalties offered by this life, obviously needs a very different sort of drug, one which, by opening the dampers that regulate our inner fires, will restore that healthy glow now almost stifled in a cloud of poisonous smoke.

We will consider first the tranquilizing agents, the "ataraxies." Man's need for such agents goes back beyond the dawn of history, for never has there been a time or a place in which he failed to find himself assailed by care. "Care," wrote Goethe in *Faust*, "soon makes her nest within the depths of the heart, secretly working, destroying joy and peace. Daily she hides behind a different mask. She comes as house and hearth, as wife and child, as fire or water, dagger or poison. You shrink from blows which do not fall, and weep for things you did not even lose."

There is nothing new in this. The story is as old as humanity. From the beginning man has walked among real and imaginary enemies, anxiously casting glances over his shoulder. A quaint fallacy which has gained currency at the present time represents the modern age as specifically the "age of anxiety" and depicts contemporary man burdened to breaking point under "the stresses and strains of modern life." Those who adopt this point of view apparently visualize our ancestors living spacious, gracious, and leisurely existences into whose stately harmonies no troublesome discords ever intruded. In actual fact, with the exception of a few pampered aristocrats, our forebears faced life on terms which to us moderns would seem almost unendurable. Haunted by a thousand terrors that they could hardly define, in dread of a host of gods and goddesses, of omens, of goblins, of witches, of devils and of damnation, they lived in the midst of a forest of shadowy fears, all of which would seem laughable to the sophisticated modern. Their lives, far from being spacious or gracious, were threatened by plague and pestilence in countless forms, endangered by famine, burdened by heavy labor, shortened by every variety of deficiency disease from rickets and scurvy to beriberi and pellagra. Only quite recently, within the last fifty years, have these sources of anxiety and misery been more or less banished from the lives of one small section of mankind, by the devices of Western science. But Western man, despite the fact that he is better protected, clothed, fed, enjoys better health and a longer average life than man has ever known in the million years of his existence, shows little gratitude for the good gifts showered upon him by the scientist but peevishly grumbles about the "age of anxiety" as if he had more cares on his shoulders than all his ancestors put together.

There is, however, an explanation for this paradox. Western man, being so much healthier than were his forebears, can afford to give more attention to those vague ills of mind and emotions which his ancestors, plagued by harsher pains and sorrows, passed over unnoticed. Nor can one deny that, along with countless benefits it has conferred, the machine age has imposed peculiar stresses. To be hoisted, in a period of less than fifty years, from the seat of the horse and buggy to that of the automobile and jet plane is an experience sufficient to unsettle even man's sturdy psyche. In the inner as well as the outer world of man there have been upheavals. Old faiths have crumbled, new ones have not been created, and in the resulting vacuum man wanders, lost. Tied to the minute hand of the clock, a servant of steel machines whose laws are inflexible, goaded by ambitions and aspirations, scrambling for gain in a crowded, jostling world, harassed by the ever pressing need to keep up with the Joneses, the modern man can hardly be blamed if he counts his ulcers instead of his blessings and cries out to his physician for relief from his inner tensions, for something to give him tranquillity and peace of mind.

The physician, if he happened to have read St. Thomas à Kempis, might reply with a quotation from the *Imitation of Christ:* "Peace is what all men desire, but all do not care for the things which pertain to true peace." He might point out that the true aim of both philosophy and religion is to give man an inward peace which the storms of life cannot ruffle. But since patients expect pills from physicians rather than sermons, and since the doctor is in any case far too busy to philosophize, he will probably make a note of his patient's blood pressure, scribble some hieroglyphics on a prescription form, and assure his visitor that, with this new tranquilizing drug in his system, he will gain all the consolations of religion and philosophy without suffering the inconvenience of having to practice self-discipline.

What then are these drugs whose action is so special that we have to borrow a new Greek word to describe it? The first of the ataraxics is not new at all. It is an extremely ancient remedy and has been used for at least twenty-five hundred years in India by practitioners of a system of medicine known as the Ayur-Veda. This drug, known in India by the name *sarpaganda,* is the powdered root of a small bush belonging to the family Apocynaceae, the Latin name of which is *Rauwolfia serpentina*. In English the plant is commonly referred to as snake root, a practice inviting errors, for this name is also applied to several entirely different drug plants (e.g., *Eryngium aquaticum, Asarum canadensis, Polygala senega*). Confusion can be avoided if one simply refers to the plant as Rauwolfia, a name bestowed upon it by Plumier in honor of Dr. Leonhard Rauwolf, a sixteenth-century German physician who had traveled widely in India collecting medicinal plants.

Rauwolfia was endowed with so many virtues by the Ayurvedic physicians that it appears to have been regarded as a universal panacea. It was prescribed as a cure for insanity, insomnia, cholera, dysentery, blindness, fever, stomach ulcers, and snakebite. It was chewed by holy men to assist them in their meditations (the late Mahatma Gandhi used it extensively); it was given by mothers to soothe their crying babies. Indian physicians who had had contact with Western science also found virtue in the plant. Drs. Gananth Sen and Kartick Chandra Bose described it as a "drug of rare merit" in treating nervous disorders; Dr. Rustom Jal Vakil extolled it as a safe means of lowering high blood pressure; Sir Ram Nath Chopra did considerable work on the chemical composition of the active extracts. To natives on the opposite side of the world, in the tropical forests of Colombia and Guatemala, the virtues of Rauwolfia were also known, the drug being used as an anti-malarial and for treatment of snakebite. In Guatemala it was called *chalchupa*, in Colombia *piñique-piñique*. In fact the only people who seemed unaware of the virtues of Rauwolfia were the great omniscient scientists of the West.

It is curious indeed that a remedy so ancient and one on which so much excellent research had been carried out by several Indian scientists should have been ignored by Western researchers until the year 1947. This situation resulted, in part at least, from the rather contemptuous attitude which certain chemists and pharmacologists in the West have developed toward both folk remedies and drugs of plant origin, regarding native medicines as the by-products of various old wives' tales and forgetting that we owe some of our most valued drugs (digitalis, ephedrine, and quinine, to name only a few) to just such "old wives' tales." They further fell into the error of supposing, because they had learned the trick of synthesizing certain substances, that they were better chemists than Mother Nature, who, besides creating compounds too numerous to mention, also synthesized the aforesaid chemists and pharmacologists. Needless to say, the more enlightened members of these professions avoided so crude an error, realizing that the humblest bacterium can synthesize, in the course of its brief existence, more organic compounds than can all the world's chemists combined. But even those who were well disposed toward native remedies and regarded with proper respect the chemical potentialities of the plant kingdom were inclined to be skeptical about Rauwolfia. Ayurvedic practitioners had claimed so many virtues for this drug that they made it sound slightly ridiculous in Western ears, like the famous drug plant *ginseng*, so esteemed by the Chinese, which has never proved capable of curing anyone of anything.

That the secret of Rauwolfia's potent action was finally brought to light was due to the curiosity of an eminent biochemist, Sir Robert Robinson, and the enterprise of Dr. Emil Schlittler of the Swiss pharmaceutical firm of Ciba, at Basle. Sir Robert was interested in an alkaloid of Rauwolfiia called adjmaline and persuaded Dr. Schlittler to prepare this substance from the ground roots of *Rauwolfia serpen-*

tina. After the adjmaline had been crystallized there remained large amounts of muddy, unattractive residue which Schlittler, with that thrift which is the hallmark of every good chemist, refused to discard until he had further explored its make-up. His exploration of this muddy resinous residue proved profitable beyond his wildest dreams, for the pharmacologists to whom he sent this material discovered, on testing it in animals, indications of that curious tranquilizing effect for which the drug has now become justly famous. Spurred on by this report, Dr. Schlittler set out to isolate the chemical substance responsible for this activity.

In a problem of this kind, success is dependent always upon the harmonious co-operation of two different kinds of experts: the chemist whose task it is to purify the desired material, and the biologist or pharmacologist whose function is to determine its effect in the animal. These two are chained together in the way criminals used to be in the bad old days and neither can move a step without the other. Lack of co-operation between these two may bring to nothing the most important lines of research, as happened in the case of penicillin, which remained unpurified and unavailable to the medical profession for eleven years after its presence was first discovered. In the case of reserpine, however, the chemical labors of Dr. Schlittler and his young colleague Johannes Muller were backed up by the work of an imaginative and co-operative pharmacologist, Dr. Hugo Bein. Their combined attack on the problem was crowned with success.

In September of 1952, just five years after Sir Robert Robinson had presented his request for some adjmaline, the three Ciba scientists, Schlittler, Muller, and Bein, finally published an account of their labors. The few grams of shining white crystals they had obtained from the muddy resinous extract of Rauwolfia represented the fruit of a prodigious amount of work. Every crystal was equivalent in activity to more than ten thousand times its weight in the crude drug. "We have long intended," wrote Schlittler and his colleagues, "to isolate the sedative substance of crude Rauwolfia extracts. This hypnotic principle had been examined earlier by Indian authors, but they did not get any further than the crude 'oleoresin fractions.' Starting from these fractions, we have now been able to isolate the carrier of the sedative effect in pure crystalline form." To this crystalline substance they gave the name reserpine.

A few months later Dr. Bein published a second report which revealed that reserpine, besides producing sedation, also lowered the blood pressure of the experimental animals. The drug reduced blood pressure slowly and safely, taking a fairly long period to attain its maximum effect. As high blood pressure is a particularly common ailment in America it is not surprising to find that one enterprising American physician, Dr. Robert W. Wilkins of Boston University, had already given the crude Indian drug a trial. Pure reserpine was not available to him. It had not at that time been isolated. Instead he used tablets of the crude drug imported from India with which he treated more than fifty patients suffering from high blood pressure.

By 1952, Wilkins and his colleagues were able to report progress:

> We have confirmed the clinical reports from India on the mildly hypotensive [blood-pressure lowering] effect of this drug. It has a type of sedative action that we have not observed before. Unlike barbiturates or other standard sedatives, it does not produce grogginess, stupor or lack of coordination. The patients appear to be relaxed, quiet and tranquil.

One of the doctors at a later scientific meeting supplied this statement: "It makes them feel as if they simply don't have a worry in the world."

It was this observation, that the drug not only lowered blood pressure but also relaxed the tensions and anxieties by which high blood pressure is often accompanied, that aroused the interest of psychiatrists. Here, they reflected, might be the drug for which they had so long been seeking. Until the discovery of Raùwolfia no drug available to psychiatrists would really tranquilize the agitated, anxious, restless patients who so often came to them seeking help. The bromides were short-acting and apt to be toxic. The barbiturates made the patients too sleepy to carry on with their work; chloral and paraldehyde suffered from the same drawbacks. Valerian, an ancient botanical remedy long esteemed as a specific for the treatment of hysteria, could not be relied upon to exert any effect at all. Thus, although Freud himself stated that "behind every psychoanalyst stands the man with the syringe," thereby showing that he foresaw the era of chemopsychiatry, the psychiatrist still had no drug with which to fill his syringe until crystalline reserpine, with its extraordinary capacity to soothe without stupefying, was made available to the profession by the labors of Schlittler and his colleagues.

As soon as the drug did become available a flood of scientific publications poured from the presses; indeed so great was the interest that for a time one rarely opened a medical journal without finding within it at least one article on Rauwolfia. Information about the effects of the drug was rapidly accumulated and summarized in several excellent symposia, two sponsored by the New York Academy of Science, and one organized by the American Association for the Advancement of Science and published under the title *Psy-*

chopharmacology. The following accounts are drawn mainly from these sources.

Reserpine is an extraordinary drug in more ways than one and its mode of action is hard to understand. It acts slowly and takes several weeks to exert its full effects, and these effects when they come follow a definite pattern. Dr. Nathan S. Kline, who has used reserpine extensively on mental patients in Rockland State Hospital, New York, summarizes his findings as follows: When reserpine is given by mouth, very little response is noted for several days. This suggests that the drug is transformed in some way in the body and that the substance which really produces the effect may not be reserpine itself but some product of reserpine. When the effects do begin to be seen they follow a very definite sequence. First comes the *sedative phase.* Patients behave more normally. They become less excited, assaultive, and agitated, appetite improves, and they begin to gain weight. Then, at the end of the first week, the patient enters the *turbulent phase.* During this phase the mental state seems suddenly to worsen. Delusions and hallucinations increase. Patients complain of a sense of strangeness; they do not feel like themselves, do not know what they are going to do next, have no control over their impulses. A physician who does not expect such manifestations may be alarmed at these symptoms and discontinue the use of the drug. Medication, however, should not be reduced until the patient has been able to get "over the hump." The *turbulent phase* may last for two or three weeks or may pass in a few hours. In some patients it was not observed at all. Finally, if all goes well, the patient enters the *integrative phase,* becomes quieter, more co-operative, friendly, and more interested in his environment. Delusions and hallucinations become less marked. This is followed by recognition on the patient's part that he has actually been ill.

Dr. Kline noted that healthy urges are often freed by the drug and that many patients for the first time in years enjoy such simple pleasures as eating, physical contact with others, and physical activity in other forms. There was a tendency toward an increase in expressive movements; several patients turned to playing the piano, which they had not done for many years. Success of the treatment seemed to depend on the patient's capacity to reorganize his inner life. Reserpine provided the conditions for this reorganization but could not provide the ability to reorganize if it was not there.

The same sort of release took place in neurotics. Liberation of these pent-up forces at times took rather embarrassing forms. A neurotic young attorney, who usually absorbed whatever his wife or anyone else handed out to him, became outgoing enough, on being treated with reserpine, to throw a dish of tomatoes at his wife when she provoked him. On the whole, however, the response of the neurotics was less extreme. Such people obtained from the drug a capacity to view their difficulties more objectively. They gained perspective and saw their troubles as if from a distance. "I no longer 'bleed' if I don't get everything done," said one of Dr. Kline's patients, a chronic worrier, "I do what I can and that's that." "It's not that I don't worry," said another. "I do that as much as before—but I don't worry about my worries." This man, an alcoholic, had been consuming about a pint of liquor a day and had found, once he started drinking, that it was beyond his power to stop. This problem also vanished under the magical influence of reserpine. He found himself under no compulsion even to complete one drink and observed, "It's peculiar. Now that I find I can drink, I don't care whether I do or not."

The statistics offered by Dr. Kline are impressive. In a series of 150 chronically disturbed psychotics who had failed to improve when treated with electroshock or insulin, 84 per cent showed improvement with reserpine, and 21 per cent of these patients maintained their improvement after medication had been discontinued. Electroconvulsion treatment was largely abandoned. Dr. L. E. Hollister and his colleagues report from California that reserpine produced significant improvement in 98 out of 127 chronic schizophrenics. Drs. Tasher and Chermak (Illinois) report excellent results in 221 chronically ill schizophrenics. The drug has been used with success in the treatment of emotionally disturbed children, in the treatment of skin diseases in which nervous factors were involved, in headache of the tension and migraine type. Its value in the treatment of withdrawal symptoms in narcotics has been mentioned elsewhere.

Needless to say, this chorus of praise contains a few discordant notes. Dr. J. C. Muller and his co-workers, in an article in the *American Journal of Medicine*, declare that the tranquilizing action of reserpine may on occasion go too far and lead to a depression. High doses of the drug produce definite side effects which may be troublesome. The nose may become stuffy and the patient may experience drowsiness and dizziness. The drug, of course, lowers blood pressure and this effect may have to be watched rather carefully. It is definitely not a medicament to be taken without medical supervision, but the side effects it produces are of minor importance compared with the tremendous benefits it can confer.

The second of the new ataraxics has a history entirely different from that of reserpine. Here there was no romantic background of ancient folk medicine. The remedy originated in the chemical laboratory and its full title, 3-dimethyl-amino-propyl-2-chlorphenothiazine hydrochloride, is awe-inspiring to anyone but a chemist. The Rhone-Poulenc Specia Laboratories in France, which developed this valuable drug, gave it the name chlorpromazine, by which it is now generally described. To ensure the greatest possible confusion, however, various trade names were also given to this substance. In the United States it is met with as "Thorazine," in Britain and Canada it goes under the name of "Largactil." It has also been called "R.P. 4560" and "Megaphen." *

Chlorpromazine, like reserpine, rose to fame with rocket-like velocity. In 1953 it was almost unheard of, in 1955 it was known to every physician in the country and reports on its use were eagerly studied, especially by those responsible for the care of the mentally sick. Dr. Douglas Goldman of Cincinnati published one of the first reports on large-scale use of this medicament in a mental hospital. So encouraging were the effects that, in the words of his colleague, Dr. Fabing, he took a new lease on life.

The reduction in assaults, the lessened use of restraint, the increased granting of privileges to locked ward patients, the lessened need for repeated electroshock treatment to control explosive behavior, and the beginnings of an improved discharge rate of patients from the hospital all stem from the use of this drug in his hands and parallel the kind of improved state of affairs which Kline reports with reserpine at Rockland.

* Reserpine may also be met with under various trade names, such as "Serpasil" (Ciba). "Raunormine" (Penick) is not reserpine but a closely related alkaloid from *Rauwolfia canescens*

Goldman likes to tell the story about Willie. Willie was a dishevelled, mute, untidy schizophrenic who had to be spoon fed and who managed to tear off just about all the clothes anyone tried to put on him. Willie received an eight weeks' trial with chlorpromazine but at the end of that time Goldman was not greatly impressed with his improvement. He announced that he was going to withdraw Willie's drug, whereupon an orderly raised a clamor, pleading for its continuance, insisting that Willie was much better. He said, "Wait a minute. I'll prove it to you. I'll get Johnny." In a moment he returned with Willie's identical twin. "See, they were both alike two months ago," he said. They stood side by side. Johnny's hair fell in his face, he was soiled, his pants were torn, and he was barefoot. Willie was fully clothed, barbered, shaved, clean and wore shoes. The difference was obvious. Instead of taking a patient off chlorpromazine he put another on.

This feeling of enthusiasm, suitably qualified by those cautious asides which any clinician working with a new drug is bound to use, pervades Dr. Goldman's report in the *Journal of the American Medical Association:*

The initial observations justify a sense of optimism that has rarely resulted from the trial of new techniques in the treatment of psychotic states. . . . In patients who show a great deal of initial excitement . . . the medicament is practically specific. . . . Patients cease to be loud and profane and . . . can sit still long enough to eat and take care of normal physiological needs. . . . In states of excitement associated with the prolonged use of alcohol, the drug is practically specifically effective. Hallucinatory states subside within less than 24 hours. . . . In the more chronic psychotic states, the effect of the drug is much less immediately dramatic, but, for those experienced with the relief of psychotic symptoms from other measures, the use of the drug produces results that are equally gratifying when compared with results in the more acute situations. . . . After a period of one to six weeks, various psychotic components gradually resolve. Hallucinations are almost specifically relieved in many patients relatively early in the treatment. . . . Severe paranoid ideation subsides more gradually. An interesting instance of this is the patient who had many ideas of passivity and control in various ways by the communists; even her bowel function was under their control. After $5\frac{1}{2}$ weeks of administration of the drug and after 2 weeks of administration of 200 mg every eight hours, she announced one morning to the nurse in charge that everything was different, that she was now herself again. On careful interview it was found that all of the paranoid ideas had been resolved and the patient had become cooperative, mild and even ingratiating.

Goldman also pointed out that chlorpromazine, when used with barbiturates, so greatly enhanced the effectiveness of these drugs that excited patients could be sedated with doses of a barbiturate which would barely have produced somnolence if given by itself.

In the same issue of the *Journal* Dr. Robert Gatskie reported enthusiastically on the value of chlorpromazine in the treatment of emotionally maladjusted children. Such children, rejected by their parents on account of their aggressive, violent, and destructive behavior, were housed in a cottage-type treatment center, 150 of all ages ranging from four to sixteen years. Nine of these children were treated with chlorpromazine and within a week all showed improved behavior. They became calm, co-operative, and more communicative. Their social behavior improved and they became more amenable to cottage supervision. Last but not least, they established rapport with the therapist.

No unusual side effects were noted, and no complications were encountered in this series of cases; however, further study and observation with larger groups of children seem to be indicated, as chlorpromazine is a valuable drug and has a definite place in the treatment of emotionally malad-justed children.

On occasion chlorpromazine exerts an influence that may quite justifiably be called miraculous. An example is given by Dr. L. H. Margolis and coworkers in their paper "Psycho-pharmacology." The patient on whom the drug was tried was the despair of psychologists, a thirty-four-year-old para-noid schizophrenic who had been treated with insulin coma and electroconvulsions, despite which his condition had re-mained unchanged. His brain was filled with delusions of grandeur and of persecution and his whole life was spent amid a collection of systematized delusions. As neither in-sulin nor electroconvulsion had helped him lobotomy was recommended but his wife refused to consent to the opera-tion. Finally in August 1954 chlorpromazine was recom-mended "as a desperation measure in a hopeless case." If it failed lobotomy and/or return to the state hospital were planned.

Soon after treatment with chlorpromazine was started the night staff began to report a subtle change in the patient's attitude. On the fiftieth day of treatment he began to emerge from his world of delusions. By the fifty-seventh day he ceased to show any evidence of mental derangement. He de-veloped an interest in the world of reality, broadened his interests and soon began to lay plans for his future. For the first time since he had been committed to the state hospital he was allowed to go home, where his wife was so impressed by his improvement that she began at once to make plans for his discharge and return to normal life. This patient was fortunate indeed. Only by his wife's refusal of her consent was he saved from a mutilating operation which, while it might have freed him from some of his delusions, would have left him with an irreparably injured brain. Chlorpromazine accomplished all that might have been done by the surgeon's knife *without* doing any damage to those precious lobes on the integrity of which the highest aspects of the personality depend. Some workers have referred to the action of chlorpromazine as "chemical lobotomy." It produces some of the good effects of the operation without the mutilation.

Dr. V. Kinross-Wright states that it is often desirable to maintain patients on the drug for longer periods than were first thought necessary. Quite a number of elderly patients who responded well relapsed when the drug was withdrawn within a six months' period. It seems that, in some cases, patients may have to be kept on this drug almost indefinitely. One patient, a thirty-five-year-old paranoid schizophrenic, was maintained on chlorpromazine for over a year and every attempt to drop the dosage was attended with relapse.

She responds almost as a diabetic would to lack of insulin, and as soon as she is reinstated on chlorpromazine, her symptoms disappear quite rapidly. While she is on it she is completely symptom free. She works, she does housework, looks after her family, and enjoys life. If the dosage is omitted, as has happened several times when she ran out of medicine, or once or twice when she went out of town and miscalculated her supply, signs of relapse have immediately appeared.

Another new member of the ataraxic group is azacyclonal, a synthetic substance manufactured by the Wm. S. Merrell Co. of Cincinnati under the name of "Frenquel." Dr. Fabing has shown this drug to be capable of blocking the development of those "experimental psychoses" which are produced by mescaline and LSD-25. An account of one of these reactions to LSD and of its resolution by "Frenquel" runs as follows:

> Complete and insoluble confusion and anxiety reigned, and the knowledge that its cause was a drug was my sole and small reassurance. This time I crawled onto the bed early, and planned to stay there beforehand. I was not nearly so eager to relate my experience or to cooperate with the experimenters—I was just going to wait it out this time.
>
> One hallucination was that of lying flat on a slowly revolving cloud-like object. There were other similar objects all around, touching gently and revolving "in gear." I just rolled slowly down into the depths of the arrangement. Another one I recall is that of a flowerbed type of pattern, or perhaps a purposeless pin-ball machine, with the lights arranged in rows and columns. The lights—or flowers—were growing, then bursting, in irregular fashion, one at the left, then the center, and so on.
>
> Next occurred the phenomenon that has happened both times I "lost," and perhaps I have neglected to mention it previously. Things seemed to clear up and I felt sane, yet knew I wasn't. I seemed to wake up to a new world—the same situation, same people and environment—yet everything, that is, my mental state, my life, had been altered.

I was a stranger in this world. I could no longer speak to anyone as a person. And that was my state when I was given the shot, bewildered, confused, afraid to say a word till I could be sure of what was happening, in which world I was.

I realize that what happened to me in those few minutes after the injection has a tremendous significance. Because of this realization, I have worked it over often since then. But God help me, I can't tell you a thing. It just happened. There was no crescendo, no fitting together of the pieces, no breaking through the surface. All of a sudden I found myself willing to cooperate, able to follow the conversation more easily, just less anxiety-ridden. I don't know how or why. I'm sorry, but that's all I can report. . . . But I was having none of the second injection, since it was a trick. Then the doctor's reassuring voice, and after I pondered awhile, agreed to take it. And again, nothing to report. I just realized I was back again in the real world, and began trying to describe my sensations.

Several other similar cases are described in Dr. Fabing's paper. Even the multicolored bugs, which one victim of *delirium tremens* saw crawling on the ceiling, yielded to the gentle influence of "Frenquel" and politely withdrew fifteen minutes after the patient had received an injection of the drug. It seems, however, to be curiously inconsistent in its action and has been described by Fabing as an "exasperating in-and-outer." It seems valuable in those cases where confusion or hallucination is the result of the action of some poison, and is useful for the treatment of senile patients who often go through troublesome confusional states. For the treatment of schizophrenics, however, it seems not to be in the same class with the great ataraxics, chlorpromazine and reserpine.

The other new ataraxic, meprobamate (trade names "Miltown" or "Equanil"), is a member of a group of chemicals classed as muscle relaxants, some of which also have sedative effects. In "Miltown" the tranquilizing action seems to predominate over the muscle-relaxing effect, though it is very probable that the two go hand in hand. It has been shown by several psychological studies that the condition we call "anxiety" is accompanied always by certain muscular tensions, indeed it is questionable whether anxiety could be experienced by any individual whose muscles were perfectly relaxed. It is exactly in this connection that "Miltown" is so effective. It promotes general muscle relaxation, which results in a reduction of tension, irritability, and restlessness. Tension headache, discomfort due to abdominal cramp, conversion hysteria, and the tremors of *paralysis agitans* may all be greatly relieved by this drug. Clinical tests by Drs. Selling and Borrus show that "Miltown" is remarkably non-toxic, for despite its muscle-relaxing qualities it does not seem to affect the heart or respiration. In short this is a valuable remedy for those lesser ailments of the spirit whose chief manifestations are anxious fear and inward tension. For the more major ailments, the hallucinations and delusions of schizophrenia for example, "Miltown" appears to be not so promising.

Before leaving the subject of agitation we should consider that error in the body's chemistry which results in the disorder called "thyrotoxicosis" or "Graves disease." This state is the direct consequence of a breakdown in the glandular harmony of the body. The sufferer from this complaint lives always beyond his emotional means. Constantly overactive, always on edge, with nerves which seem strained to the breaking point, flaring at the least provocation into outbursts of violent rage, these people are indeed a trial both to them-

selves and to others. In them the damper which controls the
rate of burning of their inner fire is always fully open. They
blaze inwardly at a fierce, unregulated pace, literally burning themselves up both emotionally and physically.

This troublesome condition results from an overproduction by the thyroid gland of a very vital hormone, thyroxine,
which is manufactured by this gland from iodine and trypto-
phane and stored in the form of thyroglobulin. This
thyroxine is intimately concerned with the rate at which our
whole metabolism operates, and normal intellectual function is impossible without it. Thus children born with in-
adequately developed thyroids will develop into cretins
unless the deficiency is made good by injections of the missing hormone. The amount of thyroxine liberated into the
blood from moment to moment is regulated by that master
hormone factory, the pituitary, which imposes its will on the
thyroid by means of yet another hormone, the "thyroid
stimulating hormone," T.S.H. for short. In the normal individual the output of thyroxine fluctuates and his vitality
and intellectual activity fluctuate with it. At moments of
low thyroxine output he feels somewhat soggy, dull, and
vacant but, as the level becomes still lower, one of those
typical feed-back mechanisms so vital in the regulation of
body and mind comes into play, stimulating the pituitary to
produce more T.S.H., which in turn stimulates the thyroid
to produce more thyroxine, whereat the dull eye brightens,
the flaccid facial muscles regain their tone, and the fog in the
brain disperses.

In the individual suffering from thyrotoxicosis, this feed-
back mechanism does not operate properly. The cause of
the trouble seems not to lie in the thyroid itself or even,
necessarily, in the pituitary, but rather in the hypothalamus,
that vital center in the brain so intimately bound up with

our emotional manifestations. Emotional stress very often seems to be involved in the production of thyrotoxicosis but, once established, it seems to supply its own emotional stresses, perpetuating itself by a kind of vicious circle. It seems, in fact, that in some susceptible individuals any extreme emotional stress—an unwelcome pregnancy, the death of a close relative, a robbery, a fire, a frightening sexual experience—can bring on this disease. Once the disease has started, it carries on as the result of a vicious circle, for the excessive production of thyroxine in itself produces a state of emotional turmoil which stimulates further production of the hormone.

A cure for this condition can be brought about by surgical removal of part or all of the thyroid gland, or its destruction by radioactive iodine. Neither procedure is ideal, for it may practically quench the fire of life so that the formerly frenzied thyrotoxic becomes apathetic to the point of being half dead. Drugs that prevent the formation of the thyroid hormone have now been discovered and are widely used in the treatment of this disease. Methimazole ("Trapazole") is perhaps the most widely used of these compounds. Methylthiouracil and propylthiouracil are also employed. The drugs tend to produce toxic reactions and dosage must be carefully regulated. It is suggested by Drs. Wittkower and Mandelbrote that this drug treatment should be accompanied by psychotherapy to help the patient to correct the emotional maladjustment which often underlies thyrotoxicosis

Passing to the opposite end of the psychological spectrum, the gloomy infrared of depression and melancholia, we must now consider remedies for these conditions. Melancholia, to use the time-honored name whose origin goes back to the days of Hippocrates, when the condition was thought to be due to an overproduction of black bile, is a much commoner condition than is generally realized. Dr. Howard Fabing, who describes himself as a "general practitioner of disorders of the nervous system," declares that he encounters four or five new cases of melancholia for every one of schizophrenia.

I have never gotten used to this disorder [he writes]. I am just amazed at a case I saw last week as those I saw as a student. Why or how can a normal hard-working, God-loving man or woman suddenly be thrown into a state of disturbed sleep and disordered mood which is completely disabling? I have seen this happen between a Tuesday and a Thursday. These people suddenly lose their power to concentrate their minds on the simplest activity such as reading the evening newspaper, they find all social intercourse painful and give up their friends, they believe that they are burdens on their loved ones, they develop the most illogical feelings of guilt and sin, and they quit eating. Unless something is done about them, suicide occurs all too frequently. I am just old enough to remember this torturing disorder before the shock therapies were introduced. Patients and their families crawled through months and even years waiting for the *vis medicatrix naturae,* the curative power of nature, to put these depressed minds back on the normal track again. Electroshock therapy has compressed these attacks into a matter of a few weeks, and depressed patients seldom gravitate to the back wards of state hospitals any more. But they are still with us; and although electroshock therapy is a blessing for most of them, the patients, their families and their doctors have never really liked this form of treatment. There is something assaultive and violent about it, try as we do to improve our techniques of administering it.

Dr. Fabing is an enthusiastic supporter of the chemical theory of the cause of melancholia. "There is surely something which goes awry in the patient's body chemistry in this strange illness." After stating that this is a challenge of the first magnitude for the neurochemist and neuropharmacologist, he declares that he, personally, will give a gold medal to the man who solves this riddle.

"What potions have I drunk of Siren tears, distilled from limbecs foul as hell within," writes Shakespeare who, to judge by certain passages in *Hamlet,* was personally familiar with every aspect of melancholia. The chemist must now try to reach that "foul alembic" and analyze its products, a task which is likely to tax his skill to the utmost. What shall he seek, where shall he seek it? Is melancholia also the result of an error in metabolism which leads to the production of a poison similar to the hypothetical "M" substance in schizophrenia? If so where shall we look for the poison? In blood, in urine, in lymph, in spinal fluid? But perhaps no poison is involved. Perhaps melancholia results simply from an imbalance of those potent hormones on whose quantitative relationships depend the inner harmonies of man's emotional life. This theory brings us back to the views of Hippocrates, who saw all illness as an imbalance (dyscrasia) between the four humors—blood, phlegm, yellow bile, and black bile. Alas, we have no such simple viewpoint now. If one speaks of hormones rather than humors it is probable that the number we must deal with is nearer forty than four. To trace disharmonies in an orchestra of so many members would be a hard task indeed. Not impossible, of course, but with the ridiculous pittance on which research in the field of mental illness is now expected to exist, progress will be slow indeed.

Since we cannot uncover the causes of melancholia our

quest for agents that will cure this condition has to be on a strictly trial-and-error basis. In the old days a good deal of reliance was placed on various weird concoctions known collectively as "nerve tonics." They generally contained iron, sometimes phosphates, sometimes a dash of strychnine or even arsenic. Small doses of strychnine, a poison which, in large doses, causes fearful convulsions, were thought to increase muscular tone, and it was argued that such an increase might restore the melancholic's zest for life. There is no evidence to suggest that strychnine has any value in this connection. It is a highly-dangerous substance best confined to rat poisons. As for the iron, the phosphates, and the arsenic, it is highly improbable that either melancholia or any other nervous disorder will be benefited by such agents. Where the cause of the trouble is anemia (and depression is often a by-product of this condition) the iron may help, though the vitamins folic acid and B_{12} are equally likely to be of importance. In such cases we treat not the depression itself but the anemia of which the depression is a by-product.

Far more specific in their action on the melancholy humor are various drugs belonging to the amphetamine group whose best-known member is amphetamine itself, more familiar to the public under its trade name of "Benzedrine." "Benzedrine" acts directly on the central nervous system. It stimulates, cheers, elevates, and enlivens. Its relative, "Dexedrine" is even more active in this respect Considerable studies have been carried out on this drug, especially on its use under war conditions to combat the fatigue that results from prolonged strain or effort Reifenstein and his coworkers reported progress of a depressed individual under the influence of this drug. He was, at the outset, "hopeless in his outlook and lacking ambition" An hour after taking the drug he became talkative and three hours later was feeling much better. On the fourth day he remarked that he was very happy, cheerful, and alert. On the sixth he was jovial, by the tenth he was singing and appeared to have reached approximately his normal state. The improvement, however, was not maintained and by the fourteenth day the depression began to return.

The same authors obtained favorable results in a case of catatonic schizophrenia in which the prevailing symptoms were dullness, listlessness, inactivity, and passivity. She refused to move or do anything for herself and had to be spoon-fed. She experienced delusions and auditory hallucinations. After two weeks of medication with "Benzedrine" the patient assisted with the ward work and applied herself well in occupational therapy, but was able to sleep only three hours at night and continued irritable, confused, and fearful of impending disaster. After the twenty-fifth day of medication the patient began to show definite improvement, became interested in her surroundings, was cheerful, friendly, and talked freely about herself. She remarked that she felt like a different person.

In the treatment of *delirium tremens* this drug also seems to have some value. The above writers describe a patient who "complained of visual hallucinations of snakes and worms four to eight feet long which he was pulling from his mouth, and of elephants which he saw on the wall." From delirium he lapsed into stupor but was aroused by medication with "Benzedrine." Several hours later he was cheerful and happy, stated that he felt very well, and was facetious and talkative. He was discharged ten days after admission completely recovered.

It appears from this that these "analeptic" drugs, as they are called, do have some value in the treatment of depressed states especially the condition called narcolepsy, in which the patient keeps falling asleep at inappropriate moments. But both "Benzedrine" and its close relative "Dexedrine" are apt to produce annoying side effects. For one thing they reduce appetite, so much so that "Dexedrine" is incorporated into several varieties of reducing pills. For another they tend to overstimulate the nervous system in such a way that sleep becomes difficult or impossible. On this account their use in the treatment of depression has been limited, the psychiatrist in most cases preferring to rely on E.C.T., the effects of which are more predictable.

More recently pipradrol, a close relative of "Frenquel," produced by its makers (Wm. S. Merrell Co.) under the name of "Meratran," has gained some fame as an "anti-melan-cholic." Dr. Howard Fabing found it a valuable drug, for it does not, as do the amphetamines, seriously reduce appetite or interfere with natural sleep. "On occasion the response of patients with reactive depression is sudden and dramatic, in that they note an elevation of mood and a quickening of their retarded psychomotor state within two hours after ingesting the first tablet." Similarly R. J. Amtos observed that "all subjects noted a 'lift' during the day without inter-ference with sleep. None of the subjects had the 'hepped up' feeling nor the appetite depression that they all noted with 5 mg. amphetamine."

That curious nervous disorder "narcolepsy," which may in some ways be allied to melancholia, also responds to medication with "Meratran." The disorder can be well illus-trated by one of Dr. Fabing's cases. A housewife began at the age of twenty to have attacks of narcoleptic sleep. She slept in the car, she slept in the cinema, she slept through the sermon, she slept while watching television. To keep awake she had to keep on the move, but even when on the move she sometimes became lost in a cataleptic trancelike state. So profound were these states that she would often cook a whole meal in a trance. Regular doses of "Meratran" relieved her of these symptoms but if she stopped taking the drug the symptoms recurred within forty-eight hours.

"Meratran" appears to be useful only in states of pure depression. Where depression is mixed with anxiety it tends to make the anxiety more severe. It appears that the drug stimulates the central nervous system by acting not at the level of the cortex but at the much lower level of the "old brain," known as the reticular system of the brain stem. It is this reticular system which, by alerting the cortex, causes us to awaken and keeps us awake. If this system is under-active various depressed conditions, such as narcoleptic sleep, emotional depression, general lethargy, "afternoon letdown," and a lack of interest in the world around us, may result. Underactivity at this brain level seems to be corrected by "Meratran," but if there is overactivity at this level the patient's condition is made worse by the drug. As Fabing puts it, "The manic patient becomes more excited, the deluded patient becomes more actively paranoid, an obsessive patient becomes more obsessive, an anxious pa-tient becomes more anxious, and an agitated patient be-comes more agitated." In short, to quote from Dr. W. Begg's article in the *British Medical Journal,* "The chief drawback to this drug's therapeutic usefulness is its tendency to exac-erbate pre-existing anxiety."

The newest of the analeptics at the time of writing (De-cember 1956) is methyl-phenidylacetate, another product of the Ciba laboratories marketed under the name "Ritalin." Dr. A. L. Natenshon, who studied the effect of the drug on 89 patients, has little but praise for this anti-depressant agent:

About an hour after taking the drug most patients noted the stimulating effect of the drug and this stimulation carried them for 4 or 5 hours. It gave a plateau type of stimulation, no sudden peaks, or sudden letdown, but the effects gradually tapered off with no rebound. This stimulation manifests itself to the patient by a feeling of well-being and being alive, no euphoria, but fatigue disappears and he goes along all day without being tired. There isn't the jitteriness, headache, nervousness or tense feeling which many patients feel when they take amphetamine drugs. It was noted in some that when bedtime came they felt alert and were unable to fall asleep. However, this was easily corrected by cutting the third dose in half, or if necessary eliminating the third dose and giving only two daily doses.

Natenshon administered the drug with good results to patients with cancer who had become depressed and suicidal on account of their condition. It proved useful also in resolving the depression of patients whose vitality had been left at a low ebb by winter infections. A few high-strung, extremely nervous, emotionally disturbed individuals were made worse by "Ritalin," but in such cases any form of stimulation may be expected to aggravate the already excessive tension.

The effect of "Ritalin" on schizophrenic patients has been determined by Dr. L. D. Clark and coworkers. It was found to have "modest but inconsistent analeptic properties" and in some cases reduced the tremors produced by chlorpromazine or reserpine. ". . . there was no evidence from these studies that it has special usefulness in the treatment of chronic schizophrenic patients."

On the whole it must be admitted that the ideal drug for the treatment of melancholia seems not yet to have been discovered. It is a hard problem for the pharmacologist, for one cannot produce melancholia in experimental animals. What we really need is a naturally melancholic guinea pig, the depth of whose gloom can be measured by some means or other. We could then try, by chemical agents, to restore its *joie de vivre*. But until someone devises such a beast the quest for the perfect anti-melancholic will be almost as problematical as was the hunting of the Snark.

We can now consider the impact which some of these newly discovered drugs have made on that complex, costly, and prolonged procedure loosely referred to as psychoanalysis. Behind the analyst, says Freud, stands the man with a syringe. Shall we now put all our faith in the syringe and forget about the analyst? It would be cheaper, easier, less time-consuming. Besides, there are never enough analysts to go round. How much simpler to dissolve one's complexes with a little chlorpromazine than to drag them out, bit by painful bit, from the muddy depths of the subconscious at an average cost of $20 per hour. What then are the prospects? Has the chemist made the analyst superfluous?

It is still far too early to answer this question. We can say, however, that the task of the therapist may be eased if he makes intelligent use of some of the chemical agents now available. Psychoanalysis is a procedure frequently rendered impossible by the inner fears of the patients which persistently "block" those very memories and damaging experiences from rising to the surface from the depths of the subconscious. In this way the health-giving cleansing or "catharsis" is prevented. It is this blocking which can to some extent be overcome by the judicious use of drugs, particularly such barbiturates as thiopental ("Pentathol"), which, for reasons known only to journalists, has been frequently referred to in the press as "truth serum." The drug is injected intravenously and, as it begins to take its effect, the tense, anxious, uncommunicative patient becomes more or less unguarded, receptive, friendly, and expansive. Unfortunately, this communicative stage lasts for a rather short time. As the action of the barbiturate continues the patient becomes increasingly drowsy and is apt to fall asleep on the analyst's couch, which makes the procedure highly unprofitable for the patient.

Attempting to overcome this difficulty, Drs. Rothman and Seward combined the soporific "Pentathol" with a stimulant of the "Benzedrine" type called methamphetamine, administering both drugs intravenously. This procedure decreased the excessive tension of the patient and at the same time promoted a state of alertness, spontaneity, and well-being. The isolation of the patient was broken down, a gate opened in the wall of fear and tension with which he had formerly been surrounded, wide enough for the analyst to squeeze through and establish contact. Sixteen patients formerly unanalyzable were thus rendered accessible for the first time. "Pharmacological psychotherapy enables the seemingly intractable patient—the 'excommunicated one'—to enter into a two-person relationship in which he can experience, often for the first time in his life, continuing communication, thanks to the benign interaction with another human being." This work is of great interest because it combines two drugs having pharmacologically opposite actions, one being a depressant, the other a stimulant. One might suppose that they would cancel one another's effects but this does not appear to be the case. Out of sixteen patients treated in this way thirteen showed slight to considerable improvement. The patients were "cushioned against the crippling effect of severe anxiety" and, at the

same time, experienced a "marked increase in drive, menta
alertness, and goal-oriented behavior." Thus they coul
communicate on a feeling level with less guilt and panic, n
longer immobilized by the dread of self-exposure or possibl
disintegration.

Another chemical key that has been used to unlock th
closed rooms of the mind is LSD, the hallucinogenic actio
of which has already been described. It seems strange tha
this potent drug, whose effect so closely resembles the symp
toms of schizophrenia, should prove of value in the psych
therapy of neuroses. Dr. R. A. Sandison and his colleagu
have tried it, however, and report favorably on its effec
when used under proper conditions:

> Our clinical impressions have convinced us that LSI
> *when used as an adjunct to skilled psychotherapy*, is of th
> greatest value in the obsessional and anxiety groups accor
> panied by mental tension. *We cannot emphasize too strongl*
> *however, that the drug does not fall into the group of "phy*
> *ical" treatments and that it should be used only by expei*
> *enced psychotherapists and their assistants.*

The aspect of the action of LSD which especially ir
pressed Dr. Sandison and his colleagues seems not to hav
been commented upon by others who have worked with th
drug. This is its capacity, at least in certain people, to brir
back into the mind forgotten childhood experiences. Th
experiences are not merely remembered in the ordinary wa
They are actually re-experienced. The body image of th
patient alters and he really feels himself transformed into
child. One patient, a woman twenty-nine years of ag
became a child of five or six, felt that her clothes were hu

and hanging about her, and when the doctor grasped her hand she felt her own to be as small as a child's.

In a series of experiences accompanied by intense emotion, she relived sexual assaults on her by a man during her childhood. She described a wood near her home where one of the incidents had taken place, even seeing the floor of the room apparently carpeted with wild plants and flowers. At the climax of this abreaction she told how the man repeatedly threatened to kill her if she told anyone about the occurrences. These events had been completely repressed but their emotional content was expressed in adult life in severe obsessional washing of the hands and genital region.

According to Dr. Sandison, LSD may bring up into the conscious mind of the patient those ancient primordial images which Jung has found to be part of the collective unconscious of the race. The snake, that great archetype which figures in so many myths from the plumed serpent of the Aztecs to the *nagas* of the Hindus, played a prominent role in many of the LSD experiences. One patient, in a state of deep depression and on the point of suicide, found the instinctive urges with which she had failed to come to terms entirely symbolized in these archaic forms:

I had the sensation as in my first LSD treatment of a snake curling up round me. I felt very sick and dizzy. I then began to see serpents' faces all over the wall—then I saw myself as a fat, pot-bellied snake slithering gaily away to destruction. I felt horrified and thought, "Whose destruction?" I then realized it was my own destruction—I was destroying myself. I seemed to be having a battle between life and death—it was a terrific struggle, but life won. I then saw myself on the treadmill of life—a huge wheel was going round and round with hundreds of people on it. Some were on top going confidently through life, others were getting jostled and trodden on but still struggling to go on living (I saw myself as one of these people) and then there were others who just couldn't cope with life and were being crushed to death in the wheel. I had another realization of how I was destroying myself—by carrying on this affair with this married man—how all the better side of me was gradually being destroyed through carrying on this affair and I knew it must cease and knew that I must never see him again. Also when I was watching myself as a snake going to destruction I cried for the Doctor because I wanted him to show me the right road away from self-destruction.

The Doctor came in and asked me how I felt and I told him that there were snakes everywhere. I had the sensation of being right in the middle of them. The Doctor asked me if it was like anything I had experienced before. I said it was a dream I had had as a child. He asked me if I knew what that dream represented and I said, "Sex." He said, "What sexual feelings could a small child of that age be having?" or words to that effect and I said, "I don't know." Actually at that minute I was right back as a small child with moving grass all round me and I could see snakes slithering through the grass. The whole atmosphere was as it had been when sexual incidents occurred with boys when I was about six or seven.

I then had the feeling of being back in ancient Egypt lying at the bottom of a well with high walls round and Egyptian faces all round the walls and something hovering over me. I said to the Doctor, "Something terrible is going to happen to me"—I felt as though a huge whitish snake was hovering over the top of me and might drop on me at any moment.

Then I had the feeling that I was the Devil—I could see my long, pointed tail curling round the back of the Doctor. I thought, "Poor Doctor, he doesn't know he is sitting with the Devil!"

After the Doctor had gone I had a vision of myself in Hell —of being dragged out by chains—the Doctor and other people were pulling me out and I was very reluctant to come out. I had all sorts of queer dizzy feelings, of patterns and colours all whizzing round in circles and I felt very tired but also a sense of happiness—as though I had sorted out quite a lot of problems under this LSD. I again felt that this was the treatment for me and my only way back to normality, but I also felt the need and presence of God. I felt that although the Doctor was helping me to get well through LSD, we all needed God's help above anything else. I had a vision of life as a dark murky pool and saw myself dipping my toes in gingerly with first one man then another, of being urged on by some of them to go down into the pool with them but I kept drawing back—I just had to wait for the right man to experience the pool of life with. I felt very tired all day but extremely happy and I laughed a lot. Colours looked very vivid and beautiful to me as though I were seeing them clearly for the first time.

I had the sensation of the jig-saw puzzle which I have had in each LSD treatment, but this time there were no pieces missing. All the pieces were there but not quite in line—it seemed as though it needed one jolt and all the pieces would fit in together and I should be well again. I thought, "I had better have a dose of E.C.T. and see if that will shake the jig-saw into place." I had a vision of myself and all my fears —I realized that I was afraid of being afraid—afraid of fear itself, which is surely much worse than being afraid of something tangible.

I didn't sleep that night—about 1 A.M. I had another sensation of watching myself. I was out of hell—standing on the brink and I was perfectly pure. I felt that I might be drawn back in again so I made myself run away. However, I was drawn back and looked down into Hell, and there was my snake still down in Hell. I jumped back into Hell—right into the snake's mouth and became the snake. Then I started the ascent out of Hell, but it was a terrific struggle—I seemed to be carrying a huge weight but I kept struggling to get out. Then I felt a snake biting my tail—then I realized I was biting my own tail and eating myself up. The struggle to get out of Hell was too great and I thought, "Oh, well, it isn't such a bad Hell after all," and curled up in Hell and went to sleep.

In another of Dr. Sandison's cases, a woman whose various personal difficulties had led "to a progressive severing of all human ties and emotional relationships until she was faced with despair and suicide," began to recover her zest for life under the influence of the drug.

As far back as I can remember, even into childhood, there has been something lacking in my life, no spark, a feeling of not really being here, incomplete. Since having my first LSD at times, all of me has come alive, I have really lived and been aware of everything about me. I have been able to know and express my emotions, a great sense of freedom of mind and spirit.

In this particular case the patient encountered her own emotional difficulties in the form of a spider, "a huge, ugly terrifying and menacing animal quite out of her control." As the LSD treatments continued, however, she developed the capacity to be aware simultaneously of both conscious and subconscious minds. She felt herself divided into two, one part watching the other, an experience often described by those that have taken mescaline.

Sometime after this I found myself inside a cell of my subconscious mind. It contained my spider, no longer alert and frightening and vivid, but tired, beaten and almost dead, it looked pathetic. With the spider there were thoughts and feelings and from these, the conscious person, myself, sitting on the bed, had to learn a lesson. It was a most peculiar sensation. I found that my conscious self "A" was speaking to my subconscious self "B." "A" was learning and speaking the lesson, "B" was teaching it by sending out waves of thoughts and feelings. "A" spoke the following words— "The love I felt"—at this "B" sent a wave of pure love pulsing through my body—"The tears I shed"—a strong feeling of emotion came to my throat and tears to my eyes—"The pain"—with this a terrific weight on my body. At this point I got confused, "A" substituted the words "unhappiness" and "burden" for pain, but "B" did not seem satisfied with any of these words. All the above was repeated again and again, always getting confused at "the pain." Eventually I cried because I was unable to understand and learn my lesson. I came out of my subconscious and sat on the bed thinking about what had just happened. I realized that I had been in the cell of memory containing my mother's death, that in it were the mistakes I had made at that time and from it I could learn a very valuable lesson. I decided to try again, but though I tried with all my power of mind to learn the lesson, I could not, the words, the feelings and meanings were all there but I was too tired to hold them together. I lay down and cried with disappointment and exhaustion. Later I re-

alized that the room and everything it contained was dripping with tears, and that I was crying inside my throat
though not from my eyes as it all had been earlier in the day.
This continued until about 4 P.M.

In both the cases described above the outcome was satisfactory. The drug, by its curious action on the deeper levels
of the mind, enabled the patient to reach those buried
regions which had proved inaccessible to psychotherapy
alone. The treatment appears to be of particular value in
obsessional neurotics in whom damaging memories are particularly strongly repressed. In such cases the memory is
often so deeply repressed and detached from consciousness
that it cannot at first be recognized when resurrected by
LSD. Such a memory may be brought out in serial form,
each treatment bringing further details into consciousness.
As many as forty treatments were found necessary in some
cases. The authors caution that improvement should not be
expected immediately.

We have been greatly impressed by this surging up of repressed experiences which has caused some of the most intense abreactions we have ever seen but it would be a mistake to suppose that all such experiences bring about an
immediate cessation of neurotic symptoms. Obsessional neurotics, in particular, may be made worse for a time. For these
patients, in whom the mechanism of repression is so strong,
everything depends on whether they can come to terms with
their repressed memories as they emerge into consciousness.
This is not always possible, but we can definitely claim that
LSD-25 is of the greatest value to the classical obsessional
neurotic. Provided treatment is sufficiently prolonged, our
results suggest that most cases will be relieved or cured.

Before we leave the subject of the sick minds mention should be made of that much-misunderstood ailment, epilepsy. This illness, so dramatic in its manifestations, has occupied the attention of physicians from the earliest times. In the days of Hippocrates it was known as the "Sacred Disease," a concept which aroused the scorn of the Father of Medicine who, with his usual common sense, rejected the idea "that the body of man can be polluted by a god." He wrote a treatise on epilepsy and announced, with an insight surprising for the times, that "its origin, like that of other diseases, lies in heredity." By the Jews, however, it was regarded as a form of demonic possession as may be seen from the well-known passage in the Gospels: "And lo, a spirit taketh him, and he suddenly crieth out, and it teareth him that he foameth again, and bruising him hardly departeth from him."

One can hardly feel surprised that the ancients attributed the disease to the work of an evil spirit, for an attack of the most violent type of epilepsy ("grand mal") is always a distressing experience for those who witness it. The sufferer may be aware in advance of the approaching fit, for the "aura" occurs in many cases just before the trouble develops. In such a case the victim can at least lie down and avoid the risk of falling and hurting himself. Often, however, as in the Gospel story, there is no advance warning. The storm bursts suddenly and, with a violent shriek, the epileptic falls to the ground. This shriek sounds like a scream of pain and is liable to strike horror into the hearts of those who hear it. Actually it has nothing to do with pain. The epileptic is already unconscious as he utters the cry, which is produced by the violent contractions of muscles in the throat and chest.

As the seizure develops these violent contractions spread

to the other muscles. The jaw is clenched. The muscles of the chest become rigid. Breathing ceases and the face becomes red or purple, the veins standing out like cords on temples and forehead. During these "tonic convulsions" the normal reflexes are abolished. The pupils dilate widely and become insensitive to light. Saliva and perspiration pour from the body and the body pressure rises sharply. Then, with the passing of the "tonic phase," air is sucked violently into the oxygen-starved lungs and foam, often flecked with blood from bitten lips or tongue, is blown from the mouth. Now the whole body becomes shaken with shocklike "clonic" jerks. The bowels and bladder are often violently evacuated and the limbs are bathed in an evil-smelling sweat. Finally, the bewildered epileptic recovers consciousness and looks about him in confusion. His attack is often followed by heavy sleep, by vomiting, headache, muscular soreness, or depression. In exceptionally severe cases one convulsion follows another without intervening periods of consciousness. This is the so-called "status epilepticus," a serious condition which may prove fatal.

A more gentle form of epilepsy is the "petit mal" or "little illness" (for some strange reason the medical profession insists on talking French when describing this disease!). It is characterized by momentary loss or impairment of consciousness which may be accompanied by certain peculiar movements. The rather alarming convulsions which are characteristic of "grand mal" do not occur in "petit mal." These lapses of consciousness may happen several times a day and occur most frequently in adolescence. In later life they may disappear spontaneously. Another form of epilepsy, the psychomotor type, involves confusion which may last from a few seconds to hours. During this condition the patient is out of touch with his environment but may continue to perform purposeful acts. When the confusion passes he has no recollection of anything that happened during the seizure.

It is in connection with epilepsy that that wonderful instrument, the electroencephalograph, has given us so much information. All the outward symptoms of epilepsy are the direct results of an electrical storm in the brain. The storm begins with violent electrical discharges from a small group of neurones. This violence, like panic in a densely packed crowd, spreads to the other neurones until in a few seconds the whole great mass of the cortex is discharging in unison. These massive discharges, registered by the pen of the electroencephalograph, are so distinctive that the veriest amateur can spot them. Each kind of epilepsy shows its own kind of disturbed brain wave. The three-per-second "dome and spike" of "petit mal" are entirely different from the eight-per-second spikes of "grand mal" which, in turn, differ from the slow waves of the psychomotor seizure. Oddly enough these abnormal brain waves may occur in people who have never had an epileptic fit. They have, however, a tendency to the disease and, if exposed to certain stimuli, such as a flickering light flashing at a critical rate per second, may develop the outward symptoms of epilepsy.

Few ailments have yielded more dramatically to the combined attack of the modern chemist and pharmacologist than has epilepsy. Research on the disease was made possible by the discovery that convulsions typical of epilepsy could be induced in cats by passing an electric current through their heads. Here was a tool which could be used for the mass screening of chemical substances for anti-convulsive activity. It was seized upon by Merritt and Putnam of Parke, Davis, who tested seven hundred chemicals for their ability to prevent such artificially induced fits, and emerged triumphantly with diphenylhydantoin ("Dilantin"). "Dilantin" differs from the bromides and such barbiturates as phenobarbital, both of which have been used in the treatment of epilepsy, in not rendering the patient drowsy. It appears to act by preventing the spread through the brain of that "electrical storm" of which the convulsions and unconsciousness are the outward and visible signs. "Dilantin" is effective against "grand mal" and psychomotor epilepsy. Complete relief from seizures is generally experienced by 60 to 65% of patients suffering from "grand mal" and in 20% the number and severity of convulsions are reduced. For those afflicted with "petit mal" another drug, trimethadoine ("Tridione"), is available. It will generally keep the patient completely free from seizures. In addition to these two agents several other anti-convulsants are on the market. Their names are legion: "Mesantoin," "Mysolin," "Miltonin," "Hibicon," "Diamox," "Paradione," "Phenurone," "Gemonil," "Peganone." If one proves ineffectual the physician can always try another. In this particular disease he has a remarkably wide choice of remedies.

Unfortunately for the epileptic, public education has not kept pace with these triumphs of the pharmacologist. The old horror which, in the past, was associated with epilepsy is still far too prevalent today and the epileptic suffers more from public ostracism than he does from his illness. In actual fact even "grand mal" epilepsy need not interfere too seriously with the life of the individual who suffers from it. Epileptics are frequently perfectly normal intellectually. They may be outstanding. Dostoevsky and Julius Caesar both suffered from the disease. With modern medication it is generally possible to prevent the development of convulsions. Even when they cannot be prevented there is no reason why one who suffers them should be treated as a leper. His ailment actually, except in extreme cases, is no more serious than migraine or dysmenorrhea. Obviously one prone to epileptic seizures should not work with dangerous machinery or drive a car but otherwise there is no reason why he should not perform a useful function in society. If he happens to develop a fit it is merely necessary to loosen his clothing, prevent him from hurting himself, and put a gag in his mouth to stop him from biting his tongue. Horror and disgust will not help him and are not called for. There are about 1,000,000 epileptics in the United States, the majority of whom can perform a useful function if society will let them and abandon its rather medieval attitude toward this disease.

[NOTE: Recently an immense amount of research has been devoted to discovering other substances like iproniazid ("Marsilid") which Dr. Nathan Kline defined as a psychic energizer. Substances in this group have one thing in common. They inhibit the action of an enzyme called monoamide oxidase which plays a role in the inactivation of adrenalin. Substances having this action are often quite active anti-depressants and a number of new ones have now appeared on the market under such trade names as "Catron," "Nardil," and "Niamid." "Deaner," another new anti-depressant, belongs in a somewhat different chemical category. At this time (October 1959) it is too early to say just how valuable these new drugs are going to prove.]

Brews Strange and Brews Familiar

A number of drug plants remain to be described, some of which, like tea and coffee, are so familiar that almost everyone has experienced their effects, whereas others, like *caapi* or *ololiuqui*, are so rare that only a few specialists have ever heard of them. All these plants exert some effect on mind or emotions, some having an influence so gentle that it is scarcely perceived, others acting so violently that their effect produces what appears to be raving madness. These various brews can be divided into two groups. Those dependent for their action mainly on caffein, such as tea, coffee, *guarana*, will be described first; accounts of the less-known brews will follow.

It is fitting that we begin these descriptions with the story of coffee, a drug whose hold on the American people is so powerful that, in the year 1953, they swallowed the watery extract of 21,000,000 bags of coffee beans. Coffee is not a very ancient drug; compared with cannabis and opium, it is a newcomer. Just when and how the virtues of the bean were discovered we have no way of knowing, but fantasy has supplied the information which history fails to provide.

Among the Arabs and Persians it is related that coffee was
brought to earth by the Archangel Gabriel, and that this
august spirit presented a brew of the beans to the Prophet
Mahomet, who derived much benefit and comfort there-
from. Others declare that the Mufti, Jemal-ed-din Dhabhani,
learned about the drug while traveling on the west coast of
the Red Sea. He brought some home with him to Aden,
whence pilgrims carried it to Mecca and the rest of Arabia.
Faustus Nairo, however, declares that the Prior of a certain
Mahometan monastery was told by his shepherds that goats
which had eaten the beans of the coffee plant gamboled
about all night. He decided to use the beans to help him
and his dervishes keep awake during the long night prayers
in the mosque. The beverage was called *kahweh*—that which
stimulates.

No sooner did coffee become popular in the East than it
brought down upon itself, as usual, the wrath of various
officious characters who declared it to be the very brew of
the Devil and did everything they could to suppress its use.
In fact the "coffee bugaboo" in sixteenth-century Egypt
caused almost as much fuss as has the "marihuana bugaboo"
in contemporary United States. Sale of coffee was prohibited;
wherever stocks of coffee were found they were burned.
Those who were convicted of having drunk coffee were led
through the town mounted on a donkey; its use was declared contrary to the spirit of the Koran. All this fuss only
had the result of interesting more people in the brew and
its use spread steadily. Finally all laws against it were re-
pealed, in fact so far did the pendulum swing in the opposite direction that a Turkish law proclaimed that refusal
of a husband to give his wife coffee was legal grounds for
divorce.

By 1551 coffee had triumphed in Asia Minor, Syria, and

Persia and was enjoyed by almost the entire population. Knowledge of the drink penetrated slowly into Europe and it was not until 1643 that the first coffeehouse was established in Paris. The habit, once established, spread swiftly. In 1690 there were two hundred and fifty coffeehouses, in the reign of Louis XV six hundred had been established, and by 1782 there were eighteen hundred. In America the first coffeehouse appears to have been located in Boston in 1689 and was known as the "London Coffee House." The "Merchants Coffee House" in New York was started in 1743. In all the main cities of both Europe and America coffeehouses sprang up and became the natural meeting places for wits, wags, poets, and philosophers, a very appropriate tribute to the drug whose fascination depends upon the fact that it stimulates the brain.

As for the culture of coffee, it has spread to such an extent that scarcely a single country in the tropics fails to produce it in one form or another It grows in Arabia, India, Java, Malaya, Guatemala, El Salvador, Colombia, and Costa Rica. As for Brazil, it is difficult to decide whether coffee has been that country's blessing or its greatest curse, so totally has its economy come to depend on a little brown bean which, delightful as its properties may be, is nonetheless an utterly needless luxury So great has been the overproduction in Brazil that, in the ten-year period ending in 1940, 68,000,000 bags had to be destroyed. Recently a sudden scarcity caused prices to rise to the astronomical level of $1.30 per pound so that even the American coffee addict seriously considered turning to tea. Now, with prices falling again, Brazil once more faces difficulties. It is hard to build a stable economy on coffee beans.

Older than coffee and with an origin even more romantically improbable is the tea plant, *Camellia thea.** This plant is reliably stated to have sprung not from seed but from the venerable eyelids of the Buddhist saint, Bhodidharma. This saint, who brought Buddhism to China and was the originator of the Zen sect, arrived in China in the year A.D. 519. Living constantly under the open sky, mortifying his flesh, and mastering his passions, the saint finally vowed to meditate for ten years without closing his eyes in sleep. After two years sleep overcame him and his eyes closed. Filled with disgust at having been unable to fulfill his vow, he cut off the offending eyelids and threw them away. Where they fell there sprang up two plants from the leaves of which the saint prepared a brew of which he drank with pleasure. Soon he experienced a feeling of renewed alertness and was able to plunge once again into his contemplation of the ultimate. The delightful beverage of which he had partaken was tea.

This fragrant product of the eyelids of Bhodidharma soon found its way into homes and temples in every part of the East. In Japan the consumption of tea became not so much a form of indulgence as a way of life, inseparably connected with the refinements of Buddhist philosophy, with the worship of balance, harmony, and inward perfection. A gentle humor blended with a noble philosophy reached its highest form in the Japanese tea ceremony. No one has ever expressed this spirit more vividly than Okakura-Kakuzo who, besides being an authority on tea, wrote English prose with the stylistic skill of Charles Lamb:

> The heaven of modern humanity is indeed shattered in the cyclopean struggle for wealth and power. The world is groping in the shadow of egotism and vulgarity. Knowledge is

* Originally called *Thea sinensis* by Linnaeus.

brought through a bad conscience, benevolence practiced for the sake of utility. The East and West, like two dragons tossed in a sea of ferment, in vain try to regain the jewel of life. We need a Niuka again to repair the grand devastation, we await the great Avatar. Meanwhile let us have a sip of tea. The afternoon glow is brightening the bamboos, the fountains are bubbling with delight, the soughing of the pines is heard in our kettle. Let us dream of evanescence, and linger in the beautiful foolishness of things.

The proper mode of making tea was described by the tea masters of China, especially in a three-volume work of the Tang poet Luwuh. Water should be chosen from a mountain spring, heated with discrimination in a suitable kettle. There are three stages of boiling: the first stage is when little bubbles like the eyes of fish swim on the surface; the second boil is when bubbles are like crystal beads rolling in a fountain; the third boil is when the billows surge wildly in the kettle. Cake-tea is roasted before the fire until it becomes soft like a baby's arm and is shredded into powder between pieces of fine paper. A little salt is put in the first boil and the tea in the second with a dipper of cold water to revive "the youth of the water." The beverage was poured into cups and drunk. O nectar! The filmy leaflets hung like scaly clouds in a serene sky or floated like water lilies on emerald streams. Such a brew inspired the writings of the poet Lotung:

The first cup moistens my lips and throat, the second breaks my loneliness, the third cup searches my barren entrails but to find therein some five thousand volumes of odd ideographs. The fourth cup raises a slight perspiration—all the wrong of life passes away through my pores. At the fifth cup I am purified, the sixth cup calls me to the realms of the immortals. The seventh cup—ah, but I could take no more! I only feel the breath of cool wind that rises in my sleeves. Where is Elysium? Let me ride on this sweet breeze and waft away thither.

Tea culture is more or less confined to Asia. There is no particular reason why it should be. The plant is not so frost-sensitive that it has to be grown in the tropics; in fact there was once a tea plantation in South Carolina. It failed not because the tea plants died but because its culture proved economically impossible. Tea is one crop that never has been and never will be harvested mechanically. Though, when left to itself, the tea tree attains a height of thirty to forty feet, it is so constantly pruned in the plantations that it rarely rises above three feet in height. The leaves must be picked individually and with discrimination, for excessive removal of leaves would kill the shrub. Picking is therefore continuous and is done by women and children whose understanding of the niceties of tea picking is almost instinctive, they having lived among tea plants practically since birth. Tea of fabulous value is prepared in China from the buds and tenderest leaves, a distinguished product once reserved for the emperor, now used to lend distinction to the more expensive blends. Leaves from lower down the stem go into ordinary tea and the oldest and coarsest leaves are used in cheap mixtures. Expert tea tasters can recognize hundreds of grades of manufactured tea, from the most delicate green teas to those coarse brews that resemble in taste and color a decoction of shoe leather, for, like shoe leather, tea contains much tannin which is drawn from the leaf by prolonged and careless stewing.

There is much of both art and science in the manufacture

and blending of tea. Black or "Indian" teas are prepared from leaves that have been allowed to wilt in the sun. The leaves are then twisted and rolled to release enzymes and the heap undergoes a process of natural fermentation in the course of which many substances responsible for flavor and aroma are generated. This fermentation is abruptly halted at the correct moment by the application of heat. The moist, twisted leaves are carefully dried and are then ready for shipment. Green tea is heated before the fermentation has set in, the leaves being shaken in pans in much the same way as coffee is roasted. Special fragrant teas are prepared by adding to tea in the course of manufacture various scented flowers such as those of orange, jasmine, rose, or *Osmanthus fragrans.*

Tea made its appearance in the West during the sixteenth century, a rare, exotic, and fabulously expensive luxury, the costly gift of kings, princes, and lords. Its use spread rapidly as its price declined. In England its consumption became almost as much a ceremony as did tea drinking among the Japanese. The habit of interrupting the day's work for afternoon tea has been a national custom ever since it was introduced by the Duchess of Bedford in the early nineteenth century. Consumption of tea in Britain is prodigious. Its popularity in the United States has never rivaled that of coffee, though its use is increasing.

Cocoa, the third beverage in this group, also has romantic origins. In the court of the Aztec monarch Montezuma a drink was prepared, the name of which was *chocolatl.* It was prepared from the seeds of a certain tree which were ground up and mixed with pepper and other plants, a foul-tasting, bitter brew beaten up into a frothy mass. "From time to time they brought him, in cup-shaped vessels of pure gold, a certain drink made from cacao, which he took when he was going to visit his wives." Apparently, like saffron and damiana and a number of other plant substances, cocoa enjoyed in the Aztec court the reputation of being an aphrodisiac. Never was reputation less deserved. There is nothing whatever in cocoa that could, by any stretch of the imagination, be construed as having any effect on sexual desire. It is highly probable that Montezuma's pick-me-up would have been totally forgotten by posterity, for it was so bitter that even pirates would not drink it, had it not happened that some nuns in Chiapas discovered the magical effect of serving powdered chocolate liberally mixed with sugar and vanilla. So popular did this drink become that the ladies of Chiapas could not consume enough of it but had to have it served to them in church. The priests, aware of its reputation as an aphrodisiac, had no hesitation in describing it as a "violent inflamer of the passions" and in attributing to its intemperate consumption much of the moral laxity of the age. It is amusing to think that this mild and muddy beverage managed for more than a century to carry such a flamboyant reputation. In the early eighteenth century chocolate became very popular in London and such wits as Addison and Steele spent much of their time in White's or the Cocoa Tree, which became the first and most aristocratic club in England. So greatly was chocolate appreciated that the great Linnaeus, casting about for an appropriate name for the cocoa tree, gave it the generic name of *Theobroma*, "food for the gods."

The cocoa tree is extraordinary in one respect. Like the familiar Forsythia, it bears its flowers on the main stem and the reddish pods which contain the cocoa beans hang from the tree trunk in a most unnatural manner. The tree grows best in moist tropical climates, much of it being produced on the Gold Coast of Africa. After harvesting, the cocoa beans are removed from the husks, placed in boxes or pits and allowed to ferment, dried and roasted. The product is called "cocoa nibs." Apart from their active principles, which will be described later, these cocoa nibs contain as much as 50 per cent fat which, when expressed, constitutes cocoa butter. In chocolate manufacture the nibs are ground between heated stones and the resulting paste, mixed with sugar, milk, or both, is shaped into suitable forms in chilled molds. This chocolate, though long ago deprived of its lurid reputation as an aphrodisiac, still represents something of a menace to the American girl, whose concern for her figure exceeds, in some cases, her concern for her virtue. Chocolate is, in fact, an extremely rich source of calories. As the United States Dispensatory points out, 3⅓ ounces of chocolate represents between 500 and 600 calories, whereas a mutton chop of the same weight would represent only about 250 calories. Cocoa used for drinking differs from chocolate in having been deprived of a large proportion of its fat, and its caloric value, as a result, is much less than that of chocolate.

The remaining plants belonging to this group need be mentioned only briefly. *Kola* is a nut, native to tropical Africa, product of a tree, *Cola nitida*, which in some ways resembles an apple tree. Like tea and coffee, the *kola* has its quota of legends. It was, so the story goes, laid aside by the Creator when He was last on earth and absent-mindedly left in the Garden of Eden. Adam seized and began to chew the morsel despite the protests of Eve, who objected to his tasting this "food of God." Adam swallowed the *kola* and was promptly seized by the indignant Deity, the pressure of whose fingers caused him to regurgitate. To this day every man bears on his throat a swelling (the Adam's apple) that marks the pressure of the fingers of a wrathful Deity deprived of His *kola*.

Kola nuts are highly valued in Africa and in places are used as currency. On the banks of the Niger a slave can be bought for a few nuts. Symbolically the nut enters into many aspects of the lives of these people. A proposal of marriage is accompanied by a gift of white *kola*, a refusal by red nuts. Oaths are sworn on the *kola* nut, friendships and hostilities are symbolized by *kola*, and some nuts are even buried with the dead. When a girl is married *kola* nuts must always be included in the dowry.

This devotion to the nut is, of course, a reflection of its pharmacological properties. The native chews his *kola* or prepares from it a beverage which he imbibes with the aid of a reed. Soon his fatigue disappears, his brain becomes active, his muscles, previously weary, seem charged with new strength. This effect is not confined to natives of Africa. Europeans who have used the *kola* nut during strenuous climbs in the Alps also report an increase in muscular energy. Physical strength is augmented without the intervention of the will. Movement is facilitated and the output of the muscles is increased. Even horses, according to Lewin, show an increased output of work when fed on *kola*. In Africa it is also reputed to act as a sexual stimulant.

Another drug belonging to this group is *guarana*, used by the savage tribes inhabiting the basin of the Amazon, the Madeira, and the Orinoco. Manes and Manduru Kus of the lower and middle Tapajós collect in October the dark brown seeds of a tropical climber, *Paullinia cupana*, which they grind and form into a paste with water, then carefully dry by suspending cylinders of the paste in wood smoke. Dried *guarana* paste is brown as chocolate and hard as stone. It is transported down the swift rivers and finds its way into

commerce, for the use of *guarana* is widespread in Bolivia
and Matto Grosso. Many Bolivians drink the beverage on
awakening and can scarcely face the day's work without it.
For consumption the hard cylinders of paste are scraped on
a grater generally prepared from the hard palate of the
piraracu, a kind of fish. The scrapings are added to a glass of
sweetened water and then swallowed. Stimulation follows,
for *guarana* contains more caffein than any other plant
source, having sometimes as much as 5 per cent compared
with 2 per cent in coffee or *kola*.

We can now consider what makes these beverages so at-
tractive. Why is the American's appetite for coffee, the Eng-
lishman's thirst for tea, the African's craving for *kola* so
potent a passion? The answer is that caffein, which all these
substances contain, has such comforting properties that the
popularity of caffein-containing beverages is more or less
inevitable. Caffein is not a complex chemical substance and
does not, correctly speaking, belong to the group of alkaloids, so many of which have valued medicinal properties.
Chemically it is a purine, a group of nitrogen-containing
substances of vital importance to the economy of the body.
It acts on the higher levels of the brain, the cerebral cortex,
to produce a gentle, agreeable stimulation. Thoughts flow
more clearly, sensations are more keenly appreciated. The
deathly drowsiness and clinging pessimism which enfold
many people around three o'clock in the afternoon are dispersed by the drug as the sun disperses fog. Furthermore the
drug increases muscular capacity while at the same time dis-
sipating the sense of fatigue. The weary typist, with a cup
of strong coffee inside her, finds her fingers dancing over the
keys with renewed nimbleness.

All these gifts are conferred by this beneficent drug without any dangerous secondary effects. Caffein does not

258 Drugs and the Mind

threaten its devotees with madness as does cocaine, with inebriation as does alcohol, with slavery as does morphine. Gentle, elevating, and singularly non-toxic, it acts so imperceptibly that many who take it barely recognize its effect. True it is that a few hypersensitive individuals find themselves sleepless if they drink coffee before bedtime, but for them the remedy would seem to be obvious enough. Others with peptic ulcers may find it harmful, for caffein certainly augments gastric secretion in man. It is also diuretic, definitely enhancing the flow of urine. It is not suitable for administration to children. A child's metabolism is, in most cases, already lively enough and, under the influence of this drug, may become entirely too active for the good of the child or the peace of his parents. Though a puritan might represent the American's reliance on coffee as a "drug habit," no legislator as yet has come forward with the suggestion that coffee be banned. This may seem surprising in view of the passion for prohibitions which runs through so much American legislation; coffee, however, is as sacred in the United States as the coca leaf was sacred to the Incas. Woe to him who raises his hand against it!

As for tea and cacao, they contain theophylline and theobromine in addition to caffein. Both substances are closely related to caffein but their action on the body differs in several respects. Theophylline is less stimulating to the central nervous system than is caffein but has a more powerful action on the heart. It causes a widening of the coronary artery, that vital blood vessel which supplies the heart itself and the blockage of which so often brings death or disablement in the form of coronary thrombosis. It is also a more powerful diuretic than caffein but the duration of its action is relatively short. Theobromine, found predominantly in cocoa, is in every respect less active than caffein and theophylline.

Among the milder beverages capable of lifting the burden of care, soothing the mind and stomach, and generally lightening the darker horizons of the soul, mention should be made of that sacred drink of the South Seas known in New Guinea as *keu*, in Fiji as *kava-kava* and in Hawaii as *ava*. The excellent qualities of this drink are all too little appreciated, nor is it easy to understand why this modest gift of the "Islands of Paradise" has been ignored by the whites who have done so much to transform these paradises into squalid little hells. The missionaries, with their usual passion for depriving Nature's children of their simple pleasures, did all they could to suppress the use of *kava* in the South Seas, with the result that this harmless brew was rapidly replaced with the more destructive alcohol, often consumed in the form of hair tonic or, worse still, as "methylated spirits."

Actually *kava* is the most harmless of drinks, completely incapable of driving its devotees to those deeds of violence and crime so common in the islands among those natives who partake of alcohol. *Kava*, declares Lewin, who was the first European scientist to appreciate its properties, never generates in those who drink it angry, aggressive, noisy, or disgusting manifestations. If the beverage is properly prepared it produces a gentle stimulation, refreshing the fatigued body, brightening and sharpening the intellectual facilities. A state of happy contentment and well-being appears, without any physical or mental excitement. Reason and consciousness remain unaffected. Excessive indulgence in *kava* brings on a pleasant somnolence leading to sleep which may last from two to eight hours but which is not followed by a hangover. The amount that must be taken to produce this somnolence is very large.

The mode of preparation of *kava-kava* in Tonga is not calculated to attract the dainty or the hygienic. Young men and girls with good teeth are specially selected to prepare the *kava* for the feast. Solemnly and slowly they take the cut-up roots in their mouths and rhythmically chew to the accompaniment of gently throbbing drums. No one is permitted to swallow the juice which accumulates in the mouth. The chewed roots are then placed in a wooden bowl which holds from one to two gallons. The chief in charge of the ceremony adds the correct amount of water, kneads and stirs the liquid with his hands, and solemnly appeals to the gods and the departed spirits. Each native then presents his receptacle, generally a half coconut shell, which is filled with the *kava* beverage and solemnly emptied to the accompaniment of special rites. The taste of the brew, according to Lewin, varies a great deal according to the mode of preparation and may be bitter or insipid, hot, aromatic, soapy, or astringent.

Kava is produced from the rhizome of a plant belonging to the pepper family, *Piper methysticum*. Little is known about the identity of the chemical substance from which its pharmacological activity is derived. The activity seems to reside in a resin named kawine which has local anesthetic properties and deadens the sense of taste. The substance would seem worthy of further study.

Turning now to Mexico, we find that, besides the *peyotl* described in an earlier chapter, two other drug plants have been used since the days of the Aztecs, both of which exert a peculiar effect on the mind. These plants are *teonanacatl*, the sacred mushroom, and *ololiuqui*, known among the

Mazatecs as "the flower of the Virgin." *Teonanacatl* belongs to the group of fungi which favor cow pats as their place of growth. During the rainy season from June to September it sprouts out of the pat, its dome-shaped cap borne on a long slender stalk. It is eagerly gathered by the Mazatec Indians and dried for future use. According to that eminent botanist, R. E. Schultes, there are professional divinators who earn a livelihood by endeavoring, while intoxicated with *teonanacatl*, to locate stolen property, discover secrets, give advice. Usually about fifteen of the mushrooms are consumed, overdoses of fifty or sixty resulting in poisoning, and continued use of large quantities producing insanity. A general feeling of exhilaration and well-being is experienced soon after the mushrooms have been eaten. This state of exhilaration is followed by hilarity, incoherent talking, and fantastic visions in brilliant colors similar to those produced by *peyotl*. It appears that the Mazatec divinators pay rather a high price for their indulgence in this mildly poisonous mushroom. They are said to age rapidly and even at the age of thirty-five have the appearance of old men.

Very recently an account of the effects of *teonanacatl* has been published by Mr. Gordon Wasson, an authority on the more exotic varieties of fungi, who, penetrating the heart of the Mixteco mountains, took part in the ceremony under the guidance of one of the native *curanderas* (*Life* magazine, May 13, 1957). *Teonanacatl* appears to be a general term which includes several hallucinogenic mushrooms. *Psilocybe mexicana* is the one most prized by the Indians. Wasson, who ate six pairs of the mushrooms, describes them as having an acrid, rancid flavor After those present had consumed their allowance of mushrooms the candle in the room was extinguished; absolute darkness reigned and in that darkness the visions began.

"They were vivid in color, always harmonious. They began with art motifs, such as might decorate carpets or textiles or wall-paper . . . Then they evolved into palaces with courts, arcades, gardens—resplendent palaces all laid over with semiprecious stones. Then I saw a mythological beast drawing a regal chariot. Later it was as though the walls of our house had dissolved, and my spirit had flown forth, and I was suspended in mid-air viewing landscapes of mountains, with camel caravans advancing slowly across the slopes, the mountains rising tier above tier to the very heavens. . . .

"The visions were not blurred or uncertain. They were sharply focused, the lines and colors being so sharp that they seemed more real to me than anything I had seen with my own eyes. I felt that I was now seeing plain, whereas ordinary vision gives us an imperfect view; I was seeing the archetypes, the Platonic ideas, that underlie the imperfect images of everyday life. The thought crossed my mind: could the divine mushrooms be the secret that lay behind the ancient Mysteries? . . . These reflections passed through my mind at the very time that I was seeing the visions, for the effect of the mushrooms is to bring about a fission of the spirit, a split in the person, a kind of schizophrenia, with the rational side continuing to reason and to observe the sensations that the other side is enjoying."

Wasson's experiences under the influence of *teonanacatl* are so similar to those described by investigators who have taken mescaline that one might suppose that the divine mushroom contains this substance. At the moment, however, we are completely ignorant as to the nature of the active principle of the fungus. It may be an entirely new hallucinogenic agent. This is another native drug which would repay further study.

The other Mexican drug, *ololiuqui,* is found in the seeds

of a plant of the bindweed family, *Rivea corymbosa* by name. The seeds were so revered by the ancient Aztecs that they called them the divine food. Elsie Clews Parsons, in her fascinating study of the Zapotecs of Mitla, describes the plant, which is called *bador* or "little children." One who drinks an infusion of its leaves or eats about thirteen of the seeds falls asleep, and in the course of this sleep the plant children, male and female, come and talk to him, informing him about future events, the whereabouts of lost property, and other occult matters. Obviously it is a handy plant to have around and the lucky family in whose back yard it happens to grow find it a modest gold mine, for they sell both leaves and seeds to those who wish to use them either for divinatory purposes or simply to escape the cares of life. Intoxication comes on rapidly and proceeds to a stage where visual hallucinations appear. The intoxication lasts about three hours and is followed by few unpleasant aftereffects. *Ololiuqui* is usually taken at night and, in contrast to *peyotl*, which is eaten in company, is administered to single individuals who seek a quiet place in which to undergo the intoxication.

Now, journeying south from Mexico, we can follow the trail of that intrepid botanist, Richard Spruce, into the dense rain forests of the Amazon. Here nature presents marvels enough to excite the mind without the aid of any hallucinating drug. Here there are forests lofty as cathedrals, huge columned trees interlaced with ropelike lianes rising sheer out of the gloom to form a roof so solid that a man can almost walk on it. Fantastic orchids grow here, suspended on the stronger vegetation with hanging roots that draw moisture from the air itself. Birds are as small as insects, insects as large as birds, plumage flashes like a polished jewel, species are innumerable, the forms of life unbelievable, for nowhere else is nature more prodigal than in these rain forests.

It would be surprising indeed if in the midst of such vegetable profusion we did not find a few drugs capable of exerting an effect on the mind. One of these is *caapi*, which is prepared from the stems of a jungle vine belonging to the family Malpighiaceae and having the botanical name *Banisteria caapi*. Spruce describes its use in an Indian feast, the "Feast of Gifts" celebrated in the village of Panuré. First the sacred drink, the *caapi*, is carefully prepared. The woody stems of the vine are beaten to a pulp with water, strained through a sieve, and poured into a special receptacle. Now, in a cleared area in the midst of the giant trees, the villagers assemble, listening for the first sounds of the sacred trumpets which boom lugubriously from the edge of the forest. At the first sound of these trumpets every female in the place, from the withered crone to the naked toddler, flees to the shelter of the community house as if her life depended on her speed. It does. Any female who sees the "botutos" is automatically condemned to death. Now, with a shout which echoes through the forest, the cup-bearer runs toward the assembled men, bearing in each hand a gourd containing a small cupful of *caapi*. Crying, "Mo, mo, mo, mo, mo," he runs in a crouching fashion, bending his knees, bowing his head, thrusting the gourds into the hands of the man he has selected, who drains the contents first of one, then of the other. In two minutes or less the recipient turns deathly pale. He trembles in every limb and there is horror in his aspect. Bursting into perspiration, he becomes possessed of a sort of frenzy Rushing to the communal house, he inflicts violent blows on the doorway and the ground, shouting,

"Thus, thus would I do to my enemy." In about ten minutes he grows calm and appears exhausted.

Among the Peruvian Indians preparations from this same
vine, *Banisteria caapi*, are known as *aya-huasca*. Its effect is
exhilarating at first and terrifying later. Sensations of heat
alternate with those of cold, wild bravado alternates with
fear. After the first feeling of vertigo has passed the Indians
see lovely lakes, trees loaded with delicious fruit, among the
branches of which fly birds of brilliant plumage. Soon the
scene changes and the delight is replaced with horror. They
see savage beasts preparing to seize them and are liable, if
not restrained by force, to grab their weapons and attack
others under the influence of these delusions. Soon the
frenzy passes and they fall into a deep sleep.

Among Indians in Colombia the use of *caapi* during the
yurupari whipping ceremony was described by Paul H.
Allen. The deep booming of drums from within the *naloca*
heralded the appearance of the mystic *yurupari* horns. All
females fled. The whipping ceremony is a strictly male affair. Soon the forest echoed with deep lugubrious notes, for
the *yurupari* horns are four or five feet long and give off a
tone as deep as a bassoon. Old men in brilliantly colored
ruffs made from the red and yellow plumage of tropical
birds gravely prepared the youths for their painful ordeal.
The master of ceremonies entered carrying a strangely
shaped jar of *caapi*, and the thick brown bitter liquid was
served in pairs of tiny round gourds. Each youth swallowed
the contents of two gourds and many, as the drug began to
work, vomited copiously. The flare of fantastic visions in
beautiful colors was soon replaced by terrifying hallucinations. Driven to frenzy by these delusions, the youths began
whipping each other, flinging the whip far back with a dramatic gesture, bringing down the lash with a sound like a

pistol shot. The first lashes were applied to the legs and
ankles, then to buttocks, waist, and back. Soon the bodies of
the youths were covered with bloody welts and, as the frenzy
induced by the *caapi* passed, they sank down exhausted.
Then tiny naked lads of not more than six rushed in and,
picking up the abandoned whips, joyfully began to imitate
the antics of their elders.

Few European observers have ever experimented with
caapi but those who have report effects similar to those described by the Indians.

> When I have partaken of *aya-huasca* [writes Villavicen-
> cio] my head has immediately begun to swim, then I have
> seemed to enter on an aerial voyage, wherein I thought I
> saw the most charming landscapes, great cities, lofty towers
> and other delightful things. Then, all at once, I found myself
> deserted in a forest and attacked by beasts of prey against
> which I tried to defend myself. Lastly I began to come
> round, but with a feeling of excessive drowsiness, headache
> and sometimes general malaise.

Iberico writes of the properties of this drug as follows:

> *Banisteria caapi* or *ayahuasca* serves the aborigines of
> various forest regions of South America for the preparation
> of a beverage having "psychokinetic" and "psychomotor"
> properties.
>
> Small doses of the beverage result in nervous stimulation,
> enhancement of intellectual activity and euphoria. With
> larger doses the psychosensory excitement is greater and is
> followed by a tendency to sleep accompanied by vivid imag-
> inings.
>
> At very high doses, such as the ayahuascan "priests" are

in the habit of taking, there is a tremendous augmentation of visual power. Objects appear intensely colored often shining. Later there occur hallucinations of magnificent ornaments accompanied at times by terrifying visions. The enhancement of the visual power is such that it makes vision possible in light so dim that nothing can be perceived with the normal sight. Profound sleep follows, with complete abolition of sensation during which the sleeper is visited by images of surprising richness so that one can hardly wonder the *ayahuasca* is regarded as the magical plant of divination. The images seen are microscopic and megaloscopic, fluctuating between lilliputian forms, like those seen by cocainomaniacs, and gigantic shapes.

In small doses, equivalent to 5mg. of banisterine of harmine, *ayahuasca* has a powerful action on the genital organs, producing an erection in the male and engorgement of the clitoris with vaginal spasm in the female. This accounts for the "psycho erotic" and aphrodisiac properties of the drug described by Wiffen and others.

Experiments with dogs shows that banisterine is an excitant of the central nervous system, the lethal dose being 200 mg/kg. At toxic doses it produces motor incoordination, paralysis and convulsions. Death results from respiratory paralysis.

Lewin, that versatile toxicologist, was among the first to investigate the active principles of *Banisteria caapi*. He found that the alkaloid which had been isolated from this plant and variously named "telepathine," "yageine," or "banisterine" was identical with harmine, an alkaloid from the seeds of wild rue. Hence the reference to harmine in the above quotation from Iberico. Those conversant with chemical structures will notice in the molecule of harmine the familiar indole nucleus, present also in reserpine and LSD-25. It seems improbable that the action of *caapi* is due solely to harmine and the drug quite probably contains other active principles. One curious feature of the drug, from the pharmacological standpoint, is its rapidity of action. Accounts of its use in Indian ceremonies suggest that it takes effect almost at once. One wonders what substance could be absorbed from the drug so rapidly that it has an effect on the central nervous system within five minutes. In short *caapi* presents many involved problems and would seem to deserve more attention than it has received.

Some South American tribes add to their *caapi* the extract of another liane, *Haemadictyon amazonica,* a member of the botanical family Apocynaceae. The plant is also used by itself, the leaves and branches being extracted to give a rosy liquid with a green fluoresence which becomes blue on standing. This brew the Indians of the Amazon call *yagé.* They drink at their solemn ceremonies out of a special vessel which they call *maté.* The drink makes them lively at first. They begin to jump and dance and sing and run about. Later they become sleepy and, in this dreamy state, experience many fantasies. The drink is considered to confer on those who take it the power of divination and telepathy. Domville Fife goes so far as to state that *yagé* suspends the activity of the higher centers which is essential to normal consciousness. This leaves the unconscious mind in possession and open to telepathic reception.

Rouhier, one of the few Europeans who has experimented with this rare, almost unobtainable drug, declares that 5 to 10 c.c. of the extract when swallowed produce a tendency to sleep. A period of excitement precedes this drowsiness. Beautiful and vivid hallucinations, which resemble those provoked by large doses of *peyotl*, are produced by the drug.

Yagé, however, acts in a somewhat different fashion on the visual centers, for it provokes especially the sensation of blue, every object being seen with a blue halo. Rouhier isolated from the plant two alkaloids which he called yageine ($C_{14}H_8NO_3$) and yagenine. In experimental animals he found the toxic dose to be 200 milligrams per kilogram, the animals dying in a state of total anesthesia.

Rather more is known about *cohoba*, the narcotic snuff of the inhabitants of ancient Hispanolia, used also by the Guahibo Indians under the name *niopo* and by the Catauixis, who call it *paricá*. This drug is prepared from seeds of a tree belonging to the same family as the mimosa (Leguminosae).

They throw themselves into a peculiar state of intoxication, one might almost say madness, by the use of the powder of *niopo* [writes the famous explorer Humboldt of the Otomac Indians]. They gather the long pods of a Mimosaceae, which we have made known under the name *Acacia niopo*, cut them to pieces, moisten them, and cause them to ferment. When the softened seeds begin to turn black they are ground into a paste, and after having mixed with them some flour of cassava and some lime made from the shell of an Ampullaria, they expose the whole mass to a very brisk fire, on a gridiron of hard wood. The hardened paste is given the form of little cakes. When wanted for use it is reduced to a fine powder, and placed on a dish five or six inches wide. The Otomac holds this dish, which has a handle, in his right hand, while he inhales the *niopo* by the nose, through a forked tube of a bird's bone This bone, without which the Otomac believes he could not take this kind of snuff, is seven inches long; it appeared to me to be the leg-bone of a sort of plover.

The Mura Indians of the Rio Negro have annual assemblies which last eight days and are accompanied by every sort of debauchery. These antics are much enlivened by *cohoba*, which in that part of the world is called *paricá*. The Muras, however, have little use for the snuff, which by all accounts is most irritating to the mucous membranes of the nose and causes the taker to break into a "whirlwind of sneezes," to use the words of Padre Gumilla. So the Muras, utilizing a less sensitive port of entry, extract their drug with water and administer the brew to themselves in the form of an enema. The Catauixis use the drug in a similar fashion, employing a primitive clyster made from the long shank bone of the *tuyuyu*. These Indians, after douching themselves, give the same treatment to their dogs before setting out on a hunting expedition. They believe that it clears the vision and renders the senses more alert. The effect, as described by Spruce, is drastic and immediate. "His eyes started from his head, his mouth contracted, his limbs trembled. It was fearful to see him. He was obliged to sit down or he would have fallen. He was drunk, but only for about five minutes; he was then gayer."

Quite recently this peculiar drug, *cohoba*, has been the subject of a scientific investigation. Dr. V. L. Stromberg of the National Heart Institute has examined the drug and shown that it contains bufotenin. This substance, bufotenin, was first obtained from the skin of the toad. It is closely related to serotonin, whose role in the metabolism of the brain has recently been much debated (see page 191, "The Chemistry of Madness"). Bufotenin is 2 methyl serotonin and, like serotonin, has potent effects on blood pressure.

The effect of bufotenin on the mind of man has recently been described by Drs. Howard Fabing and J. R. Hawkins in a paper in *Science*. The highest dose used was 16 milligrams, injected into the veins of a healthy young man whose reaction was almost immediate and quite spectacular. He reported a burning sensation in the roof of his mouth. His face turned a livid purple; his pupils became widely dilated and he retched and vomited. Reddish spots appeared before his eyes and red-purple ones on the floor, which were replaced by a yellow haze as though he were looking through a yellow lens filter. Sixteen minutes after the injection he stated, "When I start on a thought another one comes along and clashes with it, and I can't express myself clearly. . . . I feel dopey but not sleepy. I feel physically tense and mentally clouded. I am here and not here." Time and space perception were grossly impaired, the yellow haze persisted, and his face remained purple. Most of the effects disappeared after forty minutes.

Thus bufotenin, venomous product of the skin of a toad, does appear to have certain effects on the mind of man, though it is questionable whether we should attribute the action of *cohoba* entirely to this substance. The mention of toad skin, however, brings us within smelling distance of the classic witch's cauldron:

> Toad, that under cold stone,
> Days and nights hast thirty one,
> Sweltered venom sleeping got,
> Boil thou first i' the charmed pot!

Brews of this kind lie somewhat beyond the range of orthodox pharmacology. Accounts given by such authorities as Eliphas Levi in his *Dogma and Ritual of Magic* suggest that some of the ingredients were rare and hard to come by. Moss from the skull of a parricide, the horn of a goat that had cohabited with a girl—these and similar items must have cost the worried sorcerer many hours of anxious search. But what gave these brews their activity was not the inert ingredients mentioned above, but extracts of henbane, mandrake, or deadly nightshade, plants common enough throughout the countries of Europe, whose stupefying properties had been known for centuries. "The root being drunk with wine," wrote Dioscorides of datura, a plant of this group, "has the power to arouse not unpleasant fantasies. But two drams being drunk makes a man beside himself for three days and four being drunk kill him."

These plants were undoubtedly used in the ancient world in connection with orgiastic rites characterized by sexual excesses. Thus at the Bacchanalia, when the wild-eyed Bacchantes with their flowing locks flung themselves naked into the arms of the eager men, one can be reasonably certain that the wine which produced such sexual frenzy was not a plain fermented grape juice. Intoxication of this kind was almost certainly a result of doctoring the wine with leaves or berries of belladonna or henbane. The orgiastic rites were never totally suppressed by the Church and persisted in secret forms through the Middle Ages. Being under the shadow of the Church's displeasure, they were inevitably associated with the Devil, and those who took part in them were considered to be either witches or wizards.

As an example of the kind of thing that went on, let us consider the famous "witches' Sabbath" or night on the Brocken as depicted in the all too frequent witch trials in Bavaria during the sixteenth century. In this particular trial the proceedings were made all the more piquant by the fact that Lise, from whose confessions the trial resulted, was the sixteen-year-old daughter of the local pastor. This Lise was decoyed into evil ways by her lover, who persuaded her to take part in the secret ceremonies to be held at midnight in the depths of the Harz Mountains. The participants, having assembled in their secret meeting place, prepared with suitable incantations a drink of which all partook freely. Soon after partaking of the drink a frenzy seized them all, including young Lise who, abandoning all restraints of feminine modesty, stripped herself naked, as did the others present, and was anointed with the "witches' salve." Next she engaged in a frenzied sexual orgy accompanied by the most vivid hallucinations, in the course of which she became convinced that every devil in hell had enjoyed her body, that she had mounted a broomstick and soared over the mountains, that she had seen the ovens of hell and even smelled the aroma of roasting sinners. So vivid were these hallucinations that she firmly believed them to be real and, in a subsequent fit of remorse, related them to her father. That worthy pillar of the Church had no hesitation in handing over his own daughter to the authorities, who forthwith instituted a hunt for the other members of the midnight party and, in an orgy of torture, wrung from all of them confessions of their misdeeds. Thereupon the entire group was ceremoniously burned alive in the public square, the whole town turning out to watch the event.

Anyone familiar with the action of belladonna, henbane, thorn apple and similar members of the Solanaceae can have no doubt that the witches' brew of which these unfortunates partook contained these drugs and that the salve with which they anointed their bodies was composed of crushed belladonna leaves. These plants have long been known in some parts of Europe as "the sorcerer's herb" or "the herb of the devil." The wise thirteenth-century bishop, Albertus Magnus, informs us that henbane was always an ingredient of the brews made by necromancers when they wished to conjure up demons. The crazy activity of those who took these potions, their shameless sexual excesses, disordered flushed appearance, and widely dilated pupils all point to henbane or belladonna as the cause of their wild behavior. One cannot doubt that the poorer people of the Middle Ages, living as they did in conditions of almost unendurable squalor, sought an occasional escape from reality by using these drug plants which grew freely in the woods and meadows around them. Nourished in their absurd superstitions by a Church which was far more conscious of the Devil than of Christ, these people became convinced that the hallucinations they experienced were real and that they had indeed had intercourse with evil spirits, or ridden over the Brocken on a broomstick. These stories, magnified and distorted, resulted in a kind of mass neurosis, an almost hysterical terror of witchcraft and witches which found its final expression in that monstrous document *Malleus Maleficarum* (A Hammer for Witches), the work of a German monk in which was described the methods of discovering a witch, the ways in which she should be tortured, and the manner in which she should be burned.

More recently scopolamine, the active principle of henbane, has been used by the police in some countries to assist the extraction of confessions from accused persons. It has even been described by certain misinformed individuals as "truth serum." Scopolamine, of course, has nothing to do with serum, which is the liquid portion of blood after the clot has been removed. It has also very little to do with truth. There is no evidence to show that either scopolamine or any other drug can so relax an accused person's defenses that he unknowingly reveals truths he has been trying to conceal. Jean Rolin, in his book *Police Drugs,* describes the way in which scopolamine or sodium amytal has been used for this purpose and condemns the technique as being morally equivalent to the use of torture. Certainly it is a medically unethical procedure and confessions thus extorted should not be accepted in any properly constituted court of law. In the United States such a practice would be contrary to the spirit of the Fifth Amendment, which was specifically designed to protect accused persons from procedures which would compel them to be witnesses against themselves.

Scopolamine is also reputed to be of value in facilitating the process known as "brain washing." In the state of "twilight sleep" which the drug induces the individual is supposed to be abnormally suggestible. Ideas offered to him penetrate directly into the subconscious mind, lodge there, and reappear in the field of consciousness. The mental outlook of the individual is thus changed without his even being aware of the process. Such "psychochemical" methods are reputed to have been used to change the attitude of Cardinal Mindszenty toward Communism. Whether such drugs as scopolamine really can be used to facilitate "brain washing" seems at the moment highly questionable. It is entirely possible, however, that, as our knowledge grows, drugs will be discovered that will enhance suggestibility and render the individual open to ideas he would otherwise reject.

While we are on the subject of Solanaceous drugs it seems reasonable to mention that curious drug, tobacco, the products of whose combustion inflame lungs and poison atmospheres in practically every corner of the globe. Considering the questionable nature of the pleasures conferred by this weed, it is amazing that its use should be so widespread. De las Casas, one of the first to describe the way in which tobacco was used by Indians in the days of Columbus, observed, "I do not know what benefit they derive from it." Even the new edition of the United States Dispensatory, almost omniscient in the subject of drug action, is puzzled to explain the attractiveness of tobacco. "The explanation of the solace that habitual smokers get from nicotine is not obvious."

Lewin is somewhat readier with an explanation:

Smoking does not call forth an exaltation of internal well-being as does the use of wine, but it adjusts the working condition of the mind and the disposition of many mentally active persons to a kind of serenity or "quietism" during which the activity of thought is in no way disturbed, and from a physical point of view a certain calmness of movement occurs. . . . Although the action of tobacco in most cases consists in banishing vacancy of mind and boredom, so that the layman has the impression of a slight narcosis, it is nevertheless a mild excitation. The latter dominates or substitutes other normal or natural states of excitation of the cerebral centres and directs them into other channels so that the final impression is one of self-forgetfulness without any irritation of the brain.

Tobacco's ill effects, especially on the female species, is described by this same writer in lurid terms:

The juvenile female flower of the nation, the "Emancipata femans vulgaris," who should bear fruit in time to come . . . frequently fails to do so because the foolish consumption of cigarettes has impregnated the sexual organs with smoke and nicotine and keeps them in a state of irritation and inflammation. Such women, as vestals of the home, should nourish a fire of a very different sort, for their mouth is ordained for other things than to be transformed into a smoking chimney and to smell of tobacco juice.

Few contemporary authorities would accept the idea that tobacco smoke exerts a specific irritating action on the female genitals. It is not the genitals that are exposed to the poisonous products of this very toxic drug but the delicate lining of the lungs. Incidence of lung cancer and level of cigarette consumption are directly related to one another. This fact has been proved beyond reasonable doubt. Why men and women should offer such an insult to the precious sacs, through which we absorb the vital *pneuma*, for the sake of such poor pleasures as tobacco offers is hard to see. Consumption of the weed is enormous nonetheless. Cigarette output in the United States totalled 423,000,000,000 in 1953. Taking the price of a packet of twenty to be twenty-five cents, this works out to $5,000,000,000, which seems a large price to pay for increasing one's chances of dying of cancer of the lung.

The chief alkaloid of tobacco is, of course, nicotine, a highly poisonous substance which, like coniine, the alkaloid of hemlock, is peculiar in being a liquid. It does not produce hallucinations or euphoria but it does interfere in some way with the transmission of the nerve impulses, to which interference its poisonous properties are due. In the process of smoking, nicotine is largely destroyed and the substances entering the mouth and lungs of the smoker are mainly breakdown products of the alkaloid, which is just as well for the smoker. The amount of this substance in one cigar would be more than adequate to kill a man if the full amount of the drug entered his system.

In many ways the enormous popularity of *betel* among the peoples of southeastern Asia is as problematical as is the popularity of tobacco. About 200,000,000 Asiatics chew *betel*, which colors the saliva red and encrusts the teeth with black deposits known in those parts as tooth stone. *Betel* is not a single substance but a combination of a fragment of areca nut, a leaf from the vine *Piper betel*, which belongs to the pepper family, and a pinch of lime. The three taken together constitute the *betel* morsel, which is chewed but not swallowed by its devotees. It appears to produce a general sense of well-being and to act as a mild stimulant. Whether it has any direct effect on mind or emotions is questionable. The lime is probably of value to a people whose diet is notoriously low in calcium and the alkaloid arecoline from the areca nut may help to free the *betel* chewer of intestinal worms. It seems a harmless form of indulgence and may be mildly beneficial, though the copious streams of crimson saliva which the *betel* chewer squirts about are hardly a contribution to public hygiene.

Moving now to a very different part of the world, the icy plains bounded on the north by the Siberian Sea and on the east by the Bering Sea, we find a curious "passport to happiness" in use among the tribes who inhabit these inclement regions. The crimson fly agaric, *Amanita muscaria,* is known to most people as a decorative fungus which figures in countless illustrations of fairy stories along with dwarfs in red caps, mottled fawns, elves, and other assorted flora and fauna. The primitive peoples of northeastern Asia, the Tungus, Yakuts, Chukches, Koryaks, and Kamchadales, put this fungus to a very different use. It is called *muchamor* and is eaten as an intoxicant during the long winters when the sun scarcely rises above the horizon and total boredom is an ever present threat. Under these circumstances any form of inebriation may be considered better than none and the Koryak, whose tastes are not refined, prefers the fly agaric to any other agent and will even give a whole reindeer for a single dried mushroom, as the fungus itself does not grow so far north. The fly agaric presents other advantages which appeal to the thrifty, for the active principle is excreted unchanged in the urine and can thus be used again. Thus an agaric orgy among the Koryaks is started by the women, who chew the dried fungus and roll the chewed substance into sausages which are then swallowed by the men. As the party warms up the participants grow lively. Some shout and sing, some hold conversations with imaginary beings, some relate with delight that they have made vast fortunes, some leap to and fro across the room, imagining every tiny obstacle in their path to be so high that they must jump to get over it. Then, when the initial jollity has somewhat worn off, there are shouts of "pass the pot," and one of the women enters with a tin can into which all present urinate with enthusiasm. The can is then passed around and each partakes of the still warm urine, gaiety is restored to the party, and the leaping and singing recommence.

This is a form of social gathering which might not appeal to an aesthete but, as was mentioned above, the Koryak is not refined. Besides, the precious agarics are very expensive and the winters are long, so there is every inducement to prolong the orgy. Certainly as a euphoriant the fly agaric leaves much to be desired and excessive indulgence in the drug leads to an attack of raving madness. The hallucinations become destructive and dangerous, ending in acts of violence or, in some cases, self-mutilation. The active principle in fly agaric which produces these hallucinations appears not to have been isolated. The chief toxic substance in this fungus is an alkaloid called muscarine which, in sufficient doses, stops the beating of the heart. But whatever the substance is that affords such joy to Koryaks, Tungus, Chukches, Yakuts, et cetera, it certainly cannot be muscarine.

Two other minor "happiness drugs" deserve brief mention in this chapter. Kat, prepared from buds or fresh leaves of Catha edulis, is consumed in Yemen where it was employed even before coffee. There is a special kat market in Aden in which devotees of this plant may spend large sums each day to buy supplies of the plant. Kat, according to Lewin, belongs to the class of drugs which he calls "Excitantia" because they stimulate the central nervous system. It produces joyous excitation and gaiety. The desire for sleep is banished, energy is revived during the hot hours of the day, and the feeling of hunger on long marches is dispersed. The drug is used by messengers and warriors because, like cocaine, kat dulls the sense of hunger and enables one who takes it to go without food for several days. As always, those who depend upon this drug find that its drawbacks outweigh the advantages it offers. The kat eater is seized with restlessness which robs him of his sleep; overstimulation of the heart results in various cardiac disorders. It appears also to have a deleterious effect on that mysterious mechanism which generates in man the desire for women. It is openly stated in Yemen that inveterate eaters of kat are indifferent to sexual desire and that in no part of the Mahometan East are there so many bachelors.

The second drug, which also has a stimulating action, is iboga, used by natives on the Gabon coast of French Equatorial Africa. The drug is prepared from a plant called Tabernanthe iboga, the leaves of which, when chewed, have a stimulating effect, enabling one who takes the drug to endure fatigue with equanimity. No direct accounts appear to have been published concerning the action of this drug. It is the source of two alkaloids, ibogaine and iboganine, the structure of which is not known. *Iboga* is another native drug which deserves further study.

The Shape of the Future

As we stand at the entrance to the chemopsychiatric era and look toward the future some may feel disposed to cheer and some to shudder. What can we expect from this intrusion of the chemist into the most sacred recesses of the human soul? Some may complain that he is going too far. Cannot this inquisitive analyst leave us in peace to be masters or victims of our fate, to struggle with our difficulties, our depressions, our manias without the aid of pills? We have a hard enough time already to convince ourselves that our souls are our own. Must our very moods be by-products of the contents of a bottle, must the stuff of our lives be fashioned by a chemical formula? Let the chemist stay in the laboratory and make nylons to cover girls' legs or cosmetics to beautify their faces. But let him, for heaven's sake, leave our minds alone and not intrude into our holy of holies, the innermost sanctum of our spiritual being.

To this the chemist may answer that he has no intentions of intruding where he is not wanted. Those who are masters of their souls have no need of psychochemistry. Built into their own machinery they have all that is required to protect them from the whips and scorns of time. They are well buffered, to give a chemical term a psychological meaning. The blows of fate are cushioned by an internal system which knows how to maintain its own equilibrium. Balanced, collected, and inwardly serene, beyond the reach of the storms that blow from the outer world, these fortunate beings carry within them their own snug harbor. For them no oil need be poured on the troubled water in the form of an ataraxic or a sedative. They manage very well without such aids.

It is not for such as these that the modern chemist has plunged into this new and strange domain. Let the well-balanced philosopher steer his own ship where he wishes. Our concern is with the troubled, the unbalanced, and the insecure. For these the age of chemopsychiatry offers a smoother road on which to make the journey of life. For these the future prospect seems brighter.

Lucky neurotics! Soon the specter of care will be banished from your world, the burden of anxiety and guilt will be lifted from your souls. The restoration of your primeval innocence, your re-entry into the Garden of Eden, will now be accomplished through the agency of a pill. Soothed by reserpine, calmed by chlorpromazine, mellowed by "Miltown," elevated by "Meratran," what need you fear from the uncertainties of fortune? Tranquilly, smoothly your days will succeed one another, like the waters of a peaceful river flowing through green pastures in which graze dewy-eyed cows whose state of placid contentment resembles your own. O most fortunate of mortals, whose spiritual defects are made good by the skill of the scientist, whose personal shortcomings are supplemented by a formula. No longer need you struggle with your weaknesses or agonize over your sins. Salvation need not be purchased at the cost of spiritual war.

In the chemopsychiatric age you can buy it by the bottle.
O brave new world that has such bottles in it!

The prospect of a world so well tranquillized may awaken
some protests. Some may maintain that man was not placed
on earth to be comfortable, that he should aspire toward
something nobler than the placid concentment of a well-
pastured cow. One is reminded of the paradoxical irritation
of William James after he had spent a week at Chautauqua,
that "middle class paradise, without a sin, without a victim,
without a blot, without a tear":

> . . . What was my own astonishment, on emerging in to
> the dark and wicked world again, to catch myself quite un-
> expectedly and involuntarily saying: "Ouf! What a relief!
> Now for something primordial and savage, even though it
> were as bad as an Armenian massacre, to set the balance
> straight again. This order is too tame, this culture too sec-
> ond rate, this goodness too uninspiring. This human drama
> without a villain or a pang; this community so refined that
> ice-cream soda water is the utmost offering it can make to
> the brute animal in man; this city simmering in the tepid
> lakeside sun; this atrocious harmlessness of all things—I can-
> not abide with them. Let me take my chances again in the
> big outside worldly wilderness with all its sins and sufferings.
> There are the heights and the depths, the precipices and the
> steep ideals, the gleams of the awful and the infinite; and
> there is more hope and help a thousand times than in this
> dead level and quintessence of every mediocrity."

This disdain for an excess of tranquillity is echoed by
more contemporary commentators. Eric Hodgkins, in a recent article on the tranquillizing drugs (*Life*, October 22,
1956), quotes Dr. James H. Wall of New York Hospital: "I

don't look with any favor on a society where everybody just floats around in his own tub of butter. A certain amount of tension and alertness is essential to keep things straight in life." This reaction is quite understandable. It is obviously possible to tranquillize a man to the point at which he loses not only his anxieties but also his ambitions, ideals, creative urges, everything, in short, that distinguishes him from a contented cow. That this is undesirable goes without saying.

Our mid-twentieth-century world, however, is very far from being in so tranquil a state. It is crowded, tense, anxious, and unstable; two huge powers stand ready to blast each other with thermonuclear devices whose cumulative effects may be destructive enough to wipe out a large part of the globe's terrestrial life. Under these circumstances we can hardly share William James's enthusiasm for massacres. Even quite modest massacres have a way of getting out of hand and at this stage of the world's history we can hardly afford to indulge in them.

This mechanized, fast-moving, highly explosive culture balances on wheels as finely poised as the jeweled movements of a watch. To keep it in equilibrium men are needed who are equally well balanced. We are already in the situation described by Aldous Huxley in his futuristic fantasy, *Brave New World:* "Wheels must turn steadily, but cannot turn untended. They must have men to tend them, men as steady as the wheels upon their axles, sane men, obedient men, stable in contentment." It was to obtain this stability that the rulers of the brave new world developed "soma," a drug which combined the properties of an ataraxic with those of a euphoriant and a hallucinogen. "All the advantages of Christianity and alcohol, none of their drawbacks." Soma, in fact, was largely responsible for the stability of that imaginary technocracy and Aldous Huxley, who appreciated, twenty years ago, the social potentialities of pharmacology, might well be called the prophet of the chemopsychiatric age. There is no drug known at the moment with the properties of Huxley's "soma," which appears to have combined the more desirable qualities of *hashish*, mescaline, and reserpine. We are, however, only at the beginning of the chemopsychiatric age, and "soma," the perfect euphoriant, may at any time emerge from the test tube of the chemists. If mankind *must* take an occasional holiday from reality it is certainly high time the chemists found a more satisfactory "happiness drug" than that dreary old nerve poison, ethyl alcohol.

Meanwhile the great interest being shown in drugs which affect the mind is a cheering sign, indicating a new realization on the part of scientists of the importance of research into mental processes. The real frontier of research does not lie out in the wastes of interplanetary space; it lies within the small mass of pinkish jelly, the human brain, which Sherrington called the "organ of final cause." By using this organ man rose to a position of dominance among the living things on the planet. By *misusing* this organ man might conceivably destroy not only himself but most other living things as well. Within that "great ravelled knot," with its marvelously complex network of branching fibers, those processes take place which lead to the ultimate choice between good and evil. It is a realm the exploration of which is worthy of the utmost efforts of the serious scientist, a realm in which science, art, religion, and philosophy find their natural meeting place. Here we can go beyond our present rather childish preoccupation with rockets, space ships, and the like and face the supreme task which confronts our age: how to reach spiritual maturity before we destroy ourselves. It is not an exaggeration to say that the future progress, perhaps even the future survival, of man depends on his rate of progress in this field of endeavor.

ADDENDA

In the space of a few years the chemopsychiatric agents have grown from a very minor group of medicaments into one whose importance is second only to that of the antibiotics. In 1957 the sales of tranquilizers alone reached, in the U.S.A. the impressive value of 150 million dollars. For this reason an intensive search for drugs having this type of action is now in progress and the list of such agents grows constantly. The following have made their appearance during the time which has elapsed between the first and second printing of this book.

"Quiactin" (William S. Merrell Co.), oxanamide, 2-ethyl-3-propylglycidamide. This mild tranquilizing agent seems of special value where abnormalities in behavior have resulted from the hardening of the arteries of the brain. It has been reported to improve the behavior of "chronically irritated" female patients.

"Atarax" (Roerig), hydroxyzine hydrochloride, 1-p-chlorobenzhydryl-4,2,-(2-hydroxyethoxy) ethyl-diethylenediamine hydrochloride. This is another mild ataraxic. It is not intended for administration to psychotics or the hospitalized insane but appears to be about 90% effective in easing tense individuals into a state of emotional calm. It exerts a quieting influence on overactive or anxious children.

"Vesprin" (Squibb), triflupromazine, 10-(3-dimethylaminopropyl)-2-(trifluoromethyl) phenothiazine hydrochloride. This tranquilizer is very closely related to chloropromazine but appears to be about five times as active.

Four new classes of chemical compounds having tranquilizing

activity have been brought to light by a group of scientists at Eli Lilly and Company. Two of these (ethoxybutamoxane and chlorethoxybutamoxane) were found to be twenty times more potent than chloropromazine when tested in mice. Information regarding their effect in man is not yet available.

Iproniazid, that remarkable "psychic energizer" mentioned by Dr. Kline in his foreword, has not only proved capable of relieving depressions which have resisted all other treatments but has also relieved the pain of angina pectoris, improved the condition of patients with rheumatoid arthritis, elevated the mood of victims of advanced cancer and even reduced the disfiguring effect of acne.

A novel substance for the treatment of schizophrenia has been obtained by Dr. Mark D. Altschule from the pineal gland of the ox. This small gland is located on top of the brain and was thought at one time to be the seat or eye of the soul. Dr. Altschule states that a purified extract of this gland, containing a peptide-like substance (molecular weight about 1000), is capable of producing an improvement in the condition of chronic schizophrenics. (New England Journal of Medicine, 257: 919–922, 1957).

Attempts by Dr. Robert G. Heath and co-workers to find a toxic substance responsible for schizophrenia have resulted in the isolation from schizophrenic serum of a proten (taraxein) capable of evoking schizophrenic reactions in both men and monkeys. (American Journal of Psychiatry, 114: 14–24, 1957).

Appendix

Structural formulae of chemopsychiatric drugs

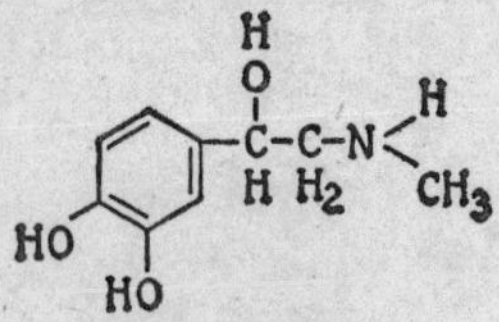

Adrenalin
Epinephrine

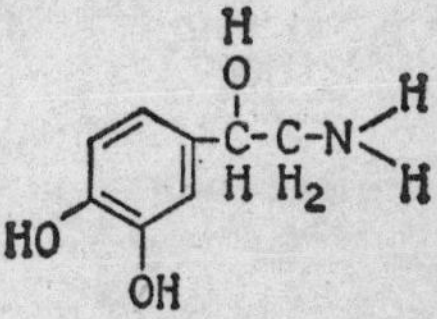

Nor-Adrenalin
Nor-Epinephrine

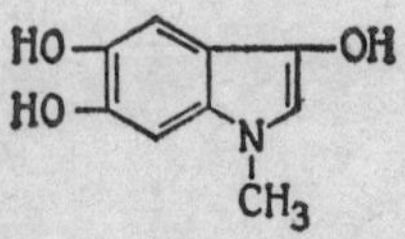

Adrenoxine

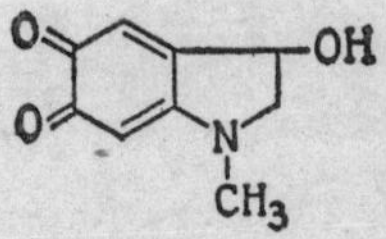

Adrenochrome

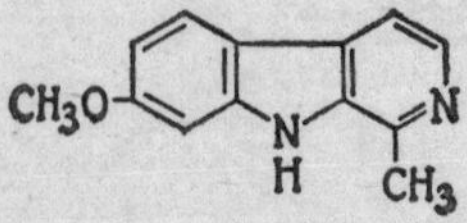

Harmine

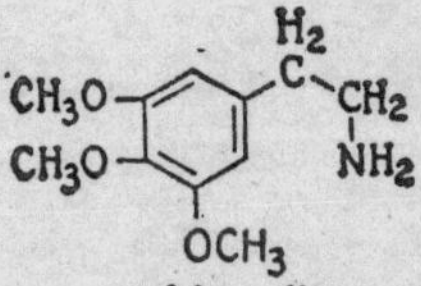

Mescaline

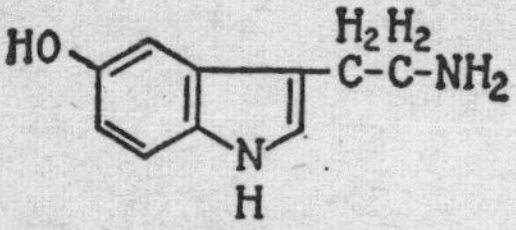

HO —[indole ring]— CH_2–CH_2–NH_2

Serotonin

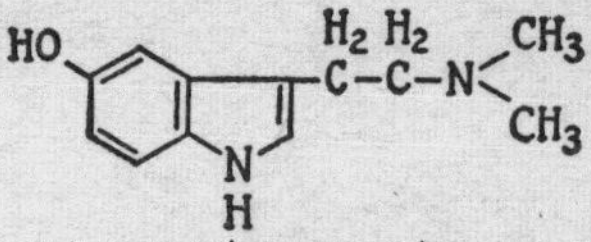

HO —[indole ring]— CH_2–CH_2–$N(CH_3)_2$

Bufotenin

[phenyl]– CH(CH_3)–CH_2–NH_2

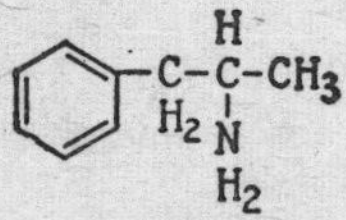

Amphetamine
"Benzedrine"

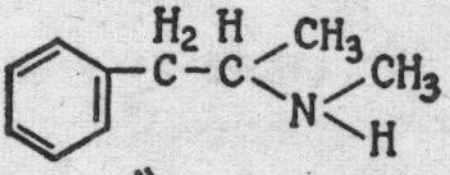

[phenyl]– CH_2–CH(CH_3)–NH–CH_3

"Methedrine"

$\left[CH_3\text{–}\overset{\displaystyle CH_3}{\underset{\displaystyle CH_3}{N}}\text{–}CH_2\text{–}CH_2\text{–}O\text{–}\overset{\displaystyle O}{C}\text{–}CH_3 \right]^{+} OH^{-}$

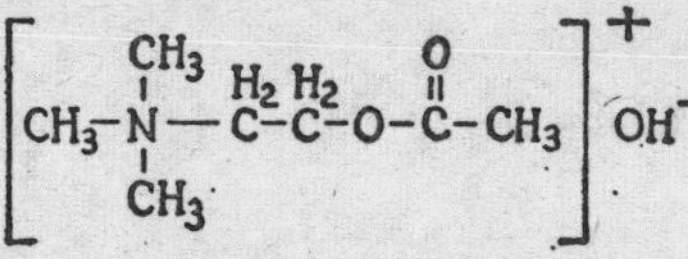

Acetylcholine

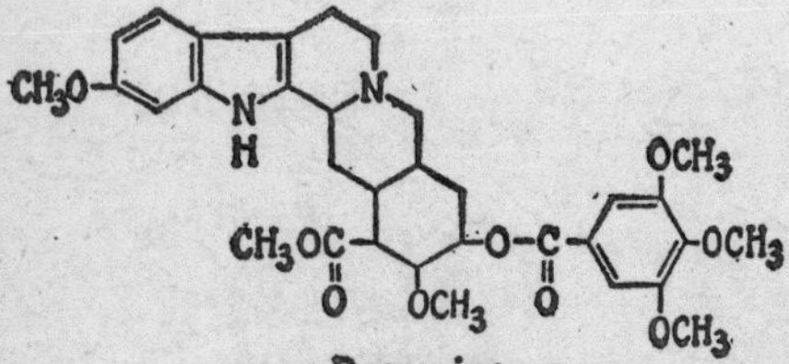

Reserpine

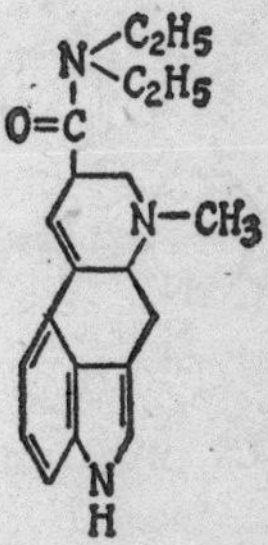

Lysergic acid diethylamide
LSD-25

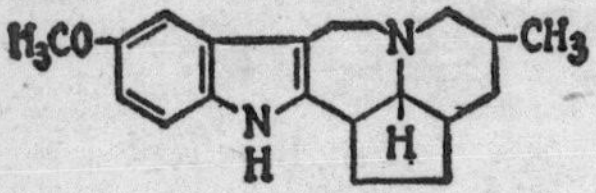

Iboqaïne
(*Proposed by R. Goutarel*)

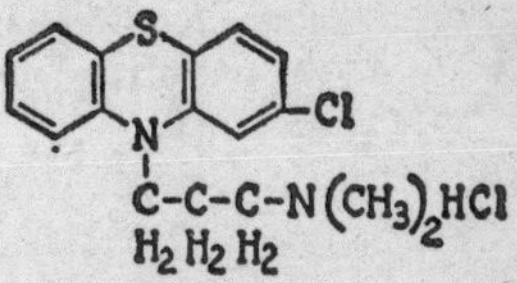

Chlorpromazine
"Thorazine"

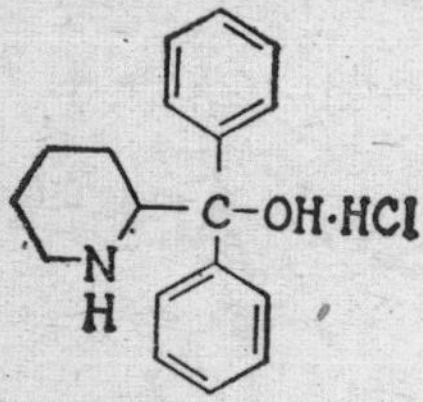

Pipradrol
"Meratran"

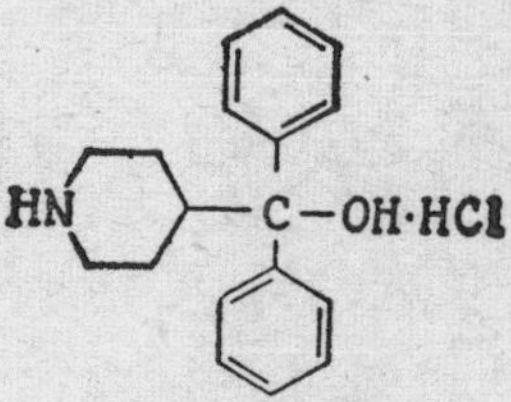

Azacyclonol
"Frenquel"

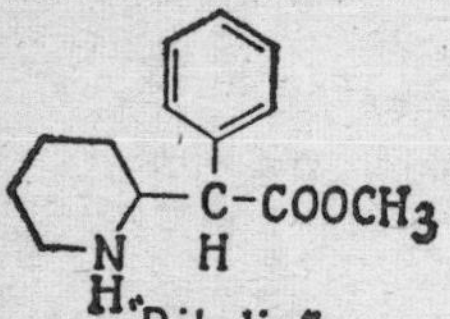

Ritalin

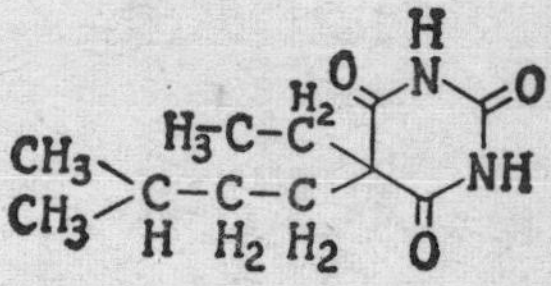

Amobarbital
"Amytal"

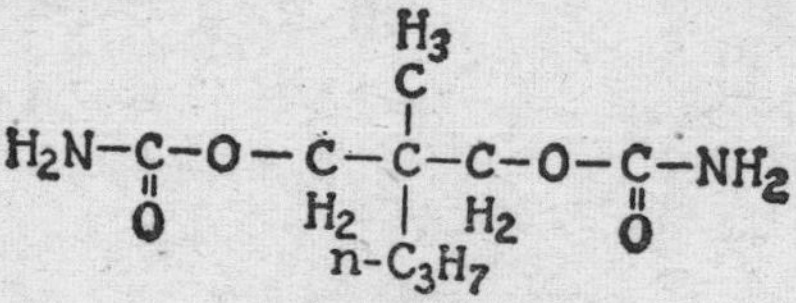

Meprobamate
"Miltown"

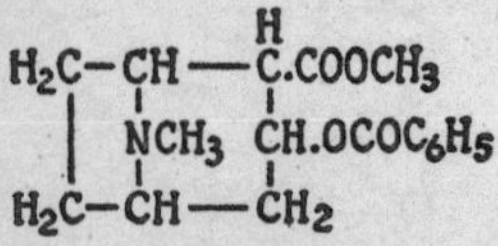

$H_2C - CH \quad \overset{H}{C.COOCH_3}$
$\quad\quad NCH_3 \quad CH.OCOC_6H_5$
$H_2C - CH \quad\quad CH_2$

Cocaine

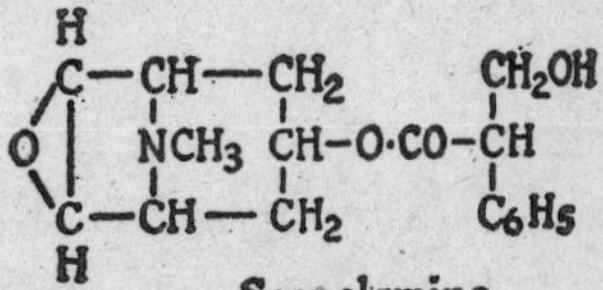

$\overset{H}{C} - CH - CH_2 \quad\quad CH_2OH$
$O \quad NCH_3 \quad CH - O \cdot CO - CH$
$\underset{H}{C} - CH - CH_2 \quad\quad C_6H_5$

Scopolamine

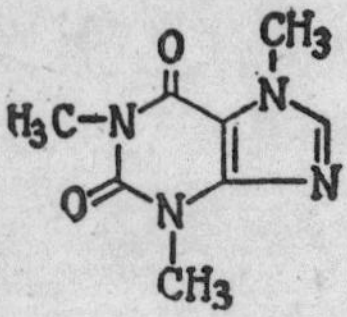

Caffein

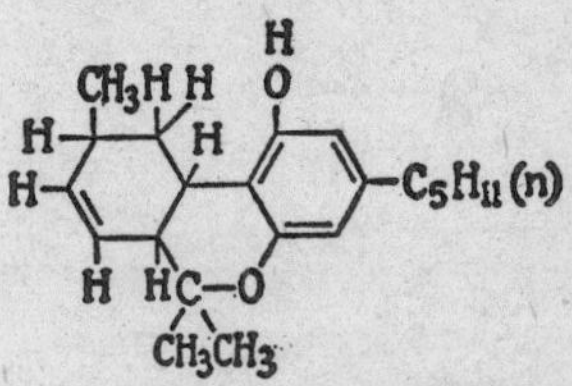

Tetrahydrocannabinol
(one of several possible forms)

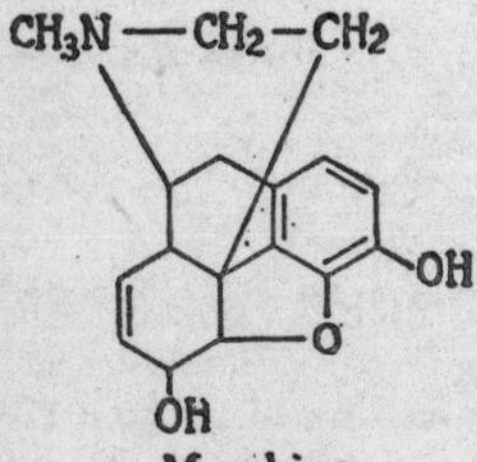

Morphine

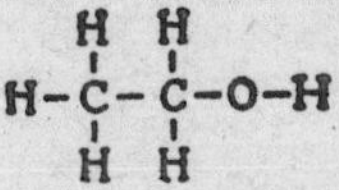

$H - \overset{H}{\underset{H}{C}} - \overset{H}{\underset{H}{C}} - O - H$

Ethyl Alcohol

Bibliography

MIND AND MATTER

Adrian, E. D. *The Physical Background of Perception*. Oxford University Press, New York, 1947.

Aird, R. B. "Barriers in the brain," *Scientific American*. *194*:101–108, 1956.

Ashby, W. R. *Design for a Brain*. Wiley and Sons, New York, 1953.

Cannon, W. B. *The Wisdom of the Body*. Norton and Co., New York, 1932.

Dale, H. "A chemical phase in the transmission of nervous effects," *Endeavour*. *12*:117–123, 1953.

Fulton, J. F. *The Physiology of the Nervous System*. Oxford University Press, New York, 1949.

Funkenstein, D. H. "The physiology of fear and anger," *Scientific American*. *192*: No. 5. pp. 74–80, 1955.

Grey Walter, W. *The Living Brain*. Norton and Co., New York, 1955.

Ingram, W. R. "The hypothalamus," Ciba Clinical Symposium. *8*:117–156, 1956.

Katz, B. "The nerve impulse," *Scientific American.* *187*:55–65, 1952.

Lewin, L. *Phantastica; die betäubenden und erregenden Genussmittel fur Ärtze und Nichtärzte.* G. Stilke, Berlin, 1924.

Lewin, L. *Phantastica—Narcotic and Stimulating Drugs.* E. P. Dutton & Co., New York, 1931.

Olds, J. "Pleasure centers in the brain," *Scientific American.* *195*:105–117. 1956.

Olds, J., Killam, K. F., Bach-y-Rita, P. "Self-stimulation of the brain used as a screening method for tranquilising drugs," *Science. 124*:265–266. 1956.

Papez, J. W. "A proposed mechanism of emotion," *Archives of Neurology and Psychiatry. 38*:725–743. 1937.

Penfield, W. "Some observations on the cerebral cortex of man," *Proceedings of the Royal Society, B, 134*:329–347. 1947.

Sherrington, C. S. *Man on His Nature.* Cambridge University Press, London, 1940.

Sherrington, C. S. *Integrative Action of the Nervous System.* Cambridge University Press, London, 1947.

THE MIND AND MESCALINE

Beringer, K. *Der Meskalinrausch.* Springer, Berlin, 1927.

Bromberg, W., Tranter, C. L. "Peyote intoxication: some psychological aspects of the peyote rite," *Journal of Nervous and Mental Disorders. 97*:518–527, 1943.

Ellis, H. "Mescal, a study of a divine plant." *Popular Science Monthly. 41*:52–71, 1902.

Ellis, H. "Mescal, a new artificial paradise," *Annual Report of the Smithsonian Institution.* Pp. 537–548, 1898.

Huxley, A. *The Doors of Perception.* Harper and Brothers, New York, 1954.

Klüver, H. *Mescal: The "Divine" Plant and Its Psychological Effects.* Kegan Paul, Trench, Trubner and Co., London, 1928.

Knauer, A., Maloney, W. J. M. A. "A preliminary note on the psychic action of mescalin, with special reference to the mechanism of visual hallucinations," *Journal of Nervous and Mental Disorders. 40*:397, 425, 1913.

La Barre, W., McAllester, D. P., Slotkin, J. S., Stewart, O. C., Tax, S. "Statement on peyote," *Science. 114*:582–583, 1951.

Mitchell, S. Weir. "The effects of Anhalonium Lewinii, (the mescal button)," *British Medical Journal.* 2:1625, 1896.

Patzig, B. Block, W. "Zur Auffassung des schizophrenen Prozess-geschehens-nach Tierversuchen mit C[14] radioaktivem Meskalin," *Naturwissenschaft. 1*:13–17, 1953.

Quastel, J. H., Wheatley, A. H. M. "Narcotics and brain oxidations. Reversibility of narcotic action *in vitro*," *Biochemical Journal. 28*:1521, 1934.

Quastel, J. H., Wheatley, A. H. M. "The effect of amines on oxidations of the brain," *Biochemical Journal.* 27:1609, 1933.

Rouhier, A. *Le Peyotl.* Doin et Cie., Paris, 1927.

Shonle, R. "Peyote: the giver of visions," *American Anthropologist.* 27:53, 1925.

Sturtevant, F. M., Drill, V. A. "Effects of mescaline in laboratory animals and the influence of ataraxics on mescaline response," *Proceedings of the Society of Experimental Biology and Medicine. 92*:383, 1956.

Taylor, N. *Flight from Reality.* Duell, Sloan and Pearce, New York, 1949.

THE MIND AND MARIHUANA

Adams, R. "Marihuana," *Harvey Lectures.* Series *37*:168–197, 1941–42.

Adams, R., Harfenist, M., Loewe, S. "New Analogs of Tetra-hydrocannabinol. XIX," *Journal of the American Chemical Society.* 71:1624–1628, 1949.

Allentuck, S., Bowman, K. M. "The psychiatric aspects of mar-ihuana intoxication," *American Journal of Psychiatry.* 99: 248–251, 1942.

Baudelaire, P. C. *Les Paradis artificiels.* Poulet-Malassis, Paris,. 1860.

Brotteaux, P. *Hachich; herbe de folie et de rêve.* Vega, Paris, 1934.

Burr, C. W. "Two cases of Cannabis indica intoxication," *Therapeutic Gazette.* 32:554, 1916.

Carlson, J. R. *Cairo to Damascus.* Knopf, New York, 1951.

Chopra, R. N., Chopra, G. S., Chopra, I. C. "Cannabis sativa in relation to mental disease and crime in India," *Indian Journal of Medical Research.* 30:155–171, 1942.

Editorial. "Effects of alcohol and cannabis during labor," *Journal of the American Medical Association.* 94:1165, 1930.

Editorial. "Marihuana problems," *Journal of the American Medical Association.* 127:1129, 1945.

Editorial. "The Marihuana Bugaboo," *The Military Surgeon.* 93:94–95, 1943.

Egyptian Government. "Hashish" (Chapter VIII). Egyptian Government Central Narcotics Intelligence Bureau. Annual report for the year 1944. Cairo, 1945.

France, Hector. *Musk, Hashish and Blood.* Privately printed. Falstaff, New York.

Gautier, T. *Le Club des hachischins.* Feuilleton de la Presse Médicale. 10, VII, 1843.

Goodman, L. S., Gilman, A. *The pharmacological basis of therapeutics.* Macmillan, New York, 1955.

Loewe, S. "Cannabiswirkstoffe und Pharmakologie der Cannabinole," *Arch. exper. Path. u. Pharmakol.* 211:175–193, 1950.

Ludlow, Fitz Hugh. *The Hasheesh Eater; being passages from the life of a Pythagorean.* Harper and Brothers, New York, 1857.

Ludlow, Fitz Hugh. "The apocalypse of hasheesh," *Putnam's Monthly Magazine. 8:*233–239, 1857.

Mayor's Committee on Marihuana. *The Marihuana Problem in the City of New York.* Jaques Cattell Press, Phila., Pa., 1944.

Meunier, R. *Le Hachich, essai sur la psychologie des paradis éphémères.* Blond et Cie., Paris, 1909.

Milks, H. J., Eichorn, A. *Veterinary Pharmacology, Materia Medica and Therapeutics.* Chicago, Alex Eger, Inc., 1949.

Parker, C. S., Wrigley, F. "Synthetic cannabis preparations in psychiatry: synhexyl (pyrahexyl)," *Journal of Mental Science. 96:*276–279, 1950.

Taylor, N. *Flight from Reality.* Duell, Sloan and Pearce, New York, 1949.

Todd, A. R. "The hemp drugs," *Endeavour. 2:*69–72, 1943.

United States Government Printing Office. Narcotic internal revenue regulations relating to the importation, manufacture, production, compounding, sale, dealing in, dispensing, prescribing, administering and giving away of Marihuana. Washington, D.C., 1937.

Walton, R. P. *Marihuana: America's New Drug Problem.* Lippincott, Philadelphia, Pa., 1938.

Walton, R. P. "Marihuana problems," *Journal of the American Medical Association. 128:*383, 1945.

Williams, E. G., Himmelsbach, C. K., Winkler, A., Ruble, D. C. "Studies on marihuana and pyrahexyl compound," Public Health Report. *61:*1059, 1946.

Wollner, H. I., Matchett, J. R., Levine, J., Loewe, S. "Isolation of a physiologically active tetrahydrocannabinol from *Cannabis sativa* resin," *Journal of the American Chemical Society. 64:*26–29, 1942.

Wood, H. C. "On the medical activity of the hemp plant as grown in North America," *Proceedings of the American Philosophical Society.* 11:226–232, 1869–1870.

Yawger, N. A. "Marihuana; our new addiction," *American Journal of Medical Science.* 195:351–357, 1938.

ADDICTS AND ADDICTIONS

Aivazian, G. H. "Chlorpromazine in the withdrawal of habit forming drugs in addicts," *Diseases of the Nervous System.* 16:57–60, 1955.

Cocteau, J. *Opium: The Diary of an Addict.* Longmans, London, 1932.

De Quincey, T *Confessions of an English Opium-Eater.*

Diethelm, O. *Etiology of Chronic Alcoholism.* C. C. Thomas, Springfield, Ill., 1955.

Emerson, H. *Alcohol and Man.* Macmillan, New York, 1953.

Gerard, D. L., Weisselberger, D., Kritz, D. "Reserpine in the Postwithdrawal Rehabilitation of Adolescent Opiate Addicts," *Archives of Neurology and Psychiatry.* 76:106–109, 1956.

Greenberg, L. A. "Alcohol in the body," *Scientific American.* 189:86–91, 1953.

Haggard, H. W., Jellinck, E. M. *Alcohol Explored.* Doubleday, Doran, New York, 1942.

Hald, J., Jacobsen, E. "A drug sensitising the organism to ethyl alcohol," *Lancet.* 2:1001–1004, 1948.

Hawkins, J. A. *Opium: Addicts and Addictions.* Author's publication. Danville, Va., 1937.

Herman, M., Nagler, S. H. "Psychoses due to amphetamine," *Journal of Nervous and Mental Diseases.* 120:268, 1954.

Hirsch, J. *The Problem Drinker*. Duell, Sloan and Pearce, New York, 1949.

Isbell, H., Fraser, H. F. "Addiction to analgesics and barbiturates," *Pharmacological Review*. 2:355–397, 1950.

Isbell, H. "Medical aspects of opiate addiction," *Bulletin of the New York Academy of Medicine*. 31:886–902, 1955.

Ivy, A. C., Krasno, L. R. "Amphetamine (benzedrine) sulfate. A review of its pharmacology," *War Medicine*. 1:15–42, 1941.

Knapp, T. M. "Amphetamine and addiction," *Journal of Nervous and Mental Disorders*. 115:406–432, 1952.

Kolb, L. "Pleasure and deterioration from narcotic addiction," *Mental Hygiene*. 9:699–724, 1925.

Lasagna, L., von Felsinger, J. M., Beecher, H. K. "Drug-induced mood changes in man," *Journal of the American Medical Association*. 157:1006–1020, 1955.

Lolli, G. "Alcoholism as a Medical Problem," *Bulletin of the New York Academy of Medicine*. 31:876–886, 1955.

Newman, H. W. *Acute Acoholic Intoxication*. Stanford University Press, Stanford, Calif., 1941.

Reifenstein, E. C., Davidoff, E. "The psychological effects of benzedrine sulphate," *American Journal of Psychology*. 52:56–64, 1939.

Sheldon, W. H., Stevens, S. S. *The Varieties of Temperament*. Harper and Brothers, New York, 1942.

U.S. Senate Report #1850. *Treatment and Rehabilitation of Narcotics Addicts*. 1956.

U.S. Senate Subcommittee Report. *Illicit Narcotics Traffic*. 4896 pp., 1955.

Wikler, A. *Opiate Addiction*. C. C. Thomas, Springfield, Ill., 1953.

THE CHEMISTRY OF MADNESS

Bellak, L. *Dementia Praecox*. Grune and Stratton, New York, 1948.

Benditt, E. P., Rowley, D. A. "Antagonism of 5-hydroxytryptamine by chlorpromazine," *Science. 123*:24, 1956.

Cerletti, A., Rothlin, E. "Role of 5-hydroxytryptamine in mental disease and its antagonism to lysergic acid derivatives," *Nature. 176*:785–786, 1955.

Frank, J. "Some aspects of lobotomy (prefrontal leucotomy) under psychoanalytic scrutiny," *Psychiatry. 13*:35–42, 1950.

Freeman, W., Watts, J. W. *Psychosurgery*. C. C. Thomas, Springfield, Ill., 1950.

Gantt, W. H. "Principles of nervous breakdown—schizokinensis and autokinensis," *Annals of the New York Academy of Science. 56*:143–163, 1953.

Gerard, R. W. "Biological roots of psychiatry," *Science. 122*:225–230, 1955.

Guttmann, E. "Artificial psychoses produced by mescalin," *Journal of Mental Science. 82*:203–221, 1936.

Hoagland, H. "Schizophrenia and stress," *Scientific American. 181*:44, 1949.

Hoffer, A., Osmond, H., Smythies, J. "Schizophrenia: a new approach II," *Journal of Mental Science. 100*:29–45, 1950.

Hoffman, J. L. "A clinical appraisal of frontal lobotomy in the treatment of psychoses," *Psychiatry. 13*:355–360, 1950.

Hoskins, R. G. *The Biology of Schizophrenia*. Chapman and Hall, London, 1946.

Kalinowski, L. B., Hoch, P. H. *Shock Treatments, Psychosurgery and Other Somatic Treatments in Psychiatry*. Grune and Stratton, New York, 1952.

Marrazzi, A. S., Hart, E. R. "Relationship of hallucinogens to adrenergic cerebral neurohumors," *Science. 121*:365-367, 1955.

Osmond, H., Smythies, J. "Schizophrenia—a new approach," *Journal of Mental Science. 98*:309-315, 1952.

Osmond, H. "Inspiration and method in schizophrenia research," *Disorders of the Nervous System. 16*:101-110, 1955.

Rinkel, M., Hyde, R. W., Solomon, H. C. "Experimental psychiatry III: a chemical concept of psychosis," *Diseases of the Nervous System. 15*:259-264, 1954.

Rinkel, M., De Shon, J. H., Morimoto, K., York, R. M., Salvatore, H. "Experimental psychoses," *Scientific American. 192*:34-39, 1955.

Rosen, J. N. "The treatment of schizophrenic psychoses by direct analytic therapy," *Psychiatric Quarterly. 21*:3-37 and 117-119, 1947.

Shore, P. A., Silver, S. L., Brodie, B. B. "Interaction of serotonin and lysergic acid diethylamide on the central nervous system," *Experentia. 11*:272-273, 1955.

Shattuck, F. M. "The somatic manifestations of schizophrenia, *Journal of Mental Science. 96*:32-142, 1950.

Silverstein, A., Kline, N. S. "Autonomic Pharmacology in Schizophrenia," *Archives of Neurology and Psychiatry. 75*:389-400, 1956.

Stockings, G. T. "Clinical study of the mescaline psychosis with special reference to the mechanism of the genesis of schizophrenic and other psychotic states," *Journal of Mental Science. 86*:29-47, 1940.

Stoll, W. A. "Ein neues, in sehr Kleinen Mengen wirksames, Phantasticum," *Schweizerische Archiv von Neurologie. 64*:483, 1949.

Tow, P. M. *Personality Changes Following Frontal Leucotomy.* Oxford University Press, London. 1955.

Trew, A., Fischer, R. "Faulty Detoxication in Schizophrenia,"
   Lancet. 268:402, 1955.
Woolley, D. W., Shaw, E. "A biochemical and pharmacological
   suggestion about certain mental disorders," *Proceedings of
   the National Academy of Sciences.* 40:228–231, 1954.

SICK MINDS, NEW MEDICINES

Bein, H. J. "Pharmacology of reserpin, a new alkaloid from
   Rauwolfia serpentina," *Experentia.* 9:107–110, 1953.
Bradley, C. "Benzedrine and dexedrine in the treatment of chil-
   dren's behaviour disorders," *Pediatrics.* 5:24–36, 1950.
Chopra, R. N., Gupta, J. C., Bose, B. C., Chopra, I. C. "Hypnotic
   effect of Rauwolfia serpentina," *Indian Journal of Medical
   Research.* 31:71–74, 1943.
Ciba Pharmaceutical Products. *The Story of Serpasil.* Summit,
   N. J., 1955.
Clark, L. D., Ellsworth, R. B., Barrett, W. W., Thurman, A. C.,
   Holland, W. "Studies of the Behavioral Effects of Ritalin,"
   Diseases of the Nervous System. 17:317–321, 1956.
Fabing, H. D. "Clinical experiences with Meratran," *Disorders
   of the Nervous System.* 16:10–15, 1955.
Fabing, H. D. "The new pharmacologic attack in psychiatry,"
   Drug and Cosmetic Industry. 78:32, 1956.
Fabing, H. D. "Frenquel, a blocking agent against experimental
   LSD-25 and mescaline psychosis," *Neurology.* 5:319–332,
   1955.
Fabing, H. D., Hawkins, J. R. "A year's experiences with Fren-
   quel in clinical and experimental schizophrenic psychoses,"
   Diseases of the Nervous System. 16:329–339, 1955.
Gerard, R. W. "The biological roots of psychiatry," *American
   Journal of Psychiatry.* 112:83–90, 1955.

Goldman, D. "Treatment of psychotic states with chlorpromazine," *Journal of the American Medical Association.* *157*: 1274–1278, 1955.

Himwich, H. E. "Prospects in Psychopharmacology," *Diseases of the Nervous System.* *17*:109–117, 1956.

Himwich, H. E. "The new psychiatric drugs," *Scientific American.* *193*:80–87, 1955

Jacobson, A. "Ritalin, a new agent for mild depressions. (A preliminary report)," *Medical Annals of the District of Columbia.* 25:491–495, 1956.

Kline, N. S. "Use of Rauwolfia serpentina Benth. in neuropsychiatric conditions," *Annals of the New York Academy of Science.* 59:107–132, 1954.

Kline, N. S. (editor). *Psychopharmacology.* A.A.A.S., Washington, D.C., 1956.

Leake, D. C. "Drugs affecting mood and behavior," *Texas Reports on Biology and Medicine.* *13*:793–819, 1955.

Lennox, W. G. "Epilepsy and the epileptic," *Journal of the American Medical Association,* *162*:118–119, 1956.

Madi, M. L., Kovitz, B. "Experiences with methyl-phenidylacetate HC₁ (Ritalin) in psychotic patients," *Antibiotic Medicine and Clinical Therapy.* 3–5:309–312, 1956.

Muller, J. C., Pryor, W. W., Gibbons, J. E., Orgain, E. S. "Depression and anxiety occurring during Rauwolfia therapy," *Journal of the American Medical Association.* *159*:836–839, 1955.

Muller, J. M., Schlittler, E. Bein, H. J. "Reserpin, the sedative principle from Rauwolfia serpentina," *Experentia.* *8*:338, 1952.

Natenshon, A. L. "Clinical evaluation of Ritalin," *Diseases of the Nervous System.* *17*:392–397, 1956.

Phillips, R. E. "Use of Meprobamate (Miltown) for the treatment of emotional disorders," *American Practitioner.* 7: 1573–1581, 1956.

Prinzmetal, M., Alles, G. A. "The central nervous system stimulant effects of dextroamphetamine sulphate," *American Journal of Medical Science.* 200:665–673, 1940.

Sandison, R. A. "Psychological aspects of the LSD treatment of the neuroses," *Journal of Mental Science.* 100:508–515, 1954.

Sandison, R. A., Spencer, A. M., Whitelaw, J. D. A. "The therapeutic value of lysergic acid diethylamide in mental illness," *Journal of Mental Science.* 100:491–507, 1954.

Schiele, B. C., Anderson, R. W., Simon, W. "Current status of chlorpromazine and reserpine in psychiatric practice," *Lancet.* 76:179–186, 1956.

Schroeder, H. A., Perry, H. M., Jr. "Psychosis apparently produced by reserpine," *Journal of the American Medical Association.* 159:839–841, 1955.

Selling, L. S. "Miltown, a new tranquilising drug," *Journal of the American Medical Association.* 157:1594, 1955.

Turvey, S. E. C. "Meprobamate (Equanil) for relief of anxiety and nervous tension from various causes," *Canadian Medical Association Journal.* 74:863, 1956.

Vakil, R. J. "A clinical trial of *Rauwolfia serpentina* in essential hypertension," *British Heart Journal.* 11:350–355, 1949.

Wilkins, R. W., Judson, W. E. "The use of Rauwolfia serpentina in hypertensive patients," *New England Journal of Medicine.* 248:48–53, 1953.

BREWS STRANGE AND BREWS FAMILIAR

Allen, P. H. "Indians of Southeastern Colombia," *Geographical Review,* 37:567–582, 1947.

Delourme-Houde, J. "Contribution à l'étude de l'Iboga," *Ann. Pharm. Franc.* 4:30–36, 1946.

Fabing, H. D., Hawkins, J. R. "Intravenous Bufotenine Injection in the Human Being," *Science.* 123:886–887, 1956.

Hough, W. "Kava drinking as practised by the Papuans and Polynesians," *Smithsonian Institution, Miscellaneous Collection.* 47:85–92, 1904.

Iberico, C. C. "Ayahuasco," *Bol. Museo List nat. Janier Prado.* (Lima, Peru). 5:313–321, 1941.

Kennan, G. *Tent Life in Siberia.* G. P. Putnam's Sons, New York, 1910.

Okakura-Kakuzo. *The Book of Tea.* T. N. Foulis, Edinburgh, 1919.

Parsons, E. C. "Mitla—Town of the Souls." Chicago, 1926.

Perrot, E. "L'Ayahuasca, le Yajé et le Huanto, boissons toxiques des Indiens du nord-ouest de l'Amazone," *Bulletin des Sciences Pharmacologiques.* 30:107–110, 1923.

Raymond-Hamet, M. "L'Iboga, drogue défatigante mal connue," *Bulletin de l'Académie de Médicin* (Paris). 124:243–255, 1941.

Reutter, L. "Du yagé ou Aya huesca," *Schweiz. Apotheker-Zeitung.* 65:289–291, 1927.

Rolin, J. *Police Drugs* (trans. L. J. Bendit). Philosophical Library, New York, 1956.

Rouhier, A. "Documents pour servir à l'étude du yagé," *Bulletin des Sciences Pharmacologiques.* 33:252–261, 1926.

Schultes, R. E. "The identification of teonanacatl, a narcotic basidiomycete of the Aztecs," Botanical Museum Leaflets. 7:37–56, 1939.

Schultes, R. E. *A Contribution to Our Knowledge of Rivea Corymbosa, the Narcotic Ololiuqui of the Aztecs.* Botanical Museum of Harvard University, 1941.

Spruce, R. *Notes of a Botanist in the Amazon and the Andes* (editor, Alfred Russel Wallace). Macmillan, London, 1908.

Stromberg, V. L. "The isolation of bufotenine from Piptadenia peregrina," *Journal of the American Chemical Society.* 76: 1707, 1954.

Index